Second Edition

Digital Experiments Emphasizing Systems and Design

To Accompany FLOYD, DIGITAL FUNDAMENTALS

David Buchla

Yuba College

Merrill Publishing Company
A Bell & Howell Information Company
Columbus □ Toronto □ London □ Melbourne

NOTICE TO THE READER

The publisher and the author(s) do not warrant or guarantee any of the products and/or equipment described herein nor has the publisher or the author(s) made any independent analysis in connection with any of the products, equipment, or information used herein. The reader is directed to the manufacturer for any warranty or guarantee for any claim, loss, damages, costs, or expense, arising out of or incurred by the reader in connection with the use or operation of the products and/or equipment.

The reader is expressly advised to adopt all safety precautions that might be indicated by the activities and experiments described herein. The reader assumes all risks in connection with such instructions.

Cover photo: Joseph Drivas/The Image Bank

Published by Merrill Publishing Company
A Bell & Howell Information Company
Columbus, Ohio 43216

This book was set in Times Roman.

Administrative Editor: David Garza
Production Editor: Carol Driver
Art Coordinator: Vincent A. Smith
Cover Designer: Cathy Watterson

International Standard Book Number: 0-675-21180-8
Printed in the United States of America
1 2 3 4 5 6 7 8 9–94 93 92 91 90

MERRILL'S INTERNATIONAL SERIES IN ELECTRICAL AND ELECTRONICS TECHNOLOGY

Preface

In digital logic, the lowest level of complexity contains only simple logic gates. As the complexity of circuits increases, the technician must apply more abstract relationships in order to achieve understanding and skill in working on circuits. Digital systems can range from simple combinational logic to such complex systems as digital video processors. The goal of this experiment manual is to build the student's skill and confidence in working with digital logic by solving the relatively simple problems posed in combinational logic systems to the more abstract and complex sequential logic problems that are the basis of most digital logic systems. An important part of the system concept is that most circuits presented in this manual are used in specific applications. As the student's skill in constructing small systems increases, the difficulty is gradually increased to help develop the abstract problem-solving and troubleshooting skills so necessary for technicians.

Although this manual is primarily oriented to digital systems and design, the need for developing troubleshooting skills in these systems is not forgotten. Troubleshooting small systems provides the added bonus of signal-tracing skills not available to students who have merely tested a collection of ICs. (For example, Experiment 24 describes a detailed signal injection and tracing technique.) In addition, troubleshooting questions are included in virtually every experiment. Instruments, including the oscilloscope, logic analyzer, logic pulser, current tracer, and logic probe, are explained.

This new edition has a number of changes designed to help the learner as well as the instructor. In keeping with the needs of many schools to have written laboratory reports, the format of the experiments has been changed to include a "preformatted" report section, including blank data tables and space for a written conclusion. All experiments retain flexibility by having a *For Further Investigation* section, which can be assigned as an enhancement or as part of the experiment depending on time constraints. The Further Investigations tend to be more open-ended investigations, frequently with a design problem associated with them. *Evaluation and Review* questions have been expanded to include many more troubleshooting questions and are now part of the student report. In addition, a new feature, called *Checkup,* has been added. Checkup questions relate to both the laboratory work and the text material and can be removed from the manual for submission.

Another feature is the inclusion of additional experimental design problems. Problem-solving skills are enhanced by requiring students to think out the solution to simple design problems. These problems require the student to develop an original solution to the problem, solve the problem, and write a formal report. This type of practical problem solving is the key to having students who can successfully encounter new situations in electronics. For example, one experiment, suggested to me by a former student, is the Fallen Carton Detector. The circuit, which can be designed with only two ICs, was given as an assignment shortly after he took his first job as an electronics technician. It is left to students to find their own unique solution to the problem posed. These problems, Experiments 8, 9, 14, and 22, are indicated with a grid design in the contents.

The laboratory work includes many of the successful applications from the first edition such as the logic probe (Experiment 2), the Perfect Pen-

v

cil Machine (Experiment 8), the Electronic Lock (Experiment 24), and the digital light meter (Experiment 25). In addition, eight new experiments have been added with continued emphasis on small systems. These small systems give students good practical experience in construction, testing, and troubleshooting. New applications include a time division multiplexing application (Experiment 11), an automated IC logic test circuit (Experiment 20), a circuit to half-step a stepper motor (Experiment 21), a memory test circuit (Experiment 23), a liquid-level detector interfaced to a display over a bus (Experiment 26), a simulation of the GPIB (Experiment 27), and more. Additional experimental work is included on J-K flip-flops, including a new design experiment and a new experiment using shift register counters. Although these additional experiments are more than most digital courses could possibly use, it is hoped that they will furnish choices for instructors as well as a series of interesting, small circuits that can be used for class discussion and evaluation.

Except for special design problems, each experiment includes a list of *Objectives, Reference Reading, Materials Needed, Summary of Theory, Procedure, For Further Investigation, Report* section, and *Evaluation and Review Questions*. The *Checkup* appears at the end of each group of experiments and is referenced to a corresponding chapter in Floyd's *Digital Fundamentals,* 4th ed. (See the cross reference Table on page vii). Appendix A contains manufacturers' data sheets for all ICs called for in the experiments. Appendix B includes a list of materials for the experiments and includes a page reference to the manufacturer's data sheet to facilitate finding information about a specific IC.

Experiments are designed to fit onto 47-row protoboards available from Radio Shack and other suppliers. All experiments except the electronic lock (Experiment 24), the liquid-level sensor (Experiment 26), and the GPIB handshake (Experiment 27) have been constructed on 47-row protoboards (similar to Radio Shack #276-174). These later experiments have been constructed using two boards. To avoid redundancy, laboratory equipment is not listed in the experiments. Each laboratory station should have a 5.0 V regulated power supply, a TTL-compatible, variable frequency pulse generator, a multimeter, and a dual-channel oscilloscope. Experiment 25 also requires a 12 V supply.

A number of persons have contributed suggestions for this manual, and I appreciate their help. These include my colleagues, Gary Snyder, Audry West, Phil Postel, and Bill Frandrup, all from Yuba college, as well as many students who have worked the experiments. I also appreciate the efforts and suggestions of the following reviewers: Francis Erazmus, Computer Hardware Institute; Steve Harsany, Mt. San Antonio College; Richard Schulmeister, Heald College; and Jerry Stierwalt, Tulsa County Vo-Tech. As always, it is a pleasure to work with the staff at Merrill. There have been many hours devoted to refining and improving this manual. I would like to express my appreciation to David Garza, Steve Helba, Carol Thomas, Carol Driver, Mary Harlan, and Vince Smith of Merrill, and to Linda Thompson, who copyedited the manuscript. Finally, I want to express my appreciation to my wife of 28 years, Lorraine. She has been the light at the end of the tunnel and has always lent support to my various projects. She is worth more than two sentences.

David Buchla

Contents

Introduction to the Student

Circuit Wiring

An important skill needed by electronics technicians is that of transforming circuit drawings into working prototypes. The circuits in this manual can be constructed on solderless protoboards ("breadboards") available at Radio Shack and other suppliers of electronic equipment. These boards use #22 or #24 gauge solid core wire which should have ⅜ inch of the insulation stripped from the ends. Protoboard wiring is not difficult, but it is easy to make a wiring error which is time-consuming to correct. Wires should be kept neat and close to the board. Avoid wiring across the top of integrated circuits (ICs) or using wires much longer than necessary. A circuit that looks like a plate of spaghetti is difficult to follow and worse to troubleshoot.

One useful technique to help avoid errors, especially with larger circuits, is to make a wire list. After assigning pin numbers to the ICs, tabulate each wire in the circuit, showing where it is to be connected and leaving a place to check off when it has been installed. Another method is to cross out each wire on the schematic as it is added to the circuit. Remember the power supply and ground connections, because they frequently are left off logic drawings. Finally, it is useful to "daisy-chain," in the same color, signal wires that are connected to the same electrical point. Daisy-chaining is illustrated in Figure I-1.

Troubleshooting

When the wiring is completed, test the circuit. If it does not work, turn off power and recheck the wiring. Wiring, rather than a faulty component, is the more likely cause of an error. Check that the proper power and ground are connected to each IC. If the problem is electrical noise, decoupling capacitors between the power supply and ground may help. Good troubleshooting requires the technician to clearly understand the purpose of the circuit and its normal operation. It can begin at the input and proceed toward the output; or it can begin at the output and proceed toward the input; or it can be done by half-splitting the circuit. Whatever procedure you choose, there is no substitute for understanding how the circuit is supposed to behave and applying your knowledge to the observed conditions in a systematic way.

The Laboratory Notebook

1. Purpose of a Laboratory Notebook

The laboratory notebook forms a chronological record of laboratory work in such a manner that it could be reconstructed if necessary. The notebook is a bound and numbered daily record of laboratory work. Data are recorded as they are observed. Each page is dated as it is done and the signature of the person doing the work is added to make the work official, as laboratory notebooks may be the

1

FIGURE I–1

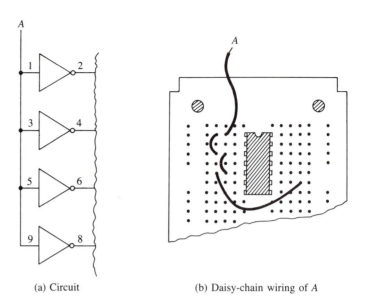

(a) Circuit   (b) Daisy-chain wiring of A

basis of patent applications or have other legal purposes. No pages are left blank and no pages may be removed.

2. General Information

The format of laboratory notebooks may vary; however, certain requirements are basic to all laboratory notebooks. The name of the experimenter, date, and purpose of the experiment are entered at the top of each page. All test equipment should be identified by function, manufacturer, and serial number to facilitate reconstruction of the experiment. Test equipment may be identified on a block diagram or circuit drawing rather than an equipment list. References to books, articles or other sources that were used in preparing for the experiment are noted if they were used. A *brief* description of the procedure is necessary. The procedure is not a restatement of the instructions in the experiment book but rather is a concise statement about what *was* done in the experiment.

3. Recording of Data

Data taken in an experiment should be directly recorded in tabular form in the notebook. Raw (not processed) data should be recorded. They should not be transcribed from scratch paper. When calculations have been applied to data, a sample calculation should be included to indicate clearly what process has been applied to the raw data. If an error is made, a single line should be drawn through the error with a short explanation.

4. Graphs

A graph is a visual tool that can quickly convey to the reader the relationship between variables. The eye can discern trends in magnitude or slope more easily from graphs than from tabular data. Graphs are constructed with dependent variable plotted along the horizontal axis (called the *abscissa*) and the independent plotted along the verticle axis (called the *ordinate*). A smooth curve can be drawn showing the trend of the data. It is not necessary to connect the data points (except in calibration curves). For data in which one of the variables is related to the other by a power, logarithmic (log) scales in one or both axes may show the relationship of data. Log scales can show data over a large range of values that will not fit on ordinary graph paper.

When you have determined the type of scale that best shows the data, select numbers for the scale that are easily read. Do not use the data for the scale; rather, choose numbers that allow the largest data point to fit on the graph. Scales should generally start from zero unless limitations in the data preclude it. Data points on the graph should be shown with a dot in the center of a symbol such as a circle or triangle. The graph should be labeled in a manner that is self-explanatory. A figure number should be used as a reference in the written explanation.

5. Schematics and Block Diagrams

Schematics, block diagrams, waveform drawings, and other illustrations are important tools to depict the facts of an experiment. Experiments with cir-

2

cuits need at least a schematic drawing showing the setup and may benefit from other illustrations depending on your purpose. Usually, simpler drawings are best; however, sufficient detail needs to be shown to enable the reader to reconstruct the circuit if necessary. Adequate information should be contained with an illustration to make its purpose clear to the reader.

6. Results and Conclusion

The section that discusses the results and conclusion is the most important part of your laboratory notebook as it contains the key findings of your experiment. Each experiment should contain a conclusion, which is a *specific* statement about the important results you obtained and will enable the reader to properly understand these results. Be careful about sweeping generalizations that are not warranted by the experiment. Before writing a conclusion, it is useful to review the purpose of the experiment. A good conclusion "answers" the purpose of the experiment. For example, if the purpose of the experiment was to determine the frequency response of a filter, the conclusion should describe the frequency response or contain a reference to an illustration of the response. In addition, the conclusion should contain an explanation of difficulties, unusual results, revisions, or any suggestions you may have for improving the circuit.

7. Suggested Format

From the foregoing discussion, the following format is suggested. This format may be modified as circumstances dictate:

1. *Title and date.*
2. *Purpose:* Give a statement of what you intend to determine as a result of the investigation.
3. *Equipment and materials:* Include equipment model and serial numbers, which can allow retracing if a defective or uncalibrated piece of equipment was used.
4. *Procedure:* Include a description of what you did and what measurements you made. A reference to the schematic drawing should be included.
5. *Data:* Tabulate raw (unprocessed) data; data may be presented in graph form.
6. *Sample calculations:* If you have a number of calculations, then give a sample calculation showing the formulas that you applied to the raw data to transform it to processed data. This section may be omitted if calculations are clear

from the procedure or they are discussed in the results.
7. *Results and conclusion:* This section is the place to discuss your results, including experimental errors. This section should contain key information about the results and your interpretation of the significance of these results.

Each page of the laboratory notebook should be signed and dated as previously discussed.

The Technical Report

1. Effective Writing

The purpose of technical reports is to communicate technical information in a way that is easy for the reader to understand. Effective writing requires that you know your reader's background. You must be able to put yourself in the reader's place and anticipate what information you must convey to have the reader understand what you are trying to say. When you are writing experimental results for a person working in your field, such as an engineer, your writing style may contain words or ideas that are unfamiliar to a lay person. If your report is intended for persons outside your field, you will need to provide background information.

2. Words and Sentences

You will need to choose words that have clear meaning to a general audience or define every term that does not have a well-established meaning. Keep sentences short and to the point. Short sentences are easiest for the reader to comprehend. Avoid stringing a series of adjectives or modifiers together. For example, the figure caption below contains a jibberish string of modifiers:

> *Operational amplifier constant current source schematic*

The word schematic has been modified five times. By changing the order and adding natural connectors such as *of, using,* and *an,* the meaning can be clarified:

> *Schematic of a constant current source using an operational amplifier.*

3. Paragraphs

Paragraphs need to contain a unit of thought. Excessively long paragraphs suffer from the same weakness that afflicts overly long sentences. The reader is asked to digest too much material at once, causing comprehension to diminish. Paragraphs should organize your thoughts in a logical format. Look for natural breaks in your ideas. Each paragraph should have one central idea and contribute to the development of the entire report.

Good organization is the key to a well-written report. Outlining in advance will help organize your ideas. The use of headings and subheadings for paragraphs or sections can help steer the reader through the report. Subheadings also prepare the reader for what is ahead and make the report easier to understand.

4. Figures and Tables

Figures and tables are effective ways to present information. Figures should be kept simple and to the point. Often a graph can make clear the relationship of data. Comparisons of different data drawn on the same graph make the results more obvious to the reader. Figures should be labeled with a figure number and a brief label. Don't forget to label both axes of graphs.

Data tables are useful for presenting data. Usually data that are presented in a graph or figure should not also be included in a data table. Data tables should be labeled with a table number and short title. The data table should contain enough information that its meaning is clear: The reader should not have to refer to the text. If the purpose of the table is to compare information, then form the data in columns rather than rows. Column information is easier for people to compare. Table footnotes are a useful method of clarifying some point about the data. Footnotes should appear at the bottom of the table with a key to where the footnote applies.

Data should appear throughout your report in consistent units of measurement. Most sciences use the metric system; however, the English system is still sometimes used. The metric system uses derived units, which are cgs (centimeter-gram-second) or mks (meter-kilogram-second). It

is best to use consistent metric units or to include a conversion chart. Whatever units are used should be used throughout your report.

Reporting numbers using powers of ten can be a sticky point with reference to tables. Table I–1 shows four methods of abbreviating numbers in tabular form. The first column is unambiguous as the number is presented in conventional form. This requires more space than if we present the information in scientific notation. In column 2, the same data are shown with a metric prefix used for the unit. In column 3, the power of 10 is shown. Each of the first three columns shows the measurement unit and is not subject to misinterpretation. Column 4, on the other hand, is wrong. In this case the author is trying to tell us what operation was performed on the numbers to obtain the values in the column. This is incorrect because the column heading should contain the unit of measurement for the numbers in the column.

5. Suggested Format

1. *Title:* A good title needs to convey the substance of your report by using key words that provide the reader with enough information to decide if the report should be investigated further.
2. *Contents:* Key headings throughout the report are listed with page numbers.
3. *Abstract:* The abstract is a *brief* summary of the work with principal facts and results stated in concentrated form. It is a key factor for a reader to determine if he or she should read further.
4. *Introduction:* The introduction orients your reader to your report. It should briefly state what you did and give the reader a sense of the purpose of the report. It may tell the reader what to expect and briefly describe the report's organization.
5. *Body of the report:* The report can be made clearer to the reader if you use headings and

TABLE I–1
Reporting Numbers in Tabular Data.

Column 1 Resistance (Ω)	Column 2 Resistance (kΩ)	Column 3 Resistance ($\times 10^3\ \Omega$)	Column 4 Resistance ($\Omega \times 10^{-3}$)
470,000	470	470	470
8,200	8.2	8.2	8.2
1,200,000	1,200	1,200	1,200
330	0.33	0.33	0.33

Correct — — — — Wrong

your report. The headings and subheadings can be generated from the outline of your report. Figures and tables should be labeled and referenced from the body of the report.

6. *Conclusion:* The conclusion summarizes important points or results. It may refer to figures or tables previously discussed in the body of the report to add emphasis to significant points. In some cases, the primary reasons for the report are contained within the body and a conclusion is deemed to be unnecessary.

7. *References:* References are cited to enable the reader to find information used in developing your report or work that supports your report. The reference should include all authors' names in the order shown in the original document. Use quotation marks around portions of a complete document such as a journal article or a chapter of a book. Books, journals, or other complete documents should be underlined. Finally, list the publisher, city, date, and page numbers.

1

Basic Laboratory Instruments

Objectives

After completing this experiment, you will be able to:

☐ Use a digital multimeter (DMM) to measure specified dc voltages from the power supply.

☐ Use an oscilloscope to measure dc voltages.

☐ Set up the function generator to obtain a transistor-transistor logic (TTL) compatible pulse of a specified frequency. Measure the pulse amplitude and the frequency with an oscilloscope.

Reference Reading

Floyd, *Digital Fundamentals,* 4th ed., Section 1–1, Digital Electronics; Section 1–2, Digital and Analog Quantities; Section 1–3, Logic Levels and Pulse Waveforms

Materials Needed

Light-emitting diode (LED)
330 Ω resistor

Optional:
Current tracer (H-P 547A or equivalent)
Logic pulser (H-P 546A or equivalent)
100 Ω resistor

Summary of Theory

Laboratory equipment needed for most electronics work includes a DMM, a power supply, a function generator, and a dual trace, triggered oscilloscope. This experiment is a brief introduction to these instruments. Since each laboratory will have instruments from different manufacturers and different models, it is recommended that you familiarize yourself with your particular lab station using the manufacturer's operating instructions.

The Power Supply

In this course, you will study digital integrated circuits and learn how to connect them to perform desired functions. An integrated circuit (IC) is one in which the transistors and other components are connected together on a single substrate. These circuits, as well as all active electronic devices, require a stable source of dc voltage in order to function properly. The purpose of the power supply is to provide the proper level of dc voltage. It is very important that the correct voltage be set *before* connecting it to the integrated circuits on your board or permanent damage can result. The power supply at your bench may have more than one output and normally will have a built-in meter to help you set the voltage. Some power supplies have meters that monitor both voltage and current. There may be more than one range or several supplies built into the same chassis, so the meter may have multiple or complex scales.

The Digital Multimeter

The DMM is a multipurpose measuring instrument that combines the characteristics of a dc and ac voltmeter, a dc and ac ammeter, and an ohmmeter in one instrument. The DMM indicates the measured quantity as a digital number, avoiding the necessity to interpret the scales as was necessary on older instruments.

Because the DMM is a multipurpose instrument, it is necessary to determine which controls select the desired function. In addition, current measurements (and often high range voltage measurements) usually require a separate set of lead connections to the meter. After you have selected the function, you may need to select the appropriate range to make the measurement. DMMs can be autoranging, meaning that the instrument automatically selects the correct scale and sets the decimal place, or they can be manual ranging, meaning that the user must select the correct scale.

The voltmeter function of a DMM can measure either ac or dc volts. For digital work, the ac voltage function is normally not used, since it will produce erroneous results with digital signals. The dc voltage function is useful to measure the voltage *difference* between two points. If the meter's red lead is touching a more positive point than the meter's black lead, the reading on the meter will be positive; if the black lead is on the more positive point the reading will be negative. In digital work, dc voltage measurements are used for checking that power supplies have the correct output and that steady-state digital signals are within their specified limits.

The ohmmeter (used for resistance measurements) of a DMM is used only in circuits that are *not* powered. The power supply should be disconnected from the circuit to avoid measuring back through the power supply. An ohmmeter works by inserting a small test voltage into a circuit and measuring the resulting current flow. Consequently, if any voltage is present, the reading will be in error. The meter will show the resistance of all possible paths between the probes. If you want to know the resistance of a single component, it is necessary to isolate that component from the remainder of the circuit by disconnecting one end. In addition, body resistance can affect the reading if you are holding the conducting portion of both probes in your fingers. This procedure should be avoided, particularly with high resistances.

The Function Generator

The function generator, or signal generator, is used to produce signals required for testing circuits. Function generators have several types of waveforms available at the output terminals. For digital circuits, a rectangular pulse is the basic signal used for testing logic circuits. It is very important that the proper voltage level be set up *before* connecting the function generator to the circuit or else damage may occur. Function generators normally have controls for adjusting the peak amplitude of a signal and may also have a means of adjusting the 0 V level. Many generators have a separate pulse output designed for use in logic circuits. Check with your instructor or instrument instructions before connecting the generator to a logic circuit.

A rectangular pulse is a signal that rises from one level to another level, remains at the second level for a time called the pulse width (t_w), and then returns to the original level. A periodic pulse train repeats in a regular manner. The time for one complete repetition of a periodic signal is called the period *(T)*. The reciprocal of the period is the frequency *(f)*, which is the number of complete repetitions per second. For pulses, the period is often called the pulse repetition time (PRT) and the frequency is called the pulse repetition rate (PRR). Another characteristic of pulses is the duty cycle. The duty cycle is the pulse width *(t_w)* divided by the period *(T)* and is usually expressed as a percentage. These definitions are illustrated in Figure 1–1.

In addition to amplitude and dc offset controls, function generators usually have switches that select the range of the output frequency. A vernier is used for fine frequency adjustments.

The Oscilloscope

The oscilloscope is a versatile test instrument, letting you "see" a graph of the voltage as a function of time in a circuit. Many digital circuits have specific timing requirements that can be readily measured with a two-channel oscilloscope. The oscilloscope allows you to measure various pulse parameters and hence is considered to be an instrument capable of *parametric* measurements. The voltage to be measured is converted into a visible display by a cathode-ray tube (CRT), a vacuum device similar to a television picture tube.

The oscilloscope contains four functional blocks, as illustrated in Figure 1–2. The input signal is coupled through a vertical section to a display section, causing the visible beam to move up

8

FIGURE 1–1
Definitions for a periodic pulse train.

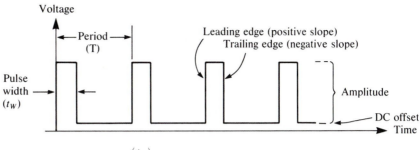

Duty cycle = $\left(\dfrac{t_W}{T}\right)$ 100%   A duty cycle of 25% is shown.

and down in the same way as the input voltage. A trigger section picks off a selected part of the input signal and generates a trigger, which is sent to the horizontal section. This trigger causes the beam to move (or sweep) across the screen. This horizontal movement must be synchronized with the vertical signal to present a stable pattern on the screen.

Although there are many controls on an oscilloscope, you can clarify their relationship if you keep in mind the four functional blocks. Controls for each of the functional blocks are usually grouped together. Frequently, there are color clues to help you identify groups of controls. Details of these controls are explained in the operator's manual for the oscilloscope; however, a brief description of frequently used controls is given here for reference:

□ *Display controls:* Display controls include INTENSITY, FOCUS, and BEAM FINDER. Their purpose is to help you find the trace and obtain a crisp, easily viewed display in different ambient lighting conditions.

□ *Vertical controls:* The vertical controls include input COUPLING, VOLTS/DIV, vertical POSITION, and channel selection (CH1, CH2, DUAL, ALT, CHOP). They are used to select the input signal and adjust the scale factor in the vertical axis to enable you to view the signal. Since most oscilloscopes

have two (or more) channels, there are duplicate controls for COUPLING, VOLTS/DIV, and vertical POSITION.

□ *Horizontal controls:* The horizontal controls are used to adjust the time base of the oscilloscope. The horizontal controls include the SEC/DIV, MAGNIFIER, and horizontal POSITION control. The SEC/DIV control determines how fast the beam moves (or sweeps) across the screen. It controls the duration of time that you can view the input signal.

□ *Trigger controls:* The purpose of trigger controls is to synchronize the start of the sweep in order to view the same part of the waveform every time. The triggering controls include MODE, SOURCE, trigger COUPLING, trigger LEVEL, and others. Usually, you will start by selecting INTernal SOURCE and AUTOmatic MODE.

With all the controls to learn, you may experience difficulty obtaining a trace. If you do not see a trace, start by setting the SEC/DIV control to 1 ms/div, select AUTO triggering, select CH1, and press the BEAM FINDER. Keep the BEAM FINDER button depressed and use the vertical and horizontal POSITION controls to center the trace. If you still have trouble, check the INTENSITY control.

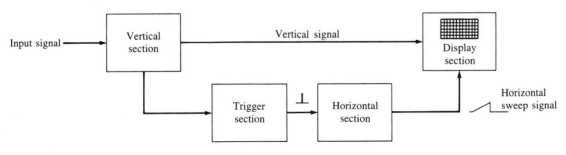

FIGURE 1–2
Basic oscilloscope.

Logic Pulser and Current Tracer

The logic pulser and current tracer are simple digital test instruments that are useful for finding certain difficult faults, such as a short between V_{CC} and ground. A problem like this can be very difficult to find in a large circuit because there are many possible places where the short could be located. The current tracer responds to pulsing current by detecting the changing magnetic field. A handheld logic pulser (see Figure 1–32 of the text) can provide very short duration, nondestructive pulses into the shorted circuit. The current tracer, used in conjunction with the pulser or other pulsating source, allows you to follow the current path, leading you directly to the short. This method of troubleshooting is also useful for "stuck" nodes in a circuit (points that have more than one path for current). The sensitivity of the current tracer can be varied over a large range to allow you to trace various types of faults. The logic pulser and current tracer are covered in more detail in the Further Investigation section of this experiment.

Logic Probe

Another handheld instrument that is useful for tracing simple logic circuits is the logic probe. The logic probe can be used to determine the logic level of a point in a circuit or determine if there is pulse activity at the point by LED (light-emitting diode) displays. Although it is used primarily for simple circuits because it cannot show important time relationships between digital signals, a good probe can indicate the presence of very short pulses that would be difficult to observe on an oscilloscope. It does this by "stretching" a very short pulse, allowing it to be easily observed. Larger circuits can generally be analyzed more completely with a logic analyzer, which quickly reveals time relationships between various signals. In Experiment 2, you will construct a simple logic probe that can be used to determine if logic levels are legitimate and use the probe to find faults in a combination logic circuit.

Logic Analyzer

One of the most powerful and widely used instruments for digital troubleshooting is the logic analyzer. The logic analyzer is an instrument which makes functional (as opposed to parametric) measurements in logic circuits. It is useful for observing the time relationship between a number of digital signals at the same time, allowing the technician to see a variety of errors, including "stuck" nodes, very short noise spikes, intermittent problems, and timing errors. Not all electronic laboratories are equipped with a logic analyzer, and it is not necessary for the experiments in this manual. Further information on the logic analyzer is given in Experiment 17, Summary of Theory.

Procedure

Measurement of dc Voltage with the DMM

1. Review the operator's manual or information supplied by your instructor for the power supply at your lab station. Generally, power supplies have a meter or meters that enable you to set the output voltage and monitor the current. Examine the meter and meter controls to assure that you understand how to monitor the output.

2. Review the operator's manual or information supplied by your instructor for the DMM at your lab station. Look for the controls that select the function. Be sure you understand how to measure AC and DC VOLTS, AC and DC CURRENT, and RESISTANCE. If your meter is not autoranging, you will need to understand how to select the appropriate range for making a measurement.

3. Set up the power supply for 0.5 V as listed on the first line of Table 1–1 (see the Report for Experiment 1) using the meter on the supply. Then assure that you have correctly set up the supply by measuring the output with the DMM. Record the reading of the DMM in Table 1–1.

4. Repeat Step 3 for each voltage listed in Table 1–1. Your measured voltages from the DMM should agree with the meter readings on the supply within ±3%.

Measurement of dc Voltage with the Oscilloscope

5. In this step, you will measure the dc voltage from the power supply using the oscilloscope. Begin by resetting the power supply to 0.5 V, as listed on the first line of Table 1–2 in the report. Set the SEC/DIV control of your oscilloscope to 1 ms and the trigger controls to AUTO and INT (internal trigger). Select channel 1, and connect a scope probe to the vertical input. Put the input coupling control on GND (to disconnect the input signal and find the ground position on the oscilloscope). Check that the vertical VOLTS/DIV variable knobs are in their calibrated positions. Adjust the beam for a sharp, horizontal line across the scope face.

6. You can move the reference ground position to any level on the scope face by using the channel 1 vertical POSITION control. Since you are measuring a positive voltage, position the ground on a convenient graticule line near the bottom of the display. Keep in mind the position of ground as it is the reference level for all dc measurements. The channel 1 VOLTS/DIV control is used to select the vertical sensitivity. Set it to 0.1 V/div to start with.

7. Move the channel 1 input coupling control from GND to the dc position. For almost all digital work, the input coupling control should be in the dc position. Clip the ground lead of the scope probe to the ground of the power supply and touch the probe itself to the power supply output. The line on the face of the oscilloscope should jump up 5 divisions. You can determine the dc voltage by multiplying the vertical sensitivity (0.1 V/div) by the number of divisions observed between ground and this line (5 divisions). This step was completed as an example in Table 1−2.

8. Set the power supply to each voltage listed in Table 1−2 using either the meter on the supply or the DMM. Measure the voltage with the oscilloscope. You will need to change the VOLTS/DIV control to a less sensitive value in order to keep the line on the display as you increase the voltage. You should select a setting that gives several divisions of deflection in order to obtain an accurate measurement. It is a good idea to recheck the ground level each time you change the vertical sensitivity (VOLTS/DIV) control.

Measurement of Pulses with the Oscilloscope

9. In this step, you will set up the function generator or pulse generator for a logic pulse and measure some characteristics of the pulse using the oscilloscope. Review the operator's manual or information supplied by your instructor for the function generator at your lab station. Select the pulse function and set the frequency for 1 kHz. (If you do not have a pulse function, a square wave may be substituted).

10. In this step, you will set up and measure the pulse amplitude of the function generator. The vertical sensitivity (VOLTS/DIV) control of the oscilloscope should be set for 1 V/div and the SEC/DIV should be left at 1 ms/div. Check that both controls are in their calibrated positions. Check the ground level on the oscilloscope as you did in Step 6 and set it for a convenient graticule near the bottom of the scope face. Switch the scope back to DC coupling and clip the ground lead of the scope probe to a ground on the generator. Touch the probe to the function generator's pulse output. If the generator has a variable amplitude control, adjust it for a 4.0 V pulse (4 divisions of deflection). Some generators have a separate control to adjust the dc level of the pulse; others do not. If your generator has a dc offset control, adjust the ground level of the pulse for zero volts.

11. If you have correctly set up the pulse generator and oscilloscope, you should observe a stable display that allows you to measure both the time and voltage of the waveform. In Plot 1 of your report, sketch the observed waveform. Measure the pulse width (t_w) and pulse repetition frequency (PRF). Show the time and amplitude on your plot.

12. Connect the LED and series limiting resistor, R_1, to the pulse generator as shown in Figure 1−3. Note that the LED is a polarized component and must be connected in the correct direction or it will not work. The schematic and an example of protoboard wiring is shown. Measure the signal across the LED with the oscilloscope and show it in Plot 2 of your report.

13. Sometimes it is useful to use an oscilloscope to measure the voltage across an ungrounded component. The current limiting resistor, R_1, in Figure 1−3 is an ungrounded component. To measure the voltage across it, connect both channels of your oscilloscope as shown in Figure 1−4. Make sure that both channels are calibrated and that the vertical sensitivity (VOLTS/DIV) is 1 V/div for each channel. Invert channel 2 and select the ADD function on your oscilloscope. (*Note:* Some oscilloscopes have a DIFF (difference) pushbutton that accomplishes this. Consult the operator's manual if you are not sure.) Measure the signal across the current-limiting resistor and show the result on Plot 3. As a check, the sum of the voltages across the components should be equal to the voltage of the generator.

14. The circuit with the resistor and diode has one path (series connection). Open the circuit between the resistor and the LED. Using the oscilloscope, can you pinpoint the open circuit? In your report, summarize a procedure you could use to locate an open in a series circuit.

For Further Investigation

More Measurements with the Oscilloscope

The oscilloscope is the most important test instrument for testing circuits, and you should become

FIGURE 1–3
Circuit for Step 12.

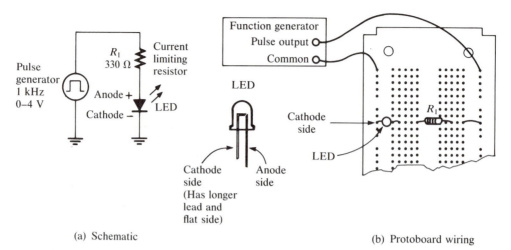

(a) Schematic

(b) Protoboard wiring

completely familiar with its operation. Adjust the pulse generator for each frequency listed in Table 1–3 in the report and obtain a stable display on the oscilloscope. If the beam is not visible, look for it with BEAM FINDER. If you still do not see a sweep, use AUTO triggering and check the INTENSITY level. When you have a stable display, measure the period and pulse width. The first line of the table is completed as an example. The computed and measured periods should agree within about 3%. The last signal, with a frequency of 1 Hz, may give you difficulty. You will need to use NORMAL triggering instead of auto triggering and you may need to adjust the trigger LEVEL control.

Using the Current Tracer

If you have a current tracer available, you can test the paths for current in the circuit you constructed. The current tracer can detect the path of *pulsing* current which you can follow. The current tracer detects fast current pulses by sensing the changing magnetic field associated with them. Set the generator to a 1 kHz TTL level pulse for this test.

Power the current tracer using a +5.0 V power supply. You will need to provide a common ground for the pulse generator and power supply, as shown in Figure 1–5(a). (Note that the current tracer has a red wire in one of the leads, which should be connected to the +5.0 V source, and a black wire in the other lead, which should be connected to the common). The sensitivity of the tracer is adjusted with a variable control near the tip of the current tracer. The current tracer must be held perpendicularly with respect to the conductor in which you are sensing current. In addition, the small mark on the probe tip needs to be aligned with the current path to obtain maximum sensitivity.

Begin by holding the current tracer above R_1. Rotate the current tracer so that the tip is aligned with the path of current. Adjust the sensitivity to about half-brightness. You should now be able to trace the current path through R_1, the LED, and along the protoboard.

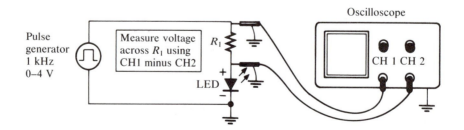

FIGURE 1–4
Measuring an ungrounded component. Both channels must be calibrated and have the same settings as the vertical sensitivity controls.

12

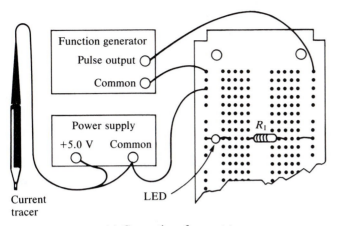
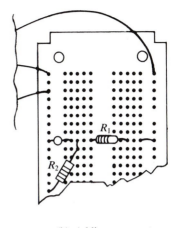

(a) Connection of current tracer

(b) Adding a current path through R_2

FIGURE 1–5

FIGURE 1–6
Stimulating the circuit with a logic pulser.

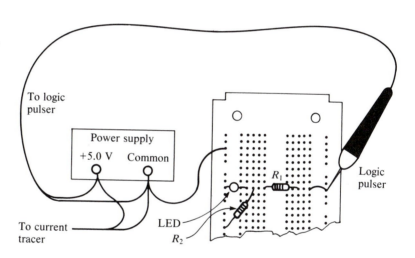

FIGURE 1–7
Simulating a short circuit. The logic pulser forces current through the short; this current can be detected with the current tracer.

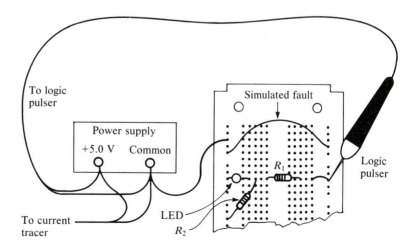

Practice tracing the path of current. Simulate a low impedance fault by installing a 100 Ω resistor (R_2) in parallel with the LED as shown in Figure 1-5(b). Test the circuit with the current tracer to determine the path for current. Does most of the current go through R_2 or through the LED?

Using The Current Tracer and Logic Pulser

Circuit boards typically have many connections where a potential short can occur. If a short occurs between the power supply and ground due to a solder splash or other reason, it can be difficult to find. A logic pulser, used in conjunction with a current tracer, can locate the fault without the need for applying power to the circuit. The logic pulser applies very fast pulses to a circuit under test. A flashing LED in the tip indicates the output mode which can be set to various pulse streams or to a continuous series of pulses. The pulser can be used in an operating circuit without damaging it because the energy supplied to the circuit is limited.

Start with the logic pulser by setting it for continuous pulses. Remove the pulse generator from the test circuit and touch the logic pulser to the test circuit, as shown in Figure 1-6. You can hold the current tracer at a 90-degree angle and against the tip of the logic pulser in order to set the sensitivity of the current tracer. You should now be able to follow the path for current as you did before.

Now simulate a direct short fault across the circuit by connecting a wire as shown in Figure 1-7. You may need to adjust the sensitivity of the current tracer. Use the logic pulser and current tracer to follow the path of current. Can you detect current in R_1? Describe the current path in the wire and in the protoboard in your report.

Report for Experiment 1

Name: _____ Date: _____ Class: _____

Objectives:

Procedure:

Data:

TABLE 1–1
DMM measurements of power supply.

Voltage Setting (use supply meter)	Voltage Reading (use DMM)
0.5 V	
1.0 V	
5.0 V	
12.0 V	

TABLE 1–2
Oscilloscope measurements of power supply.

Power Supply Setting	VOLTS/DIV Setting	Number of Divisions of Deflection	Oscilloscope (measured voltage)	DMM (measured voltage)
0.5 V	0.1 V/div	5.0 div	0.5 V	0.5 V
1.0 V				
5.0 V				
12.0 V				

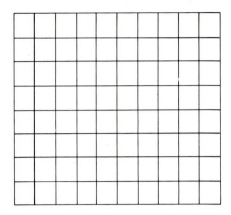

PLOT 1
Generator waveform.

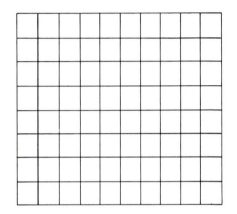

PLOT 2
Waveform across LED.

PLOT 3
Waveform across R_1.

Step 14: Procedure for locating an open in a series circuit:

Results and Conclusion:

Further Investigation Results:

TABLE 1–3

Pulse Generator Dial Frequency	Computed Period	Oscilloscope SEC/DIV	Number of Divisions	Measured Period	Measured Pulse Width
25 kHz	40 μs	10 μs/div	4.0 div	40 μs	10 μs*
6.5 kHz					
300 Hz					
1 Hz					

*Depends on particular pulse generator

Evaluation and Review Questions

1. If a DMM measures a voltage between two points of -3.5 V, what reading will be observed if the meter leads are reversed?

2. Why is it important to check the power supply voltage before connecting power to a logic circuit?

3. a. A periodic pulse waveform has the following parameters: PRR $= 4$ kHz; $t_w = 50$ μs; dc level $= 0.5$ V; amplitude $= 3.0$ V. Sketch the waveform. Label your sketch.

b. What is the duty cycle of the above waveform? _____

4. The four major sections of an oscilloscope are listed next. In your own words, state the function of each section.
a. vertical section

b. trigger section

c. horizontal section

d. display section

5. Compare the advantages and disadvantages of making a dc voltage measurement with a DMM and an oscilloscope.

2

Constructing a Logic Probe

Objectives

After completing this experiment, you will be able to:

□ Use the logic connection diagram *(pin-out)* from the data book for the 7404 inverter to determine the power supply and logic connections for a 7404 inverter.

□ Apply the correct voltage to the IC and build a simple logic probe using the 7404 inverter.

□ Use this logic probe to test a circuit.

□ Measure logic levels in the circuit with the digital multimeter (DMM) and the oscilloscope, and compare them with valid input logic levels.

Reference Reading

Floyd, *Digital Fundamentals*, 4th ed., Section 1–3, Logic Levels and Pulse Waveforms; Section 1–4, Elements of Digital Logic; Section 1–5, Functions of Digital Logic; Section 1–6, A System Application; Section 1–7, Digital Integrated Circuits; Section 1–8, Digital Testing and Troubleshooting Instruments

Materials Needed

7404 hex inverter
Two LEDs (light-emitting diodes)
Two signal diodes (1N914 or equivalent)

Resistors:
  Three 330 Ω
  One 2.0 kΩ
1 kΩ potentiometer

Summary of Theory

Digital circuits have two discrete voltage levels to represent the binary digits *(bits)* 1 and 0. All digital circuits are switching circuits. Instead of mechanical switches, they use high-speed transistors to represent either an ON condition or an OFF condition. Various types of logic, representing different technologies, are available to the logic designer. The choice of a particular family is determined by factors such as speed, cost, availability, noise immunity, and so forth. The key requirement within each family is compatibility; that is, there must be consistency within the logic levels and power supplies of various integrated circuits made by different manufacturers. The experiments in this lab book use primarily transistor-transistor logic, or TTL. The detailed performance characteristics of TTL depend on the particular subfamily. However, all TTL is designed to operate from a 5 V power supply, and the logic levels are the same for all TTL integrated circuits. The input logic levels are illustrated in Figure 2–1. They will be covered in more detail in Experiment 5.

For any integrated circuit (IC) to function properly, power and ground must be connected.

FIGURE 2–1
TTL logic levels.

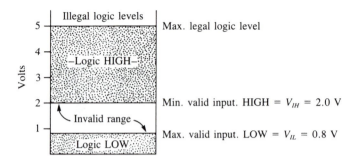

The connection diagram for the IC shows these connections, although in practice the power and ground connections are frequently omitted from diagrams of logic circuits. Appendix A contains connection diagrams as found in manufacturers' logic data books. Figure 2–2 shows the connection diagram for a 7404 hex inverter, which will be used in this experiment. Pins are numbered counterclockwise from the top, starting with a notch or circle at the top or next to pin 1; see Figure 2–3.

The circuit in this experiment is a simple logic probe. Logic probes are useful for detecting the presence of a HIGH or a LOW logic level in a circuit. The logic probe in this experiment is a simple one designed only to illustrate the use of this tool and the wiring of integrated circuits. The simple probe shown in Figure 2–4 works as follows: If the probe is not connected, the top inverter is pulled HIGH (through the 2.0 kΩ resistor) and the bottom inverter is pulled LOW (through the 330 Ω resistor). As a result, both outputs are HIGH and neither LED is on. If the probe input is connected to a voltage above approxi-

mately 2.0 V, the voltage at the input of the lower inverter is interpreted as a logic HIGH through diode D_2. As a result, the output of the lower inverter goes LOW, and the lower LED, representing a HIGH input, turns on. If the probe input is connected to a voltage below approximately 0.8 V, the upper input inverter is pulled below the logic threshold for a LOW, and the output inverter is LOW. Then the LED, which represents a logic LOW, turns on. A more sophisticated probe could detect pulses, has a much higher input impedance, and is useful for logic families other than TTL.

Procedure

A Simple Logic Probe

1. Before starting any wiring, review the guidelines for experiments given in the Introduction. If you are not familiar with the power supply and digital multimeter at your lab station, take the time to learn how to set and measure voltages with these instruments before proceeding.

FIGURE 2–2
Connection diagram from manufacturer's logic data book.

$Y = \overline{A}$

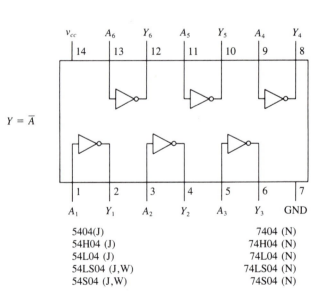

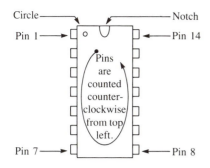

FIGURE 2–3
Numbering of pins.

2. Using the pin numbers shown, construct the simple logic probe circuit shown in Figure 2–4. Note that the LEDs and the signal diodes are polarized; that is, they must be connected in the correct direction. The arrow on electronic components always points in the direction of conventional current flow, which is from plus to minus. Signal diodes are marked on the negative side with a line. The LEDs generally have a flat spot on the negative side or are the longer element inside the diode. As a guide, Figure 2–5(a) shows an example of the wiring of the logic probe. Pin numbers are included on the drawing but usually are omitted from logic drawings.

3. Test your circuit by connecting the probe to 5 V and then to ground. One of the LEDs should light to indicate a HIGH, the other, a LOW. When the probe is not connected, neither LED should be on. If the circuit does not work, double-check your wiring and the direction of the diodes. You can test the HIGH and LOW threshold voltages of your logic probe with the circuit

shown in Figure 2–5(b). Connect the logic probe to a 1 kΩ variable resistor, as shown. Vary the resistor and find the HIGH and LOW thresholds. Use a DMM to measure the threshold voltages.

4. Now use two of the remaining inverters to wire the cross-coupled inverters shown in Figure 2–6. The input signal, V_{in}, is inverted at the output by the top inverter. The output, in turn, is inverted by the lower inverter and "latches" the input voltage at its last logic level. Connect the logic probe to V_{out}. Then momentarily touch V_{in} (pin 3) to ground. Observe the output logic and record it (high, low, or invalid) in Table 2–1 of the report.

5. Touch the input to 5 V, test the output again, and record the logic in Table 2–1.

6. Place a fault in the circuit of Figure 2–6 by removing the wire that is connected to pin 5, the input of the lower inverter. Now momentarily touch the input, pin 3, to ground. Test the logic levels at each point in the circuit and record them in Table 2–1.

7. An open circuit on the input of TTL logic has an invalid logic level. Even though it is invalid, it acts as a logic HIGH at the input to the gate. (However, open circuits should never be used as a means of connecting an input to a constant HIGH.) In this step, repeat step 6 but use a DMM to measure the actual voltages at each pin. Record the data in Table 2–1.

8. In order to gain practice with the oscilloscope, repeat the measurements of step 6 using the oscilloscope. You may want to review the procedure for making dc voltage measurements with the oscilloscope in Experiment 1. Record the measured voltages in Table 2–1.

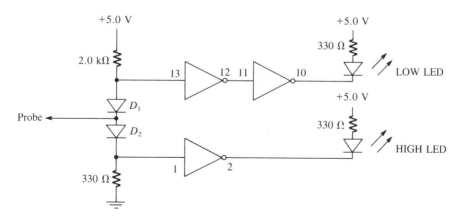

FIGURE 2–4
Simple logic probe.

FIGURE 2–5

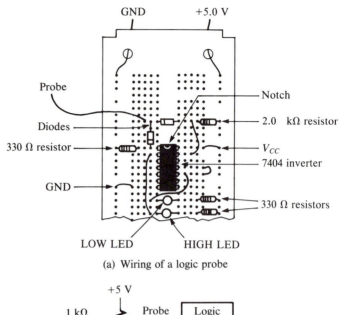

GND   +5.0 V

Probe

Notch

Diodes

2.0 kΩ resistor

330 Ω resistor

V_{CC}
7404 inverter

GND

330 Ω resistors

LOW LED   HIGH LED

(a) Wiring of a logic probe

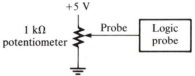

+5 V

1 kΩ
potentiometer

Probe

Logic
probe

(b) Test circuit to determine
logic thresholds

For Further Investigation

1. In this investigation, you will gain further practice making dc measurements with the oscilloscope by making measurements of voltages on the logic probe that you constructed. Begin by select-

ing channel 1 and setting the sensitivity to 1 V per division.

2. Place the input coupling control on dc. Place the scope probe on +5.0 V (with the reference side of the probe on ground). Use the oscilloscope to verify that the voltage is 5.0 V.

3. With the logic probe input disconnected, measure the voltage at each point listed in Table 2–2 of the report. Measure the voltage with the oscilloscope and check your reading with your DMM. Record the values in Table 2–2. If the deflection is small, increase the vertical sensitivity (decrease the volts per division) in order to obtain the highest accuracy. If you change the vertical sensitivity, recheck the ground level and reposition it if necessary using the vertical POSITION control.

4. Repeat the measurements in Step 3 with the probe input connected to +5.0 V; record the values in Table 2–3 of the report.

5. Connect the probe input to ground and repeat the measurements listed in Table 2–4 of the report.

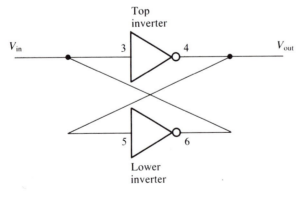

Top
inverter

V_{in}

3

4

V_{out}

5

6

Lower
inverter

FIGURE 2–6
Test circuit.

Report for Experiment 2

Name: _____ Date: _____ Class: _____

Objectives:

Procedure:

Data:

TABLE 2–1

Step		Input Logic Level (pin 3)	Output Logic Level (pin 4)	Logic Level (pin 5)	Logic Level (pin 6)
4	V_{in} momentarily on ground.				
5	V_{in} momentarily on +5.0 V.				
6	Fault condition: open at pin 5.				
7	Voltages with fault (DMM):	volts	volts	volts	volts
8	Voltages with fault (scope):	volts	volts	volts	volts

Results and Conclusions:

Further Investigation Results:

TABLE 2–2

Logic Probe Open	Measured Voltage	
	Oscilloscope	DMM
Pin 13		
Pin 12		
Pin 10		
Pin 1		
Pin 2		

TABLE 2–3

Logic Probe on +5 V	Measured Voltage	
	Oscilloscope	DMM
Pin 13		
Pin 12		
Pin 10		
Pin 1		
Pin 2		

TABLE 2–4

Logic Probe on GND	Measured Voltage	
	Oscilloscope	DMM
Pin 13		
Pin 12		
Pin 10		
Pin 1		
Pin 2		

Evaluation and Review Questions

1. a. For the circuit of Figure 2–7, what logic level would you expect at the output (pin 4) if the input at pin 3 were open?

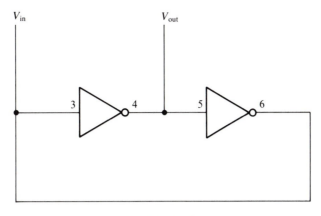

V_{in} V_{out}

3   4   5   6

FIGURE 2–7

b. What voltage would you expect to see on the input (pin 3)? _____
Is this valid? _____

2. a. How would an open output on pin 6 affect the circuit? What happens to latching action? Confirm your answer by removing the wire at pin 6 and repeating Step 5.

3. Observe the circuit shown in Figure 2–7. Is this circuit the same as the circuit in Figure 2–6?

4. Discuss the advantages and disadvantages of using a logic probe and DMM for logic measurements.

5. a. What is the equivalent logic if two inverters are connected in series, as shown in Figure 2–8?

V_{in} —————Output = ?

FIGURE 2–8

b. What action would you expect if the output of a single inverter were connected to its input?

c. What logic do you expect to see on the output of a TTL inverter if the input is open?

Checkup 1

The exercises in this checkup reflect information covered in Floyd's Chapter 1, "Introduction," and Buchla's Experiments 1 and 2.

1. State whether each of the following TTL input voltages is HIGH, LOW, or INVALID:

    a. 1.0 V _____ **b.** 2.5 V _____ **c.** 0.3 V _____ **d.** −0.6 V _____ **e.** 3.1 V _____

2. If a HIGH logic level represents a false condition (0) and a LOW logic level represents a true (1) condition, the logic is called _____ logic.

3. What is the power supply voltage for TTL logic?

4. **a.** What is a pulse?

    b. How is the rise time of a pulse normally defined?

5. Explain the difference between a periodic waveform and a nonperiodic waveform.

6. If a period pulse waveform with a frequency of 12.5 kHz has a pulse width of 20 μs, what is the duty cycle?

7. The frequency of a clock signal is 9 MHz and the duty cycle is 25%.
    a. What is the period?

    b. What is the pulse width?

8. What is the purpose of a register?

9. Compare the function of a multiplexer with that of a demultiplexer.

10. Compare the function of an encoder with that of a decoder.

11. What types of devices are needed to implement a counter?

12. What is the difference between a ROM and a RAM?

13. List the major parts of a microprocessor:

14. What are the four groups of controls on an oscilloscope?

15. a. What voltage would you expect to measure on a TTL open input? _____ V

   b. What indication would you expect to see if you were testing the open with a logic probe?

16. What advantage does an oscilloscope have over a DMM for troubleshooting?

17. Assume an experimental circuit, constructed on a protoboard, does not operate the first time it is turned on. List steps you would employ to find the problem.

18. What is the function of a logic analyzer?

19. Why is it necessary for a current tracer to be used only with pulsating current?

20. a. Explain the difference between a logic probe, a logic pulser, and a current tracer.

   b. Which instrument(s) would be useful for tracing the path to a short from the power supply voltage to ground?

3

Number Systems

Objectives

After completing this experiment, you will be able to:
- Convert between binary, BCD, octal, hexadecimal, and base ten number systems.
- Construct a circuit that demonstrates conversions between number systems.

Reference Reading

Floyd, *Digital Fundamentals,* 4th ed., Section 2–1, Decimal Numbers; Section 2–2, Binary Numbers; Section 2–3, Decimal-to-Binary Conversion; Section 2–4, Binary Arithmetic; Section 2–5, 1's and 2's Complements; Section 2–8, Octal Numbers; Section 2–9, Hexadecimal Numbers; Section 2–10, Binary Coded Decimal (BCD)

Materials Needed

Five LEDs
7447A BCD/decimal decoder
MAN72 seven-segment display
Four-position DIP switch
Resistors:
   Eleven 330 Ω
   One 1 kΩ

Summary of Theory

The number of symbols in a number system is called the *base,* or *radix,* of that system. The dec-imal number system uses ten counting symbols— the digits 0 through 9—to represent quantities. Thus it is a base ten system. In this system, we represent quantities larger than 9 by using positional weighting of the digits. The position, or column, that a digit occupies indicates the weight of that digit in determining the value of the number. The base ten number system is a weighted system because each column has a value associated with it.

Digital systems use two states to represent quantities and thus are *binary* in nature. The binary counting system has a radix of two and uses only the numbers 0 and 1. (These are often called *bits,* which is a contraction of BInary digiT). It too is a weighted counting system, with each column value worth twice the value of the column to the immediate right. Because binary numbers have only two digits, large numbers expressed in binary require a long string of 0s and 1s. Other systems, which are related to binary in a simple way, are often used to simplify these numbers. These systems include octal, hexadecimal, and BCD.

The octal number system is a weighted number system using the digits 0 through 7. The column values in octal are worth 8 times that of the column to the immediate right. You convert from binary to octal by arranging the binary number in groups of 3 bits, starting at the binary point, and writing the octal symbol for each binary group. You can reverse the procedure to convert from octal to binary. Simply write an equivalent 3-bit binary number for each octal character.

The hexadecimal system is a weighted number system using 16 characters. The column values in hexadecimal (or simply hex) are worth 16 times that of the column to the immediate right. The characters are the numbers 0 through 9 and the first six letters of the alphabet, A through F. Letters were chosen because of their sequence, but remember that they are used to indicate numbers, not letters. You convert binary numbers to hexadecimal numbers by arranging the binary number into 4-bit groups, starting at the binary point. Then write the next symbol for each group of 4 bits. You convert hex numbers to binary by reversing the procedure. That is, write an equivalent 4-bit binary number for each hexadecimal character.

The BCD system uses four binary bits to represent each decimal digit. It is a convenient code because it allows ready conversion from base ten to a code that a machine can understand; however, it is wasteful of bits. A 4-bit binary number could represent the numbers 0 to 15, but in BCD it represents only the quantities 0 through 9. The binary representations of the numbers 10 through 15 are not used in BCD and are invalid.

A simple circuit can illustrate the various number systems discussed above. The circuit in this experiment uses light-emitting diodes (LEDs) to show the binary or BCD number and a seven-segment display to show the equivalent base ten number. A seven-segment display is a special arrangement of LEDs that can form the numbers 0 through 9 and some letters. Figure 3–1 illustrates the arrangement of diodes in a seven-segment display. The circuit uses an IC called a *decoder* to convert the binary input to a seven-segment value. Decoder circuits will be studied in Experiment 11. In the Further Investigation, you will modify the circuit to form the equivalent octal representation of the four switches.

Procedure

1. Take a moment to reread "Circuit Wiring" in the Introduction to the Student before constructing this experiment. The pin numbers for the ICs in this and succeeding experiments have not been assigned; pin numbers may be found in the data sheets in the back of this lab manual or in manufacturer's data books. It is a good idea to assign the pin numbers to the schematic before you begin wiring.

Conversions Between Number Systems

2. Connect the circuit shown in Figure 3–2. Test each switch to see that it turns on an LED. This portion of the circuit represents the input binary number. A lighted LED represents a binary one, and an unlighted LED represents a binary zero. The least significant bit (LSB) is on the right and represents the 1s column. The most significant bit (MSB) is on the left.

3. Now remove power and add the circuit shown in Figure 3–3. The pin numbers for the MAN72 display are shown in Figure 3–1 and 7447A pin numbers are shown in Figure 3–4. Note that the 7447A has 16 pins and the MAN72 seven-segment display has only 14 pins. Both are

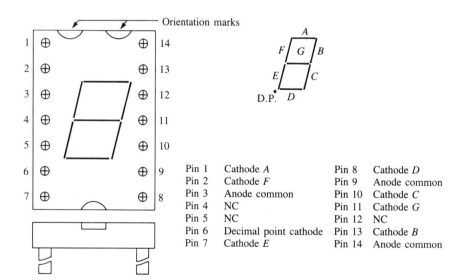

Pin 1	Cathode *A*	Pin 8	Cathode *D*
Pin 2	Cathode *F*	Pin 9	Anode common
Pin 3	Anode common	Pin 10	Cathode *C*
Pin 4	NC	Pin 11	Cathode *G*
Pin 5	NC	Pin 12	NC
Pin 6	Decimal point cathode	Pin 13	Cathode *B*
Pin 7	Cathode *E*	Pin 14	Anode common

FIGURE 3–1
MAN72 seven-segment display.

FIGURE 3–2

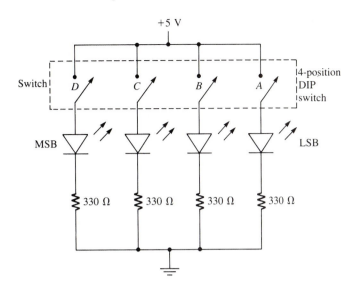

numbered counterclockwise starting from the top left.

Connect pins 3, 4, and 5 on the 7447A to a 1 kΩ resistor connected to +5 V. Connect pin 14 of the MAN72 to +5 V. Be sure to connect each output from the 7447A through a 330 Ω resistor to the seven-segment display as shown on the circuit drawing. Figure 3–5 shows an example of the wiring.

4. When you have completed wiring the cir-

cuit, test it by checking each switch combination shown in Table 3–1 in the report. Set the binary number on the switches by closing a switch for a 1 and opening a switch for a 0. Complete each column for the table by writing the input numbers as BCD, octal, and hexadecimal. Show the output from the seven-segment display in the right-hand column. The last six invalid BCD codes will show a unique code in the seven-segment display.

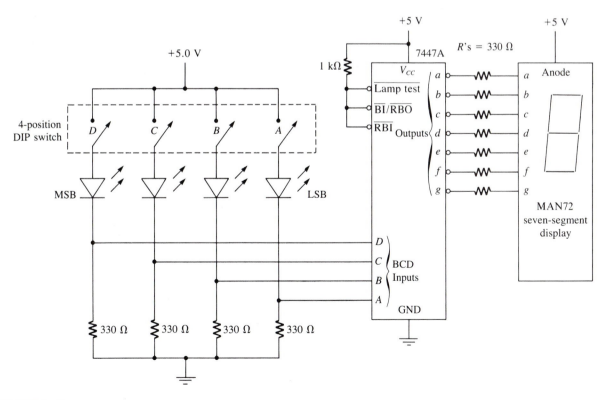

FIGURE 3–3

FIGURE 3–4

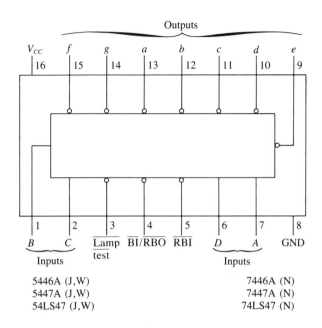

Outputs

V_{CC}	f	g	a	b	c	d	e
16	15	14	13	12	11	10	9

1	2	3	4	5	6	7	8
B	C	Lamp test	BI/RBO	RBI	D	A	GND

Inputs   Inputs

5446A (J,W)   7446A (N)
5447A (J,W)   7447A (N)
54LS47 (J,W)   74LS47 (N)

For Further Investigation

As you observed, the 7447A decoder used in this experiment actually decoded only the decimal numbers correctly.[1] The 7447A decoder is normally used for decimal decoding; however, a slight modification of the circuit can be made to correctly decode octal numbers. For this experiment, the largest octal number that we can show using the same four-position DIP switch is octal 17.

Recall that the conversion of a binary number to octal can be accomplished by grouping the bi-

nary number by threes starting at the binary point. To display the octal numbers larger than octal 7 would normally require a second display; however, we could use an LED to represent the most significant digit, which (for 4 bits) cannot be larger than 1. The seven-segment display can show the least significant digit. Your job in this further investigation is to modify the circuit in Figure 3–3 so that it correctly shows the octal numbers from 0 to 17. For example, if the switches are set to binary 1000, your circuit should light the LED representing the most significant digit and the seven-segment display should show a zero. Draw your circuit in the report, test it, and summarize how it works.

---

[1]There are decoders available (the 9370, for example) that will show the hexadecimal numbers.

FIGURE 3–5

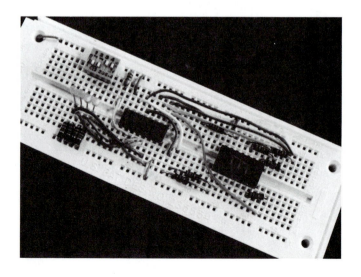

Report for Experiment 3

Name: _____ Date: _____ Class: _____

Objectives:

Procedure:

Data:

TABLE 3–1

Inputs				Output
Binary Number	BCD Number	Octal Number	Hex Number	Seven-Segment Display
0 0 0 0				
0 0 0 1				
0 0 1 0				
0 0 1 1				
0 1 0 0				
0 1 0 1				
0 1 1 0				
0 1 1 1				
1 0 0 0				
1 0 0 1				
1 0 1 0	INVALID			
1 0 1 1	INVALID			
1 1 0 0	INVALID			
1 1 0 1	INVALID			
1 1 1 0	INVALID			
1 1 1 1	INVALID			

Results and Conclusion:

Further Investigation Results:

Evaluation and Review Questions

1. Assume the switches in Figure 3–3 are set for a binary 1000, but the display shows a zero. What are three possible causes for this error?

2. Looking at the possible causes for an error from Question 1, how would you go about troubleshooting the problem?

3. Suppose that the $\overline{B1/RB0}$ input line was shorted to ground on the 7447A decoder and all other input lines were okay. Looking at the function table for the 7447A in Appendix A, determine the effect this would have on the display.

4. Explain the difference between binary and BCD.

5. Convert each number shown into the other bases:

Binary	Octal	Hexadecimal	Decimal	BCD
01001100				
	304			
		E6		
			57	
				0100 1001

Checkup 2

The exercises in this checkup reflect information covered in Floyd's Chapter 2, "Number Systems and Codes," and Buchla's Experiment 3.

1. **a.** What is meant by the *base* of a number system?

   b. What is the base of the octal number system?

2. Why are binary numbers important in the study of digital electronics?

3. **a.** How does a *weighted* number system differ from an *unweighted* system?

   b. What type of system is represented by Gray code?

4. What is the weight of the most significant bit (MSB) binary switches shown in Figure 3–2?

5. **a.** Explain how to use grouping of bits to convert a binary number to octal or hexadecimal.

   b. Explain how the procedure can be reversed to convert an octal or hexadecimal number to binary.

6. Explain the difference between 1's complement and 2's complement.

7. Explain the difference between BCD and Excess-3 code.

8. Assume the circuit shown in Figure 3–3 has all segments of the seven-segment display ON no matter what the input switches are set to. The 7447A is replaced but the condition resists. The LEDs are observed to be functional. What can account for the trouble?

9. The Baudot code is old 5-bit telegraphing code still used in some applications. How many different characters can be represented by this code?

10. Convert each number shown into the other bases:

Binary	Octal	Hexadecimal	Decimal	BCD
11110000				
	165			
		3D		
			15	
				0110 0011

11. Assume you needed to show numbers up to 255 in a seven-segment display such as the on-site display unit illustrated in the small system in Floyd's text (Figure 1–23). Assume the input number is an 8-bit binary number. What needs to be done to the input number in order to use the decoding technique illustrated in the circuit in Figure 3–3 of the experiment?

12. a. What sequence of numbers can be displayed in the seven-segment display for the circuit shown in Figure 3–6?

    b. What is the base of the number system this represents?

FIGURE 3–6

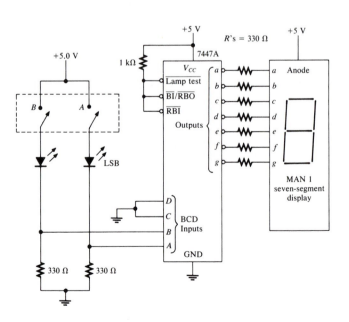

4

Logic Gates

Objectives

After completing this experiment, you will be able to:

□ Determine the truth tables for the NAND, NOR, and inverter gates.

□ Use the inverting gates (NAND and NOR) to formulate other basic logic gates and demonstrate the equivalence between the NAND/negative-OR and NOR/negative-AND.

□ Connect a simple logic circuit using the ANSI/IEEE Std. 91–1984 symbols.

□ Observe pulse waveforms in a NAND circuit and measure the propagation delay of a NAND gate.

Reference Reading

Floyd, *Digital Fundamentals,* 4th ed., Section 3–1, The Inverter; Section 3–2, The AND Gate; Section 3–3, The OR Gate; Section 3–4, The NAND Gate; Section 3–5, The NOR Gate; Section 3–6, The Exclusive-OR and Exclusive-NOR Gates.

Materials Needed

7400 quad 2-input NAND gate
7402 quad 2-input NOR gate
1 kΩ resistor
For Further Investigation: 7486 quad XOR gate

Summary of Theory

Logic deals with only two normal conditions: logic TRUE or logic FALSE. These conditions are like the yes or no answers to a question. Either a switch is closed (TRUE) or it isn't (FALSE); either an event has occurred (TRUE) or it hasn't (FALSE); and so on. In Boolean logic, TRUE and FALSE represent conditions. In positive logic, TRUE is represented by the term HIGH and FALSE is represented by the term LOW. In positive logic, the more positive voltage is TRUE and the less positive voltage is FALSE. Thus, for positive TTL logic, a voltage of $+2.4$ V = HIGH and a voltage of $+0.4$ V = LOW.

In some systems, this definition is reversed. With negative logic, the more positive voltage is FALSE and the less positive voltage is TRUE. Thus, for TTL logic, a voltage of $+0.4$ V = TRUE and a voltage of $+2.4$ V = FALSE.

Although negative logic is sometimes useful in simplifying designs, it can easily become confusing. For example, in positive logic a 2-input AND gate has a HIGH output if both input *A* AND input *B* are HIGH. But in negative logic it becomes an OR gate because if either input *A* OR input *B* is LOW (true), the output is LOW (true). Figure 4–1 illustrates this idea. The electrical signals are identical for both gates, but the logic definitions are not. The AND gate can also be drawn as an OR gate if inversion "bubbles" are added to both the inputs and the output to indicate the active-LOW signals.

FIGURE 4–1

Two ways of representing an AND gate.

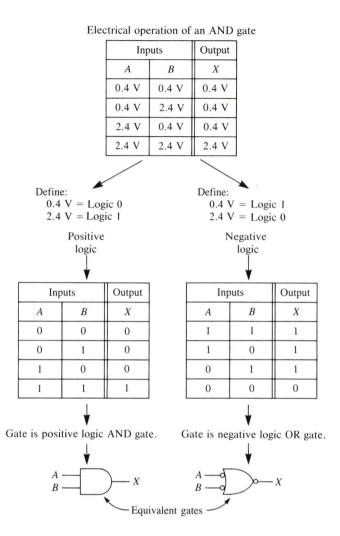

Electrical operation of an AND gate

Inputs		Output
A	B	X
0.4 V	0.4 V	0.4 V
0.4 V	2.4 V	0.4 V
2.4 V	0.4 V	0.4 V
2.4 V	2.4 V	2.4 V

Define:
0.4 V = Logic 0
2.4 V = Logic 1

Positive logic

Inputs		Output
A	B	X
0	0	0
0	1	0
1	0	0
1	1	1

Gate is positive logic AND gate.

Define:
0.4 V = Logic 1
2.4 V = Logic 0

Negative logic

Inputs		Output
A	B	X
1	1	1
1	0	1
0	1	1
0	0	0

Gate is negative logic OR gate.

Equivalent gates

Another very useful method of dealing with negative logic is to label the signal function with a bar written over the label to indicate that the signal is LOW when the stated condition is TRUE. Figure 4–2 shows some examples of this logic, called *assertion-level* logic. You should be aware that manufacturers are not always consistent in the way labels are applied to diagrams and function tables. Assertion-level logic is frequently shown to indicate an action. As shown in Figure 4–2, the action to read (R) is asserted (TRUE) when the input line

is HIGH; the opposite action is to write ($\overline{W}$), which is asserted (TRUE) when the line is LOW. Other examples are shown in the figure.

The symbols for the basic logic gates are shown in Figure 4–3. The newer IEEE rectangular symbols are shown along with the older distinctive-shape symbols. The distinctive-shape symbols for logic gates are still very popular because they enable you to visualize the standard Boolean operations of AND, OR, and INVERT immediately. The distinctive shapes also enable you to analyze

FIGURE 4–2

Examples of assertion logic.

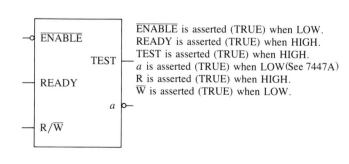

$\overline{\text{ENABLE}}$ is asserted (TRUE) when LOW.
READY is asserted (TRUE) when HIGH.
TEST is asserted (TRUE) when HIGH.
a is asserted (TRUE) when LOW(See 7447A)
R is asserted (TRUE) when HIGH.
$\overline{W}$ is asserted (TRUE) when LOW.

40

logic networks because each gate can be represented with a positive logic symbol or an equivalent negative logic symbol, as was shown in Figure 4–1 for an AND gate.

In addition to the AND, OR, and INVERT functions, two other basic gates are very important to logic designers. These are the NAND and NOR gates in which the output of AND and OR, respectively, have been negated. These gates are important because of their "universal" property; these gates can be used to synthesize the other Boolean logic functions including AND, OR, and INVERT functions. This is covered further in Section 5–3 of Floyd's text.

Two gates that are sometimes classified with the basic gates are the exclusive-OR (abbreviated XOR) and the exclusive-NOR (abbreviated XNOR) gates. These gates always have two inputs. The symbols are shown in Figure 4–3(f) and (g). The output of the XOR gate is HIGH when exactly one input is HIGH. The output is HIGH if either A or B is HIGH, but not both. The XNOR is just the opposite; the output is HIGH only when the inputs are the same. For this reason, the XNOR gate is sometimes called a COINCIDENCE gate.

The logical operation of all gates can be summarized with a truth table, which shows all the possible inputs and outputs for a combinational logic circuit. The truth tables for AND, OR, INVERT, XOR, and XNOR are shown in Table 4–1 (a) through (e). The tables are shown with 1 and 0 to represent positive logic HIGH and LOW, respectively. This notation is convenient because the numbers can be written quickly as an ordinary count sequence of binary numbers; however, in negative logic, the concepts of 1 and 0 are reversed. Except in Figure 4–1 (where negative logic is illustrated), only positive logic is used in this lab book and 1 and 0 mean HIGH and LOW, respectively.

In the experiment, you will test the truth tables for NAND and NOR gates as well as those for several combinations of these gates. Keep in

FIGURE 4–3
Basic logic gates.

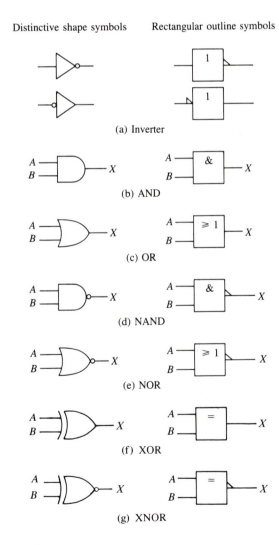

Distinctive shape symbols   Rectangular outline symbols

(a) Inverter

(b) AND

(c) OR

(d) NAND

(e) NOR

(f) XOR

(g) XNOR

TABLE 4–1 (a)
Truth table for inverter.

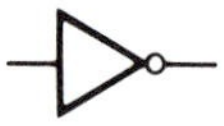

Input	Output
A	X
0	1
1	0

TABLE 4–1 (b)
Truth table for 2-input AND gate.

Inputs		Output
A	B	X
0	0	0
0	1	0
1	0	0
1	1	1

TABLE 4–1 (c)
Truth table for 2-input OR gates.

Inputs		Output
A	B	X
0	0	0
0	1	1
1	0	1
1	1	1

TABLE 4–1 (d)
Truth table for XOR gate.

Inputs		Output
A	B	X
0	0	0
0	1	1
1	0	1
1	1	0

TABLE 4–1 (e)
Truth table for XNOR gate.

Inputs		Output
A	B	X
0	0	1
0	1	0
1	0	0
1	1	1

mind that if any two truth tables are identical, then the logic circuits that they represent are equivalent. This equivalency will be investigated in this experiment. Later, in Experiment 6, you will prove the algebraic basis of these circuits.

Procedure

Logic Functions

1. Look up the connection diagram for the 7400 quad 2-input NAND gate and the 7402 quad 2-input NOR gate in Appendix A. Note that there are four gates on each of these ICs. Apply V_{CC} and ground to the appropriate pins. Then test one of the NAND gates by connecting all possible combinations of inputs as listed in Table 4–2 of the report. Apply a logic 1 through a series 1 kΩ resistor and a logic 0 by connecting directly to ground. Show the logic output as well as the measured output voltage for each case, and include both in Table 4–2. Use the DMM to measure the output voltage.

2. Repeat Step 1 for one of the NOR gates; tabulate your results in Table 4–3 of the report.

3. Connect the circuits of Figures 4–4 and 4–5. Connect the input to a 0 and a 1, measure each output voltage, and complete truth Tables 4–4 and 4–5 for the circuits.

4. Construct the circuit shown in Figure 4–6 and complete truth Table 4–6. This circuit may appear at first to have no application but in fact can be used as a buffer. In logic, a buffer can be used to provide more drive current allowing additional circuits to be connected to a gate.

FIGURE 4–4

FIGURE 4–5

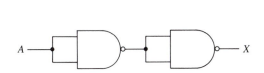

FIGURE 4–6

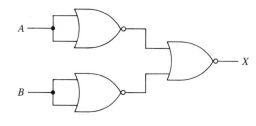

FIGURE 4–7

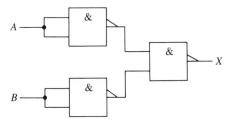

FIGURE 4–8

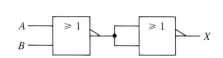

FIGURE 4–9

FIGURE 4–10

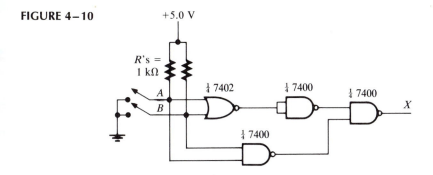

5. Construct the circuit shown in Figure 4–7 and complete truth Table 4–7. Notice that the truth table for this circuit is the same as the truth table for one of the single gates. (What does this say about the circuit?)

6. Repeat Step 5 for the circuits shown in Figures 4–8 and 4–9. Complete truth Tables 4–8 and 4–9.

7. The circuit shown in Figure 4–10 has the same truth table as one of the truth tables shown in Figure 4–1 (a) through (e). Test all input combinations and complete truth Table 4–10. What is the equivalent gate?

For Further Investigation

Pulse Response of a Logic Circuit

In this investigation you need to have a signal generator capable of supplying TTL level pulses and a two-channel oscilloscope. Check the signal generator output to insure that its output does not exceed the nominal power supply voltages (ground and +5 V).

Some additional hints for oscilloscope use with digital logic follow:

1. Normally, use dc coupling for the signal. (The input signal is directly coupled to the scope rather than capacitively coupled.)

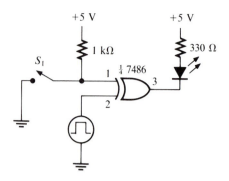

FIGURE 4–11
XOR gate.

2. Check probe compensation at the start of each lab session, and verify that variable controls are in the "calibrate" position. As a general rule, you would use an attenuating probe (×10 or ×100) to avoid capacitive loading and provide a high-frequency response.

3. Trigger the scope from only one channel. Do NOT use COMP (composite) triggering (sometimes labeled VERTICAL MODE) to avoid incorrect time relationships between the channels.

Connect the 7486 exclusive-OR gate as shown in Figure 4–11. Set the pulse generator to a frequency of 10 kHz and select a SEC/DIV setting of 0.2. Observe the signal from the pulse generator on channel 1 and the output signal from the XOR gate on channel 2. While observing the trace, close S_1. Sketch the waveforms in Plot 1 of the report.

What application can you think of for this circuit?

Report for Experiment 4

Name: _____ Date: _____ Class: _____

Objectives:

Procedure:

Data:

TABLE 4–2
NAND gate.

Inputs		Output	Measured Output Voltage
A	B	X	
0	0		
0	1		
1	0		
1	1		

TABLE 4–3
NOR gate.

Inputs		Output	Measured Output Voltage
A	B	X	
0	0		
0	1		
1	0		
1	1		

TABLE 4–4
Truth table for Figure 4–4.

Input	Output	Measured Output Voltage
A	X	
0		
1		

TABLE 4–5
Truth table for Figure 4–5.

Input	Output	Measured Output Voltage
A	X	
0		
1		

TABLE 4–6
Truth table for Figure 4–6.

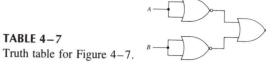

Input	Output	Measured Output Voltage
A	X	
0		
1		

TABLE 4–7
Truth table for Figure 4–7.

Inputs		Output	Measured Output Voltage
A	B	X	
0	0		
0	1		
1	0		
1	1		

TABLE 4–8
Truth table for Figure 4–8.

Inputs		Output	Measured Output Voltage
A	B	X	
0	0		
0	1		
1	0		
1	1		

TABLE 4–9
Truth table for Figure 4–9.

Inputs		Output	Measured Output Voltage
A	B	X	
0	0		
0	1		
1	0		
1	1		

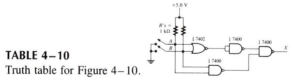

TABLE 4–10
Truth table for Figure 4–10.

Inputs		Output	Measured Output Voltage
A	B	X	
0	0		
0	1		
1	0		
1	1		

Results and Conclusion:

Further Investigation Results:

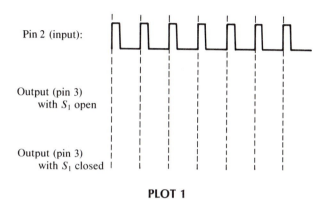

Pin 2 (input):

Output (pin 3)
with S_1 open

Output (pin 3)
with S_1 closed

PLOT 1

Evaluation and Review Questions

1. Look over truth tables in your data. If any of these tables are the same as that of an inverter (Table 4–1(a)), then the circuits are equivalent and either could be used for the inversion function, if necessary.

a. What circuit(s) did you find that are equivalent to inverters?

b. What circuit is equivalent to a 2-input AND gate?

c. What circuit is equivalent to a 2-input OR gate?

2. An alarm circuit is needed to indicate that either the temperature OR the pressure in a batch process is too high. If either of the conditions is true, a microswitch closes to ground as shown in Figure 4–12. The required output for an LED is a LOW signal when the alarm condition is true. George thinks that an OR gate is needed, but Betty argues that an AND gate is needed. Who is right and why?

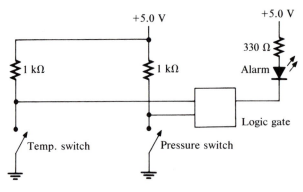

+5.0 V

+5.0 V

330 Ω

1 kΩ

1 kΩ

Alarm

Logic gate

Temp. switch

Pressure switch

FIGURE 4–12

3. a. A standard TTL circuit can drive no more than 10 standard TTL inputs. Assume you need to connect 15 inputs to the output of a NAND gate. Show how the circuit of Figure 4–6 can allow you to do this.

7 inputs

8 inputs

b. From the truth table for Figure 4–6, what does double inversion do to the logic?

4. A car burglar alarm has a normally LOW switch on each of its four doors when they are closed. If any door is opened, the alarm is set off. The alarm requires an active HIGH output. What type of gate is needed to provide this logic?

5. Suppose you need a 2-input NOR gate for a circuit, but all you have available is a 7400 (quad 2-input NAND gate). Show how you could obtain the required NOR function using the NAND gate. (Remember that equivalent truth tables imply equivalent functions.)

5

Interpreting Manufacturer's Data Sheets

Objectives

After completing this experiment, you will be able to:

☐ Measure the static electrical specifications for TTL and CMOS logic, including input and output voltage, input and output current, and noise margin.

☐ Interpret manufacturer's data sheets including voltage and current requirements.

☐ Measure the transfer curve for an inverter.

Reference Reading

Floyd, *Digital Fundamentals,* 4th ed., Section 3–7, Integrated Circuit Logic Families; Section 13–1, Basic Operational Characteristics and Parameters; Section 13–3, TTL Circuits; Section 13–5, CMOS Circuits; Section 13–6, Comparison of CMOS and TTL Characteristics

Materials Needed

7404 hex inverter
CD4081 quad AND gate
10 kΩ variable resistor
Resistors (one of each):
   300 Ω
   1 kΩ
   15 kΩ
   1 MΩ
   Load resistor (to be calculated)
0.1 μF capacitor

Summary of Theory

Experiment 2 introduced the 7404 hex inverter, a single package containing six inverters. The basic function that an inverter performs is the NOT or complement function. If the input is HIGH, then the output will be LOW; if the input is LOW, then the output will be HIGH. Ideally, the output voltage is in either of two separate states. As long as manufacturer's specifications are not exceeded, these conditions will hold; otherwise they may not. In addition, it is important not to exceed current or voltage limits to avoid damage to the IC. For these reasons, it is important to understand these specifications.

TTL logic is designed to have conventional current (plus to minus) flowing into the output terminal of the gate when the output is LOW. This current, called *sink* current, is shown on a data sheet as a positive current, indicating that it is flowing into the gate. Conventional current leaves the gate when the output is HIGH. This current is indicated on the data sheet as a negative current and is said to be *source* current. TTL logic can sink much larger current than it can source, as described in this experiment.

Another important logic family is CMOS (complementary metal-oxide semiconductor). One of the most important advantages to CMOS logic is its low power consumption. When it is not switching from one logic level to another, the power dissipation in the IC approaches zero; however, at high frequencies the power dissipation increases and can approach that of TTL. Other advantages include high fanout, high noise immunity, temperature stability, and ability to operate from power supplies from 3 V to 15 V.

CMOS logic uses two types of field-effect transistors, whereas TTL uses only bipolar transistors. As you might expect, this results in significantly different characteristics for CMOS logic than TTL logic. Consequently, CMOS and TTL logic cannot be connected directly without due consideration of their specifications, since voltage levels and current sourcing and sinking capabilities differ. In this experiment, you will learn to read and interpret the specifications for TTL and CMOS logic families; interfacing between various types of logic is determined by these specifications. (See Chapter 11 of Floyd.) In addition, all MOS families of logic are more sensitive to static electricity, and special precautions to avoid static damage should be observed when handling MOS devices. In addition to the static handling precautions listed in Floyd's text, you should use the following operating precautions:

1. Unused inputs must NOT be left open even on gates that are not being used. They should be tied to V_{CC}, ground, or an input signal.

2. Power supply voltages must always be on when signal voltages are present at the inputs. Signal voltage must never exceed the power supply.

3. CMOS devices must never be inserted into or removed from circuits with the power on.

One important specification for any logic family is *noise margin*. Noise margin is the voltage difference that can exist between the output of one gate and the input of the next gate and still maintain guaranteed logic levels. For TTL, this difference is 0.4 V, as illustrated in Figure 5–1(a). For CMOS, the voltage thresholds are approximately 30% and 70% of V_{CC}. The noise margin is 30% of the supply voltage, as illustrated in Figure 5–1(b). A technique that is employed to avoid noise problems in logic circuits is to place a small bypass capacitor (about 0.1 μF) between the supply and ground near every IC in a circuit.

A graphic tool to help visualize the characteristics of a circuit is called the *transfer curve*. The transfer curve is a graph of the input voltage plotted along the x-axis against the corresponding output voltage plotted along the y-axis. A linear circuit should have a straight-line transfer curve. On the other hand, a digital circuit has a transfer curve with a sharp transition between a high and low value. In the Further Investigation section, you will investigate the transfer curve for a 7404 inverter.

Procedure

1. The data table in the report section is the manufacturer's specified characteristics for the 7404 inverter. You will be measuring many of these characteristics in this experiment and entering your measured value next to the specified value. Begin by connecting the circuit shown in Figure 5–2(a). Inputs that are connected HIGH are normally connected through a resistor to protect the input from voltage surges and the possibility of shorting the power supply directly to ground in case the input is connected to a ground.

2. Measure the voltage at the input of the inverter, as shown in Figure 5–2(b). Since the input

FIGURE 5–1

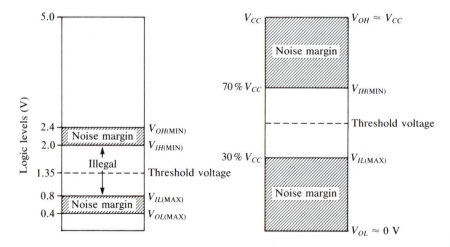

(a) TTL levels and noise margin   (b) CMOS levels and noise margin

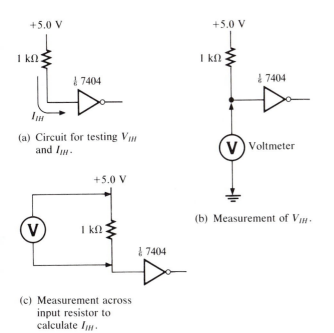

(a) Circuit for testing V_{IH} and I_{IH}.

(b) Measurement of V_{IH}.

(c) Measurement across input resistor to calculate I_{IH}.

FIGURE 5–2

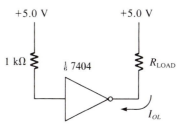

FIGURE 5–3

is HIGH, this voltage will be labeled V_{IH}. Enter your measured voltage in Table 5–1, line a. (Note that the specified V_{IH} is a *minimum* level; your measured value is probably much higher.)

3. Measure the voltage *across* the 1 kΩ resistor, as shown in Figure 5–2(c). TTL logic requires a very small current to pull it HIGH, as you will see when you measure the voltage across the resistor. Using your measured voltage and Ohm's law, calculate the current in the resistor. This current is the input HIGH current, abbreviated I_{IH}. Enter your measured current in Table 5–1, line g. Compare your measured value with the specified maximum I_{IH}. Note the sign of this current. Since it flows into the IC, the sign is positive.

4. Measure the output voltage. Since the input is HIGH, the output will be LOW. This voltage is called V_{OL}. Do not record this voltage; you will record V_{OL} in Step 5. Notice that without a load, the V_{OL} is much lower than the maximum specified level.

5. Determine the effect of a load on V_{OL}. To put the maximum specified load on the inverter, look up the maximum LOW output current I_{OL} for the 7404. Then connect a resistor, R_{LOAD}, between the output and +5 V that allows I_{OL} (max) to flow. Assume 4.8 V is dropped across the load resistor. Using Ohm's law, determine the appropriate load resistor, measure it, and place it in the circuit of Figure 5–3. Then measure V_{OL} and record it in Table 5–1, line f.

6. Measure the voltage drop across R_{LOAD}, and divide by R_{LOAD} to determine the actual load current. Record the measured load current as I_{OL} in Table 5–1, line d.

7. Change the previous circuit to the one shown in Figure 5–4. Measure V_{IL} and V_{OH}, and record the measured voltages in Table 5–1, lines b and e.

8. Calculate I_{IL} by applying Ohm's law to the 300 Ω input resistor in Figure 5–4. (Note the sign.) Record the measured I_{IL} in Table 5–1, line h.

9. Measure the output load current by applying Ohm's law to the 15 kΩ load resistor. Record this current, I_{OH}, in Table 5–1, line c. Note the units and the sign. The minus sign indicates that the current is leaving the IC. This current, called *sourcing* current, is significantly lower than the maximum LOW current, I_{OL}, which is positive current, or *sinking* current.

10. In this and remaining steps, you will test a CMOS IC for several important characteristics. Before handling the CMOS IC, review the section in the text, *Precautions for Handling CMOS*. Disconnect power from your protoboard and replace the 7404 with a CD4081 quad AND gate. Although in practice you could test any CMOS gate, this gate will be used because it is needed in the next experiment and you have already tested an inverter. Check the manufacturer's specification sheet in Appendix A. Enter the specified values for $V_{OL(MAX)}$, $V_{OH[MIN]}$, $V_{IL[MAX]}$, $V_{IH[MIN]}$, $I_{OL[MIN]}$,

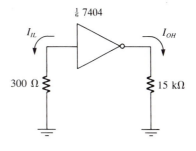

FIGURE 5–4

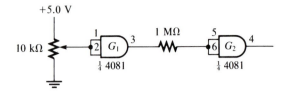

FIGURE 5-5

$I_{OH[MAX]}$ and $I_{in[TYP]}$ for a supply voltage of 5.0 V and a temperature of 25°C in Table 5-2. Notice on the pinout that the power is supplied to a pin labeled V_{DD} and ground is supplied to a pin labeled V_{SS}. Although this convention is commonly used, both pins are actually connected to transistor drains; V_{DD} is used to indicate the positive supply. (For +5.0 V supplies, the supply is often referred to as V_{CC}).

11. Connect a 0.1 µF capacitor between the supply and ground. Connect the circuit shown in Figure 5-5 and ground the inputs to all other gates except the two gates you are using. Reconnect the power supply and keep it at +5.0 V for these tests. Adjust the input voltage using the potentiometer to the manufacturer's specified value of $V_{IH[MIN]}$ for $V_{DD} = 5$ V. Record your measured value of the $V_{IH[MIN]}$ on line d of Table 5-2.

12. Read the output voltage of the first AND gate at pin 3. Notice the difference between the CMOS gate and the TTL gate you tested earlier. Since the output is HIGH, record it as $V_{OH[MIN]}$ in Table 5-2, line b.

13. Measure the voltage across the 1 MΩ test resistor. A very high impedance meter is necessary to make an accurate measurement in this step. Determine the current flowing into the input of the second gate by applying Ohm's law to the test resistor. Record this as the input current in Table 5-2, line g.

14. Adjust the potentiometer until the input voltage on the first AND gate is at the specified value of $V_{IL[MAX]}$. Record the measured input voltage in Table 5-2, line c. Measure the output

voltage on pin 3 and record this as $V_{OL[MAX]}$ in Table 5-2, line a.

15. Turn off the power supply and change the circuit to that of Figure 5-6(a). The potentiometer is moved to the output and the 1 MΩ resistor is used as a pull-up resistor on the input. This circuit will be used to test the HIGH output current of the gate. After connecting the circuit, restore the power and adjust the potentiometer until the output voltage is 4.6 V (see manufacturer's stated conditions for specification of output current). Remove the power, measure the potentiometer's resistance, and apply Ohm's law to determine the output current I_{OH}. Record your measured current in Table 5-2, line f.

16. Change the circuit to that of Figure 5-6(b). Restore the power and adjust the potentiometer until the output voltage is 0.4 V. Remove the power, measure the potentiometer's resistance, and apply Ohm's law to determine the output current I_{OL}. Record your measured current in Table 5-2, line e.

For Further Investigation

1. To further investigate the voltage characteristics of TTL, connect the circuit shown in Figure 5-7. The variable resistor is used to vary the input voltage.

2. Vary the input voltage through the range of values shown in Table 5-3. Set each input voltage; then measure the corresponding output voltage and record it in Table 5-3.

3. Plot the data from Table 5-3 onto Plot 1. Since V_{out} depends on V_{in}, plot V_{out} on the y-axis and V_{in} on the x-axis. This graph is called the *transfer curve* for the inverter.

4. Label the region on the transfer curve for V_{OH}, V_{OL}, and the threshold. The threshold is the region where the transition from HIGH to LOW takes place.

5. Disconnect the input from the inverter, and measure the voltage on the open input. Then

FIGURE 5-6

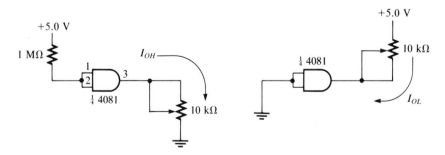

(a) Measurement of I_{OH} (b) Measurement of I_{OL}

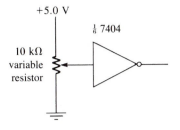

+5.0 V

$\frac{1}{6}$ 7404

10 kΩ
variable
resistor

FIGURE 5–7

measure V_{out}. Locate this point on the transfer curve.

6. The transfer curve for the CD4081 AND gate is somewhat different from that for an inverter. Consider the data points needed for the transfer curve for the CD4081. What is the shape of the AND transfer curve? If directed by your instructor, take data for the CD4081 and write a short report on your findings.

Report for Experiment 5

Name: _____ Date: _____ Class: _____

Objectives:

Procedure:

Data:

TABLE 5–1
TTL 7404.

Recommended Operating Conditions		DM5404			DM7404				
Symbol	Parameter	Min	Nom	Max	Min	Nom	Max	Units	**Measured Value**
V_{CC}	Supply Voltage	4.5	5	5.5	4.75	5	5.25	V	
V_{IH}	High Level Input Voltage	2			2			V	a.
V_{IL}	Low Level Input Voltage			0.8			0.8	V	b.
I_{OH}	High Level Output Current			−0.4			−0.4	mA	c.
I_{OL}	Low Level Output Current			16			16	mA	d.
T_A	Free Air Operating Temperature	−55		125	0		70	°C	

Electrical Characteristics over recommended operating free air temperature (unless otherwise noted)						
Symbol	Parameter	Conditions	Min	Typ	Max	Units
V_I	Input Clamp Voltage	V_{CC} = Min, I_I = −12 mA			−1.5	V
V_{OH}	High Level Output Voltage	V_{CC} = Min, I_{OH} = Max V_{IL} = Max	2.4	3.4		V

Continued.

TABLE 5–1
Continued.

Electrical Characteristics over recommended operating free air temperature (unless otherwise noted)							
Symbol	Parameter	Conditions		Min	Typ	Max	Units	Measured Value
V_{OL}	Low Level Output Voltage	V_{CC} = Min, I_{OL} = Max V_{IH} = Min			0.2	0.4	V	f.
I_I	Input Current @ Max Input Voltage	V_{CC} = Max, V_I = 5.5V				1	mA	
I_{IH}	High Level Input Current	V_{CC} = Max, V_I = 2.4V				40	μA	g.
I_{IL}	Low Level Input Current	V_{CC} = Max, V_I = 0.4V				−1.6	mA	h.
I_{OS}	Short Circuit Output Current	V_{CC} = Max (Note 2)	DM54	−20		−55	mA	
			DM74	−18		−55		
I_{CCH}	Supply Current With Outputs High	V_{CC} = Max			6	12	mA	
I_{CCL}	Supply Current With Outputs Low	V_{CC} = Max			18	33	mA	

TABLE 5–2
CMOS CD4081.

		Quantity	Manufacturer's Specified Value	Measured Value
(a)		$V_{OL[MAX]}$, low level output voltage		
(b)		$V_{OH[MIN]}$, high level output voltage		
(c)		$V_{IL[MAX]}$, low level input voltage		
(d)		$V_{IH[MIN]}$, high level input voltage		
(e)		$I_{OL[MIN]}$, low level output current		
(f)		$I_{OH[MIN]}$, high level output current		
(g)		$I_{in[TYP]}$, input current		

Results and Conclusion:

Further Investigation Results:

TABLE 5–3

V_{in} (V)	V_{out} (V)
0.4	
0.8	
1.2	
1.3	
1.4	
1.5	
1.6	
2.0	
2.4	
2.8	
3.2	
3.6	
4.0	

PLOT 1

Evaluation and Review Questions

1. In Step 4, you observed V_{OL} with no load resistor. In Step 5, you measured V_{OL} with a load resistor. What conclusion can you draw about the effect of a load resistor on V_{OL}?

2. Assume a 7404 has a logic HIGH voltage of 2.4 V. Using the specified maximum I_{OH}, determine the smallest output resistor that can be connected from the output to ground.

57

3. A hypothetical logic family has the following characteristics:

$$V_{IL} = 0.5 \text{ V}$$
$$V_{IH} = 3.0 \text{ V}$$
$$V_{OL} = 0.2 \text{ V}$$
$$V_{OH} = 3.5 \text{ V}$$

Compute the LOW and HIGH noise margin for this family.

$V_{NL}(\text{LOW}) = $ _____
$V_{NL}(\text{HIGH}) = $ _____

4. Assume that an LED requires 10 mA of current.
   a. Which of the two TTL circuits shown in Figure 5–8 is the better way to drive the LED?

   b. Why?

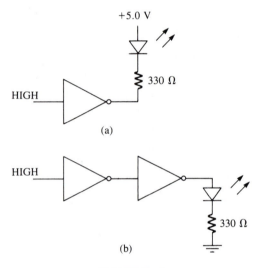

FIGURE 5–8

5. What is the maximum low voltage that a TTL input will accept to guarantee a correct logic output?

Checkup 3a

The exercises in this checkup reflect information covered in Floyd's Chapter 3, "Logic Gates," and Buchla's Experiments 4 and 5.

1. A rule for a NAND gate is, Any zero on the input produces a one on the output. How does the negative-OR symbol illustrate this rule?

2. The circuit shown in Figure 5–9 has a DATA line and an ENABLE line.
   a. When the ENABLE is HIGH, what logic is seen at the output?

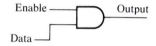

FIGURE 5–9

   b. When the ENABLE is LOW, what logic is seen at the output?

3. If the gate in Figure 5–9 is changed to a NAND gate, what logic is seen at the output when the ENABLE is HIGH?

4. A 2-input logic gate follows the rule, Any one on the input produces a zero on the output. What type of gate is this (positive logic)?

5. An interesting aspect of an XOR gate is that if an inverter is placed on either the input or on the output of the gate, the resulting combination is an XNOR. Prove that this statement is true.

6. In Problem 5, it was stated that if an inverter was added to either the input or the output of an XOR gate, the resulting combination acts as an XNOR gate. Find out if the reverse is true—that is, if an inverter is added to either the input or the output of an XNOR gate, is the resulting combination equivalent to an XOR gate?

7. If you need to make a NAND gate into an equivalent inverter, you could either tie the inputs together or

8. Why is it poor practice to leave a TTL input unconnected if you needed a logic HIGH?

9. A 2-input NOR gate is needed but only a 3-input gate is available. What could you do with the extra input to "disable" it?

10. Which logic type has the lowest power dissipation, CMOS or TTL? _____

11. The XNOR gate is sometimes called a COINCIDENCE gate. Explain.

12. If an XOR gate has a LOW output, what must be true about the inputs?

13. If you invert both inputs and the output of a 2-input OR gate, what is the equivalent positive logic gate for the combination?

14. If you invert both inputs and the output of a 2-input NAND gate, what is the equivalent positive logic gate for the combination?

15. If a counter input function is labeled UP/$\overline{\text{DOWN}}$, which action is accomplished with a logic HIGH? Explain.

Checkup 3b

The following questions reflect content from Floyd's Chapter 13 in *Digital Fundamentals*, 4th ed., and Experiment 5, and may be attempted upon completion of the referenced readings.

16. Explain the meaning of *noise immunity*.

17. If a CMOS CD4081 AND gate is operated from a +15 V supply, what are $V_{IL[MAX]}$ and $V_{IH[MIN]}$?

$$V_{IL[MAX]} = \underline{\hspace{3cm}}$$
$$V_{IH[MIN]} = \underline{\hspace{3cm}}$$

18. What is the worst-case output voltage you can expect from a TTL IC when:

a. the output is a logic LOW? _____

b. the output is a logic HIGH? _____

19. Look up the (on) state current output for the 7447A decoder for segments a through g (Appendix A). Compare this current to the equivalent output current for the 7404. Why do you think they are not the same?

20. Compare the maximum output HIGH current from a CD4071 two-input OR gate when it is operating from a supply voltage of +5 V with the maximum current when it is operating from a supply voltage of +15 V (Appendix A). What is the meaning of the minus sign shown with these currents?

6

Boolean Laws and DeMorgan's Theorem

Objectives

After completing this experiment, you will be able to:

□ Experimentally verify several of the rules for Boolean algebra.

□ Design circuits to prove Rules 10 and 11 of the Boolean algebra rules.

□ Experimentally determine the truth table for circuits with three input variables, and use De-Morgan's theorem to prove algebraically whether they are equivalent.

Reference Reading

Floyd, *Digital Fundamentals*, 4th ed., Section 4–1, Boolean Operations; Section 4–2, Boolean Expressions; Section 4–3, Rules and Laws of Boolean Algebra; Section 4–4, DeMorgan's Theorems; Section 4–5, Boolean Expressions for Gate Networks

Materials Needed

4071 quad 2-input OR gate
4069 hex inverter
4081 quad 2-input AND gate
One LED
Four-position DIP switch
Four 1 kΩ resistors
Three 0.1 μF capacitors

Summary of Theory

Boolean algebra consists of a set of laws that govern logical relationships. Unlike ordinary algebra, where an unknown can take any value, the elements of Boolean algebra are binary variables and can have only one of two values: 1 or 0 (also called TRUE or FALSE). Variables are typically letters of the alphabet.

Symbols used in Boolean algebra include the bar, which is the NOT or complement; the connective $+$, which implies logical addition and is read "OR"; and the connective $\cdot$, which implies logical multiplication and is read "AND." The dot is frequently eliminated when logical multiplication is shown. Thus $A \cdot B$ is written AB. The basic rules of Boolean algebra are tabulated in Floyd's text and are repeated here in Table 6–1 for convenience.

The Boolean rules shown in Table 6–1 can be applied directly to actual circuits, as this experiment demonstrates. For example, Rule 1 states $A + 0 = A$ (remember to read $+$ as "OR"). This rule can be demonstrated with an OR gate and a pulse generator, as shown in Figure 6–1. The signal from the pulse generator is labeled A and the ground signal represents the 0. The output, which is a replica of the pulse generator, represents the ORing of the two inputs—hence, the rule is proved. Figure 6–1 illustrates the application of this rule.

The circuits constructed in this experiment use CMOS logic. You should use static protection

TABLE 6–1
Basic rules of Boolean algebra.

1. $A + 0 = A$
2. $A + 1 = 1$
3. $A \cdot 0 = 0$
4. $A \cdot 1 = A$
5. $A + A = A$
6. $A + \overline{A} = 1$
7. $A \cdot A = A$
8. $A \cdot \overline{A} = 0$
9. $\overline{\overline{A}} = A$
10. $A + AB = A$
11. $A + \overline{A}B = A + B$
12. $(A + B)(A + C) = A + BC$

NOTE: A, B, or C can represent a single variable or a combination of variables.

as outlined in the text and Experiment 5 to prevent damage to your ICs.

Procedure

1. Construct the circuit shown in Figure 6–1. Set the power supply to 5.0 V and use a 0.1 μF capacitor between V_{CC} and ground for each IC throughout this experiment. Set the pulse generator to a frequency of 10 kHz with a 0 to 4 V level on the output. Observe the signals from the pulse generator and the output at the same time on your oscilloscope. *Important:* Whenever you do timing comparisons of digital signals, you should trigger the scope from one channel only. Do not use COMP (composite) triggering because relative time information is lost. The timing diagram and Boolean rule for this circuit has been completed in Table 6–2 as an example.

2. Change the circuit from Step 1 to that of Figure 6–2. Complete the second line in Table 6–2.

3. Connect the circuit shown in Figure 6–3. Complete the third line in Table 6–2.

4. Change the circuit in Step 3 to that of Figure 6–4. Complete the last line in Table 6–2.

5. Design a circuit that will illustrate Rule 10. The pulse generator is used to represent the A input and a switch is used for the B input. The required schematic is started in the first line of Table 6–3. Switch B is open for B = 1 and closed for B = 0. Complete the schematic, build your circuit, and draw two timing diagrams in the space provided in Table 6–3. The first timing diagram is for the condition B = 0 and the second is for the condition B = 1.

6. Design a circuit that illustrates Rule 11. Draw your schematic in the space provided in Table 6–3. Construct the circuit and draw two timing diagrams for the circuit in Table 6–3.

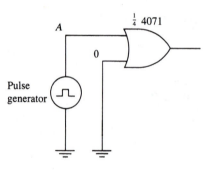

FIGURE 6–1

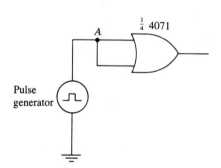

FIGURE 6–2

FIGURE 6–3

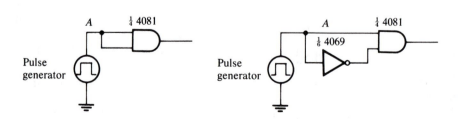

For Further Investigation

1. Build the circuit shown in Figure 6–4. Test each combination of input variables by closing the appropriate switches as listed in truth Table 6–4 in the report. Using the LED as a logic monitor, read the output logic, and complete Table 6–4.

2. Construct the circuit of Figure 6–5. Again, test each combination of inputs and complete truth Table 6–5 in the report. Observe the two truth tables. Can you prove (or disprove) that the circuits perform equivalent logic?

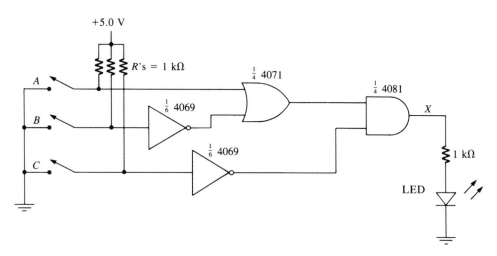

FIGURE 6–4

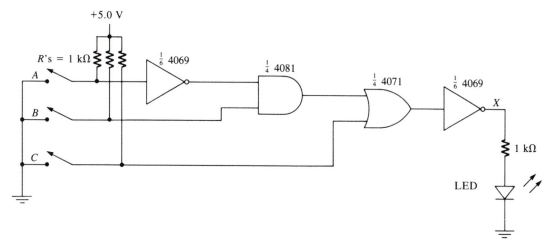

FIGURE 6–5

Report for Experiment 6

Name: _____ Date: _____ Class: _____

Objectives:

Procedure:

Data:

TABLE 6-2

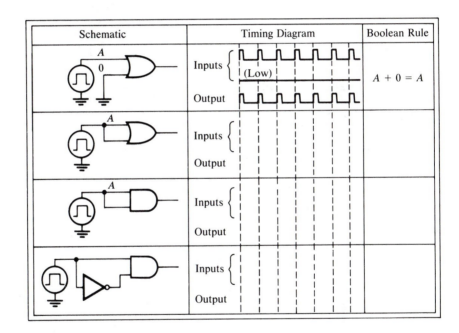

TABLE 6–3

Schematic	Timing Diagram
Rule 10:	*Timing Diagram for B = 0:* Inputs $\left\{\begin{array}{l} A \\ AB \end{array}\right.$ Output *Timing Diagram for B = 1:* Inputs $\left\{\begin{array}{l} A \\ AB \end{array}\right.$ Output
Rule 11:	*Timing Diagram for B = 0:* Inputs $\left\{\begin{array}{l} A \\ AB \end{array}\right.$ Output *Timing Diagram for B = 1:* Inputs $\left\{\begin{array}{l} A \\ AB \end{array}\right.$ Output

Results and Conclusion:

Further Investigation Results:

TABLE 6-4
Truth table for Figure 6-4.

Inputs			Output
A	B	C	X
0	0	0	
0	0	1	
0	1	0	
0	1	1	
1	0	0	
1	0	1	
1	1	0	
1	1	1	

TABLE 6-5
Truth table for Figure 6-5.

Inputs			Output
A	B	C	X
0	0	0	
0	0	1	
0	1	0	
0	1	1	
1	0	0	
1	0	1	
1	1	0	
1	1	1	

Write the Boolean expression for each circuit:

Evaluation and Review Questions

1. The equation $X = A(A + B) + C$ is equivalent to $X = A + C$. Prove this with Boolean algebra.

2. A technician is asked to provide a "black-box" circuit that has a two position switch to select between the AND function or the OR function. The inputs are A and $\overline{A}$. (See Figure 6-6.) She cleverly completes the circuit using no logic gates! Draw the circuit:

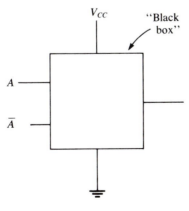

V_{CC} "Black box"

A

$\overline{A}$

FIGURE 6-6

3. Determine if the circuits in Figures 6–4 and 6–5 perform equivalent logic. Then, using DeMorgan's theorem, prove your answer.

4. Write the Boolean expression for the circuit shown in Figure 6–7. Then, using DeMorgan's theorem, prove that the circuit is equivalent to that shown in Figure 6–1.

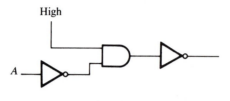

FIGURE 6–7

5. The Boolean Toy Co. produces red, white, blue, and green toys. The directions in the ordering department read: "Minimum orders are for two toys, except a single green toy may be ordered by itself. No order can contain two toys of the same color. Orders for blue toys must always include a green toy in the same order. All orders must have at least one red toy, except those orders that include both a green and a white toy. Orders for red and white toys must also include a green toy." Needless to say, the order clerks are somewhat confused by the situation and would like to have a circuit constructed that lights an LED letting them know if an order can be accepted. Write the Boolean expression for the circuit and use the Boolean rules to simplify the expression. Then draw a circuit for the simplified expression. (*Hint:* Start with a truth table.)

7

Logic Circuit Simplification

Objectives

After completing this experiment, you will be able to:

□ Develop the truth table for a combinational logic problem.

□ Read the sum-of-products expression from the table, and plot it on a Karnaugh map.

□ Use the map to simplify the expression.

□ Build and test a circuit that implements the simplified expression.

Reference Reading

Floyd, *Digital Fundamentals*, 4th ed., Section 4–5, Boolean Expressions for Gate Networks; Section 4–6, Simplification of Boolean Algebra; Section 4–7, Simplification Using the Karnaugh Map

Materials Needed

7400 NAND gate
LED
330 Ω resistor
Four 1 kΩ resistors
One 4 position DIP switch

Summary of Theory

With combinational logic circuits, the outputs are determined solely by the inputs. For simple combinational circuits, truth tables are used to summarize all possible inputs and outputs; the truth table completely describes the desired operation of the circuit. The circuit may be realized by simplifying the expression for the output function as read from the truth table.

A powerful mapping technique for simplifying combinational logic circuits was developed by M. Karnaugh and was described in a paper he published in 1953. The method involved writing the truth table into a geometric map in which adjacent cells (squares) differ from each other in only one variable. (Adjacent cells share a common border horizontally or vertically). The map simplifies application of the Boolean theorem $AB + \overline{A}B = B$. The variable that changes can be cancelled using the map by grouping two adjacent cells and reading only the common factor between the adjacent cells. Further, the mapping technique allows you to group any integer power of 2 (2, 4, 8, 16) and provides a nearly "automatic" way of applying the theorem to more than one variable at the same time.

One of the most important points to remember when you are drawing a Karnaugh map is that the variables must be written in a Gray code sequence along the sides and tops of the map. This is because the adjacent cells on the map must differ from each other in only one variable as previously stated. Each cell on the map corresponds to one row of the truth table. The output variables appear as 0s and 1s on the map in positions corresponding to those given in the truth table.

TABLE 7–1
Truth table for comparator.

Inputs				Output
A_2	A_1	B_2	B_1	X
0	0	0	0	1
0	0	0	1	0
0	0	1	0	0
0	0	1	1	0
0	1	0	0	1
0	1	0	1	1
0	1	1	0	0
0	1	1	1	0
1	0	0	0	1
1	0	0	1	1
1	0	1	0	1
1	0	1	1	0
1	1	0	0	1
1	1	0	1	1
1	1	1	0	1
1	1	1	1	1

As an example, consider the design of a 2-bit comparator. The inputs will be called A_2A_1 and B_2B_1. The desired output is HIGH if A_2A_1 is equal to or greater than B_2B_1. To begin, the desired output is written in the form of a truth table, as given in Table 7–1. All possible inputs are clearly iden-

tified by the truth table and the desired output for every possible input is given.

Next the Karnaugh map is drawn, as shown in Figure 7–1. In this example, the map is drawn using numbers to represent the inputs, a technique that is justified by considering the map as merely an extension of the truth table. The corresponding values for the output function are entered from the truth table. The map can be read in sum of products (SOP) form by grouping adjacent cells containing 1s on the map. The size of the groups must be an integer power of 2 (1, 2, 4, 8, etc.) and should contain only 1s. The largest possible group should be taken; all 1s must be in at least one group and may be taken in more than one group if helpful.

After grouping the 1s on the map, the output function can be determined. Each group is read as one of the product terms in the reduced output function. Within each group larger than one, adjacent boundaries will be crossed, causing the variable that changes to be eliminated from the output expression. A group of two adjacent 1s will have a single adjacent boundary and will eliminate one variable. A group of four 1s will eliminate two variables and a group of eight 1s will eliminate three variables. Figure 7–1 shows the groupings for the 2-bit comparator. Since each group in this case is a group of four 1s, each product term contains two variables (two were eliminated from each term). The resulting expression is the sum of all of the product terms. The circuit can be drawn directly, as shown in Figure 7–2.

The Karnaugh map method is a powerful technique for functions that contain four or fewer variables. Although it is possible to extend mapping techniques to a greater number of variables, usually tabular methods are more efficient at reducing more complicated functions. Although the map is an excellent tool, it may not always give the most efficient circuit in certain situations. For example, the map does not readily show when an exclusive-OR or exclusive-NOR gate may be implemented. Another factor in the best implementation of a circuit is number of inputs and type of gates available in each IC package. Frequently, the designer needs to keep in mind the total number of ICs, rather than the minimum number of gates, or use a different type of gate or one with extra inputs based on availability. In addition, parts of the required logic may already exist in some other part of the circuit. In this case, a portion of the circuit can be eliminated by using the already-existing logic.

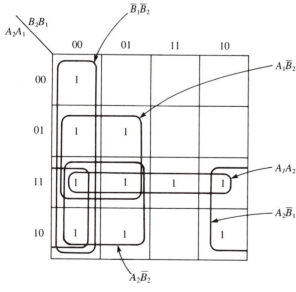

FIGURE 7–1

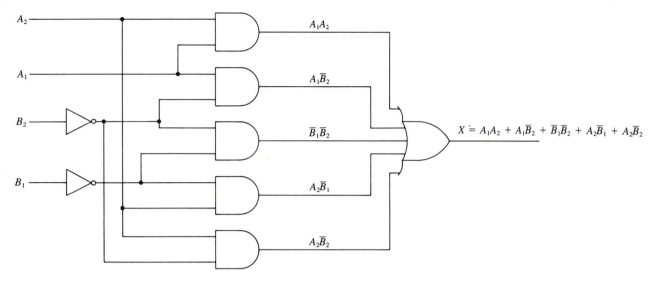

$$X = A_1A_2 + A_1\overline{B}_2 + \overline{B}_1\overline{B}_2 + A_2\overline{B}_1 + A_2\overline{B}_2$$

FIGURE 7–2

Procedure

BCD Invalid Code Detector

As you have learned, BCD is a 4-bit binary code representing the decimal numbers 0 through 9. The binary numbers 1010 through 1111 are not used in BCD. In this experiment, you will design a circuit that will detect these invalid codes.

1. First construct a truth table containing all possible inputs and the desired output. Assume that the desired output for a valid code is a 1, for an invalid code a 0. Complete the truth table shown in Table 7–2 of the report for these output values. In this example the letter D is the most significant bit, and the letter A is the least significant bit.

2. Complete the Karnaugh map shown as Figure 7–3 in the report. Group the 1s according to the rules given in Floyd's text. Read the minimum sum-of-products expression from the map, and write the Boolean expression in the space provided in the report. Your completed map should contain ten 1s and six 0s.

3. If you have correctly written the minimized sum-of-products for the preceding expression, you will see that each of the input variables is "NOTted." Apply DeMorgan's theorem to your expression, and show in the space provided in the report that it can be written as follows:

$$X = \overline{D \cdot (B + C)}$$

4. The truth table was set up with a zero for invalid codes. Recall that, for TTL logic, a LOW

can cause an LED to be on without violating the I_{OL} specification, but a HIGH causes the IC to be operated outside the I_{OH} specification. This is the reason the zero was selected for the active level for the invalid code detector. The circuit shown in Figure 7–4 directly implements the expression from the DeMorgan operation:

$$X = \overline{D \cdot (B + C)}$$

5. Although the circuit shown in Figure 7–4 satisfies the design requirements with only two gates, this may not be the easiest to implement as the two gates are different types. Using the universal properties of the NAND gate, the OR gate can be replaced with three NAND gates. This will allow the completed design to be implemented with only one IC—a 7400! Change the circuit in Figure 7–4 by replacing the OR gate with three NAND gates. Draw the circuit in the space provided in your report.

6. Construct the circuit you drew in Step 5. Test all combinations of the inputs and complete truth Table 7–3 in the report. If you have constructed and tested the circuit correctly, the truth table will be the same as Table 7–2.

7. The BCD invalid code detector can be constructed yet another way using NAND gates! By applying the distribution rule, the expression from DeMorgan's theorem can be written:

$$X = \overline{BD + BC}$$

A direct implementation of this expression is shown in Figure 7–5.

FIGURE 7–4

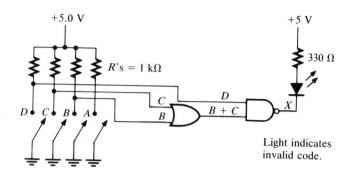

Light indicates
invalid code.

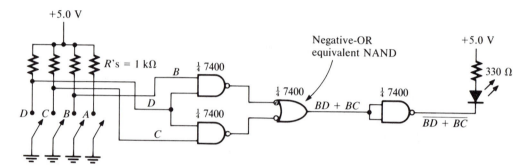

FIGURE 7–5

8. Construct the circuit shown in Figure 7–5. Then test all combinations of the inputs and complete truth Table 7–4 in the report.

For Further Investigation

Two-Thirds Majority Test

A nine-member legislative committee requires a ⅔ vote to spend a billion dollars. The vote is tabulated and converted to BCD code. If ⅔ of the committee is in favor, the vote will be the BCD representation of 6, 7, 8, or 9. Design and build a circuit that lights an LED if a majority has voted in favor of spending another billion.

1. Complete truth Table 7–5 in the report for the problem. As in the invalid code detector problem, the active output should be a zero in order to turn on an LED for TTL logic with a LOW signal. Use a one on the truth table for a vote less than ⅔ majority; use a zero for ⅔ majority and place an X ("don't care") on the table for invalid codes.

2. Complete the Karnaugh map shown in Figure 7–6. Enter the invalid BCD codes on the map as "don't cares" (X).

3. Read the minimum sum-of-products expression from the map. A "don't care" can be circled as part of a larger group. The significance of "don't care" is that it can help reduce the output expression because if the input is *not possible*, you *don't care* about the outcome. If a "don't care" is circled with a group of ones, then it too becomes a one.

4. In the space provided in the report, draw the circuit using only 2-input NAND gates.

5. Build and test your circuit.

74

Report for Experiment 7

Name: _____ Date: _____ Class: _____

Objectives:

Procedure:

Data:

TABLE 7–2
Truth table for BCD invalid code detector.

Inputs	Output
D C B A	X
0 0 0 0	
0 0 0 1	
0 0 1 0	
0 0 1 1	
0 1 0 0	
0 1 0 1	
0 1 1 0	
0 1 1 1	
1 0 0 0	
1 0 0 1	
1 0 1 0	
1 0 1 1	
1 1 0 0	
1 1 0 1	
1 1 1 0	
1 1 1 1	

DC \ *BA*	00	01	11	10
00				
01				
11				
10				

FIGURE 7–3
Karnaugh map of truth table for invalid BCD code detector.

Minimum sum-of-products read from map:

$$X = \text{_____}$$

Apply DeMorgan's theorem to the preceding sum-of-products expression:

$$X = \text{_____}$$

Step 5. Circuit for BCD invalid code detector:

TABLE 7–3
Truth table for Step 5 circuit.

Inputs	Output
D C B A	*X*
0 0 0 0	
0 0 0 1	
0 0 1 0	
0 0 1 1	
0 1 0 0	
0 1 0 1	
0 1 1 0	
0 1 1 1	
1 0 0 0	
1 0 0 1	
1 0 1 0	
1 0 1 1	
1 1 0 0	
1 1 0 1	
1 1 1 0	
1 1 1 1	

TABLE 7–4
Truth table for Figure 7–5.

Inputs	Output
D C B A	*X*
0 0 0 0	
0 0 0 1	
0 0 1 0	
0 0 1 1	
0 1 0 0	
0 1 0 1	
0 1 1 0	
0 1 1 1	
1 0 0 0	
1 0 0 1	
1 0 1 0	
1 0 1 1	
1 1 0 0	
1 1 0 1	
1 1 1 0	
1 1 1 1	

Results and Conclusion:

Further Investigation Results:

TABLE 7−5
Truth table for ⅔ majority test.

Inputs				Output
D	C	B	A	X
0	0	0	0	
0	0	0	1	
0	0	1	0	
0	0	1	1	
0	1	0	0	
0	1	0	1	
0	1	1	0	
0	1	1	1	
1	0	0	0	
1	0	0	1	
1	0	1	0	
1	0	1	1	
1	1	0	0	
1	1	0	1	
1	1	1	0	
1	1	1	1	

FIGURE 7−6
Karnaugh map of truth table for ⅔ majority test.

Circuit:

Minimum sum-of-products read from map:

$$X = \underline{\hspace{2cm}}$$

Evaluation and Review Questions

1. Assume that the circuit in Figure 7–4 was constructed but doesn't work correctly. The output is correct for all inputs except $DCBA = 1000$ and 1001. Suggest at least two possible problems that could account for this and explain how you would isolate the exact problem.

2. BCD is a 4-bit code, yet the circuits drawn in Figures 7–4 and 7–5 had only three inputs. Explain why the A switch was not connected.

3. Assume a circuit already had a 7442 BCD decoder in it and you wanted to add a BCD invalid code detector to the circuit. Design a circuit that uses only one three input NAND gate and the 7442 to turn on an LED for invalid codes. (*Hint:* Use two outputs from the 7442 and one input to the 7442.)

4. The circuit shown in Figure 7–7 has an output labeled $\overline{X}$. Write the expression for $\overline{X}$; then, using DeMorgan's theorem, find the expression for X.

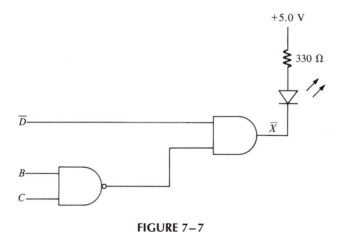

FIGURE 7–7

5. It is possible to read a Karnaugh map by grouping the zeros and reading the inverse function, $\overline{X}$. The map shown in Figure 7–8 is the same one used for the invalid code detector. The expression can be read as $\overline{X} = CD + BD$.

Prove that this expression is the same as the minimum sum-of-products expression in your report.

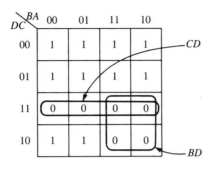

FIGURE 7–8

Checkup 4

The exercises in this checkup reflect information covered in Floyd's Chapter 4, "Boolean Algebra," and Buchla's Experiments 6 and 7.

1. Prove with Boolean algebra that the circuits shown in Figure 7–9 perform equivalent logic.

FIGURE 7–9

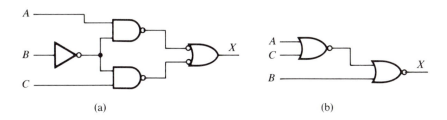

(a)   (b)

2. Assume that the inputs A, B, and C to the circuits shown in Figure 7–9 were all LOWs. What is the output?

3. Draw a logic circuit that will implement the Boolean expression $X = A\bar{B}C + \bar{A}\bar{B}C + AB\bar{C}$.

4. Simplify the expression $X = A\bar{B}C + A\bar{B} + AC$ and draw the circuit for the simplified expression.

5. Using DeMorgan's theorem, simplify each of the expressions.
   a. $X = \overline{\overline{AB}C + \overline{D}E}$

   b. $X = \overline{\overline{A + B} + \overline{C} + \overline{D}}$

6. Explain how the circuit drawn in Figure 7–2 could be changed to one in which only NAND gates were employed. (Don't forget the inverters!)

7. The Boolean expression for an XOR gate is: $X = \overline{A}B + A\overline{B}$. Show how this expression could be implemented using only NAND gates.

8. Draw a Karnaugh map for each expression. Then, write the minimum sum-of-products form for the following expressions.
   a. $X = ABC + \overline{A}B\overline{C} + AB\overline{C} + \overline{A}BC$

   b. $X = \overline{A}\overline{B}\overline{C}\overline{D} + \overline{A}B\overline{C}D + A\overline{B}\overline{C}\overline{D} + A\overline{B}\overline{C}D + ABCD + \overline{A}BCD$

9. Write the minimum sum-of-products expression for the Karnaugh map shown in Figure 7–10.

$X =$ _____

AB\CD	00	01	11	10
00	1	0	1	1
01	0	0	1	1
11	0	0	1	1
10	1	0	0	0

FIGURE 7–10

10. Suppose that the last row of entries on the Karnaugh map in Figure 7–10 were changed to "don't cares." Read the reduced minimum sum-of-products expression from the map.

$X =$ _____

11. Assume the circuit in Figure 7–11(a) has a problem. A timing diagram is taken with a logic analyzer and is shown in Figure 7–11(b). Which of the following are the possible problems with the circuit?

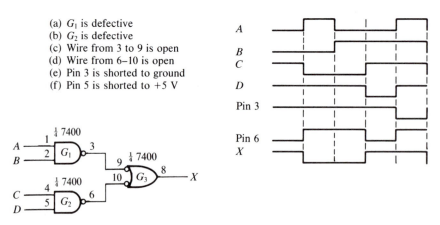

(a) G_1 is defective
(b) G_2 is defective
(c) Wire from 3 to 9 is open
(d) Wire from 6–10 is open
(e) Pin 3 is shorted to ground
(f) Pin 5 is shorted to +5 V

FIGURE 7–11

8

The Perfect Pencil Machine

Objectives

After completing this experiment, you will be able to:
□ Given a problem statement, design and build a combinational logic circuit that solves the logic problem.
□ Write a formal laboratory report describing the circuit and the results.

Reference Reading

Floyd, *Digital Fundamentals,* 4th ed., Section 5–1, Analysis of Combinational Logic; Section 5–2, Design of Combinational Logic; Section 5–3, The Universal Property of NAND and NOR Gates; Section 5–4, Combinational Logic Using Universal Gates; Section 5–5, Pulsed Operation; Section 5–6, Troubleshooting Gate Networks

Materials Needed

Two LEDs
Four-position DIP switch
Other materials as determined by student

Summary of Theory

The methods of designing a combinational logic circuit using the truth table, the equation of the function, and Karnaugh maps have been described. These methods are important tools for the design of simple combinational circuits.

The truth table is a good starting point for a combinational circuit design because it systematically lists all possible combinations of inputs and the desired output. The Karnaugh map is another way to write the truth table, and it allows the function to be reduced in a systematic way. Each 1 from the output function of the truth table appears on the map. The product of the input variables corresponding to each 1 on the map is called a minterm. The sum of all minterms is the expanded sum-of-products (SOP) form of the function.

Some combinational circuits require more than one unrelated output. Such is the case in this experiment where you will design a circuit that delivers an item (a pencil) and has another output to indicate that change is required depending on the input variables. To design this circuit, you will need a separate Karnaugh map for each output. For the analysis, consider each output a separate problem. However, keep in mind that logic needed for one of the outputs sometimes appears in the equation for the other output, and this logic may simplify the total circuit.

As an example, the original not-so-perfect pencil machine design is shown (see Figure 8–1). This machine (which was built shortly after the invention of the pencil) is based on combination logic. Back then, pencils sold for ten cents and the original pencil machine could accept either two nickels or one dime. It would deliver a pencil when at least ten cents was dropped in the machine. If someone first dropped in a nickel and then a dime, the machine was smart enough to

FIGURE 8–1
Not-so-perfect pencil machine switches.

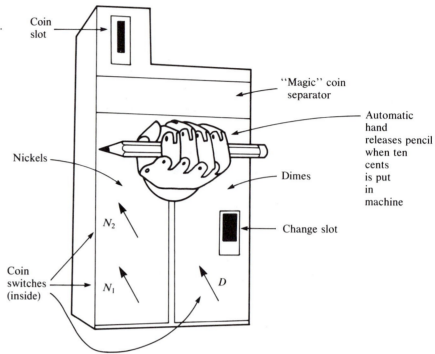

give a nickel change. Here's how the not-so-perfect pencil machine was designed.

First a truth table was filled out showing all possibilities for the input coins. There were two switches for nickels, labeled N_1 and N_2, and one switch for a dime, labeled D. The truth table is shown as Table 8–1. A one on the input side of the truth table indicated that the coin had been placed in the machine and a zero on the input side of the truth table indicated the absence of the coin. The truth table listed two outputs; the first one, labeled P, indicated when a pencil was to be delivered. The second output, labeled NC, indicated when a nickel change was to be returned. Since the circuit was planned for TTL logic, it was decided to use a zero for the "action" output—that is, the pencil or change was to be delivered when a *zero* was in the truth table's output.

Note that the two nickel switches are stacked on top of each other (see Figure 8–1). It is not possible for the second nickel to be placed in the machine until the first nickel has been placed in the machine. Nor is it possible for all three coins to be placed in the machine, since the coins are added sequentially and as soon as ten cents is added, the pencil is delivered. For these reasons, several lines on the truth table are shown as "don't care" (X). "Don't cares" appear on the table because if the input is *not possible,* then we *don't care* what the output does.

The information from the truth table was entered onto two Karnaugh maps—one for each out-

TABLE 8–1
Truth table for the not-so-perfect pencil machine.

Input			Output*	
N_1	N_2	D	P	NC
0	0	0	1	1
0	0	1	0	1
0	1	0	X	X
0	1	1	X	X
1	0	0	1	1
1	0	1	0	0
1	1	0	0	1
1	1	1	X	X

* "0" shown for active level (see discussion).

put (see Figure 8–2). The maps were read by taking "don't care" wherever it would help. The Boolean expressions that resulted surprised no one, not even the company president! From the Boolean sum-of-products, it was a simple matter to implement the not-so-perfect pencil machine, as shown in Figure 8–3.

Procedure

The Perfect Pencil Machine

1. Design a circuit that implements the perfect pencil machine problem stated below. Each

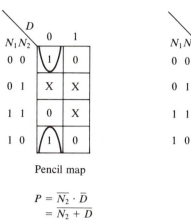
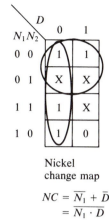

Pencil map

$$P = \overline{N_2 \cdot \overline{D}}$$
$$= \overline{N_2} + D$$

Nickel
change map

$$NC = \overline{N_1} + \overline{D}$$
$$= \overline{N_1 \cdot D}$$

FIGURE 8–2
Karnaugh maps.

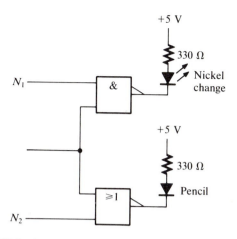

FIGURE 8–3
No-so-perfect pencil machine.

input will be represented by a switch. Outputs will be represented by LEDs. Test your design by building the circuit. Summarize your design steps and results in a formal lab report as outlined in the Introduction at the beginning of this manual. To start, review the steps shown in the summary of theory.

Problem Statement: The Perfect Pencil Company plans to sell its perfect pencils in a new vending machine. Pencils still cost ten cents (but they are smaller!). The new machine has to accept nickels, dimes, or quarters. Each coin accepted by the machine turns on one of the four switches representing a coin. There are two switches for nickels. Assume that the first nickel always turns on switch 1 and the second nickel always turns on switch 2. There is another switch for dimes and one for quarters. Three outputs are required: The first output delivers a pencil if at least ten cents has been put into the machine. The second output indicates that a nickel change is required. The third output is for a dime change. Note that if a customer inadvertently puts a nickel into the machine followed by a quarter, the customer should receive change, but the machine will give change

only for the quarter and will keep the extra nickel. A nickel, followed by a dime, should give a nickel change.

Design Hint: Since three outputs are required, the truth table should show each output for all combinations of inputs. Call the inputs N_1, N_2, D, and Q, and draw a separate map for each of the three outputs. Certain combinations are not possible and can be mapped as "don't cares." For example, a quarter-and-dime combination is not possible, since either of the coins would deliver a pencil before the other coin is put in. By assuming that the first nickel switch is always activated before the second nickel switch, you will obtain additional "don't cares" on the map. The design can be accomplished with just two ICs: a 7400 and a 7402!

For Further Investigation

Design the Model 2 perfect pencil machine in which there are four outputs. The first output is for a pencil, the second is for a nickel change, the third for a dime change, and the fourth for a second dime change.

Report for Experiment 8

Name: _____ Date: _____ Class: _____

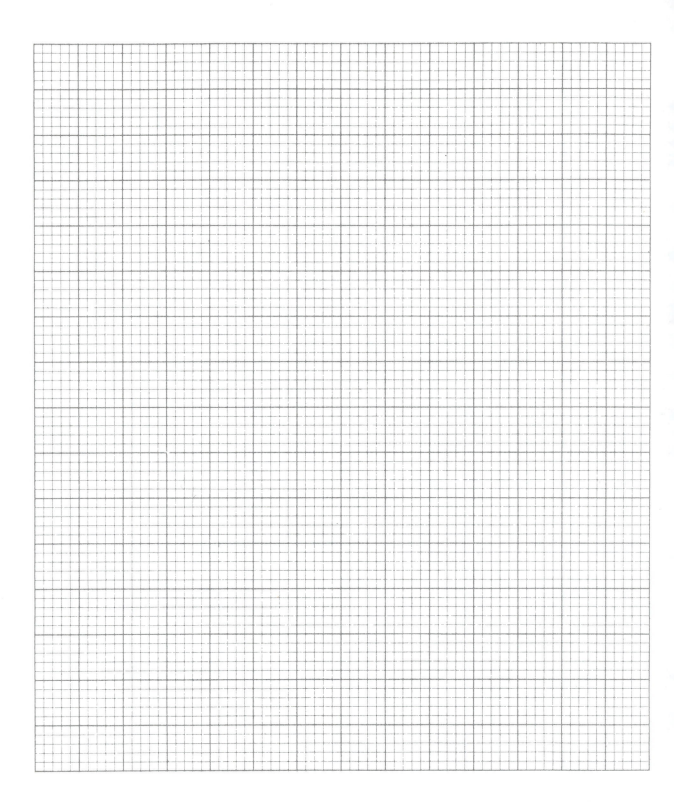

Report for Experiment 8

Name: _____ Date: _____ Class: _____

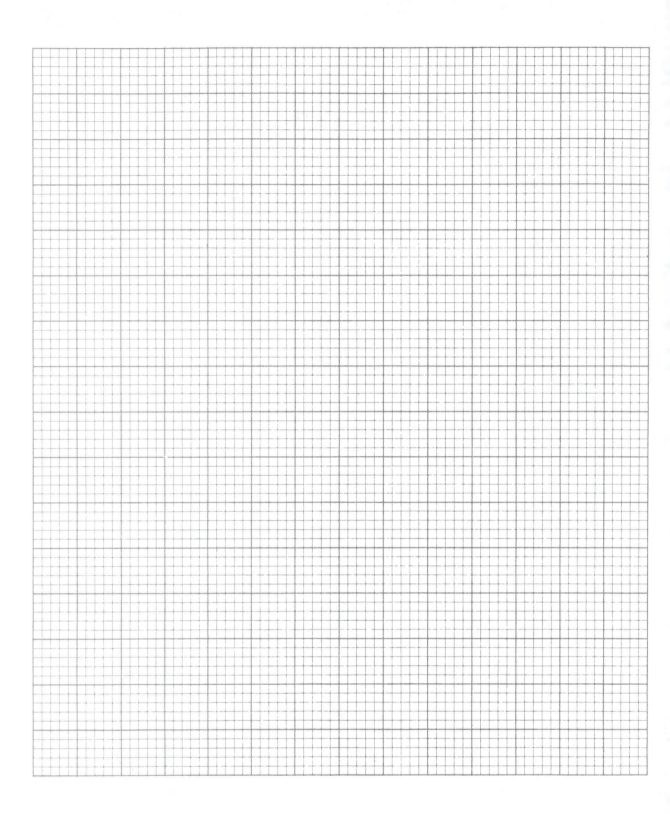

Report for Experiment 8

Name: _____ Date: _____ Class: _____

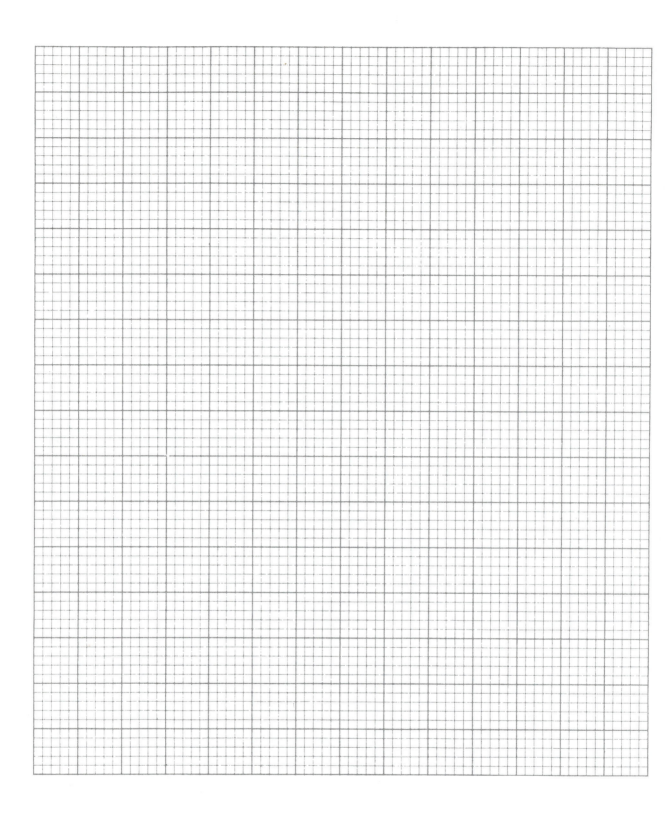

The Cattle Boat

Objectives

After completing this experiment, you will be able to:

- Design, construct, and troubleshoot a logic game.
- Submit a written laboratory report describing your circuit and results.

Reference Reading

Floyd, *Digital Fundamentals,* 4th ed., Section 5–1, Analysis of Combinational Logic; Section 5–2, Design of Combinational Logic; Section 5–3, The Universal Property of NAND and NOR Gates; Section 5–4, Combinational Logic Using Universal Gates; Section 5–5, Pulsed Operation; Section 5–6, Troubleshooting Gate Networks

Materials Needed

Three LEDs (one green, one yellow, one red)
Four-position DIP switch
Other materials as determined by student

The Story

Once upon a time, as the fictional story is told, cattle were shipped to market in the holds of large wooden craft known as cattle boats. These craft were often at sea for months at a time, so the crew would become bored and invent various games. It so happened that there were usually several holds to separate the cattle, so the crew members would take turns dropping water balloons through the breathing holes in the hatch covers to try to hit the cattle.

This may be hard to believe, but the holes in the hatch covers were always arranged in a 4 × 4 matrix. The crew members assigned numbers to the holes and used a numbering system to keep track of their shots. History doesn't reveal if the numbers were assigned a Gray code sequence; however, it is known that the covers were sometimes referred to as K maps.

The game went out of vogue many years ago but later surfaced as a schoolhouse game called battleship. Today, the cattle boat game is making something of a comeback, although, to be kind to animals, the game is now played only in digital logic classes using switches and LEDs. Your job, should you care to accept it, is to construct the logic gameboard as described in the following rules.

The "Gameboard"

Each player has an area defined by a 4 × 4 Karnaugh map. Placed on the map, at "secret" locations, are a "cow" and a "goat." The cow is represented by three adjacent logic 1s and the goat is represented by two adjacent 1s. (Diagonal 1s are not permitted). Naturally, the cow and the goat cannot occupy the same squares on the map.

The game is represented by a circuit in which the cow and goat reside strictly in the Boolean logic. There are five inputs to the circuit—four switches representing the location on the Karnaugh map for dropping the next water balloon and a "fire" pushbutton. When an opponent wishes to drop a water balloon on your animals, he or she first sets the switches to the desired location and then pushes the "fire" pushbutton. There are two outputs represented by LEDs. The first output is "HIT COW," represented by a green LED, and the second output is "HIT GOAT," represented by a yellow LED.

Rules

Each player takes turns dropping water balloons at an opponent's animals. Hits are displayed on the LEDs and recorded by the players on a blank Karnaugh map. If a player scores a hit on an opponent's animal, the appropriate LED will indicate the hit. Turns alternate between players until one player has found the location of the opponent's cow and goat.

Circuit Hint

You can map the output for "cow" and "goat" as a logic 1. The "fire" pushbutton can be connected from a normally closed pushbutton (or wire jumper) to NAND gates, as shown in Figure 9–1.

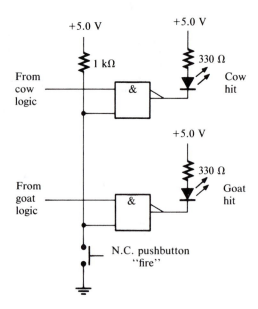

FIGURE 9–1

The output logic is then inverted when the fire pushbutton is pressed, causing a logic 1 to light the LED.

For Further Investigation

Add a red LED that indicates the water balloon missed when the "fire" pushbutton is pressed and neither the cow nor the goat is hit.

Report for Experiment 9

Name: _____ Date: _____ Class: _____

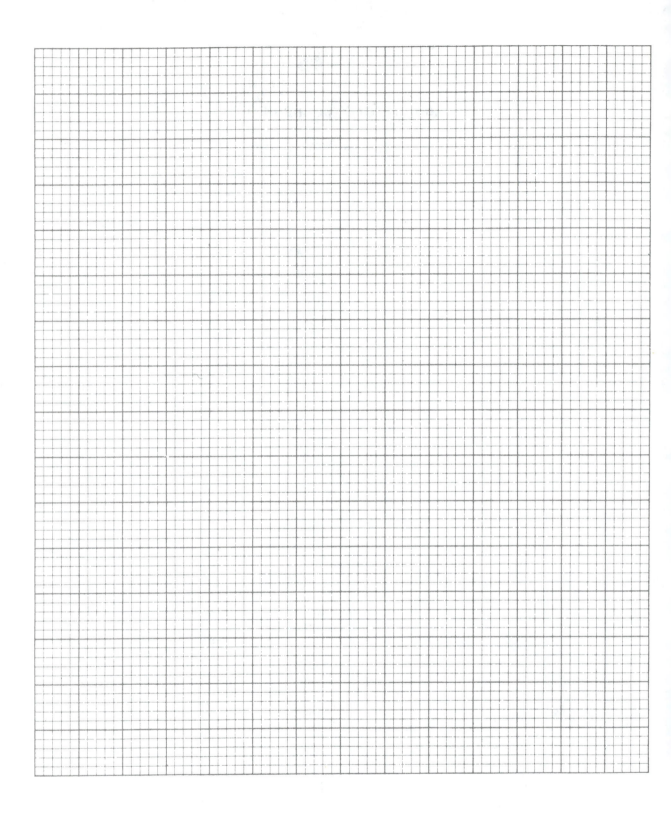

Report for Experiment 9

Name: _____ Date: _____ Class: _____

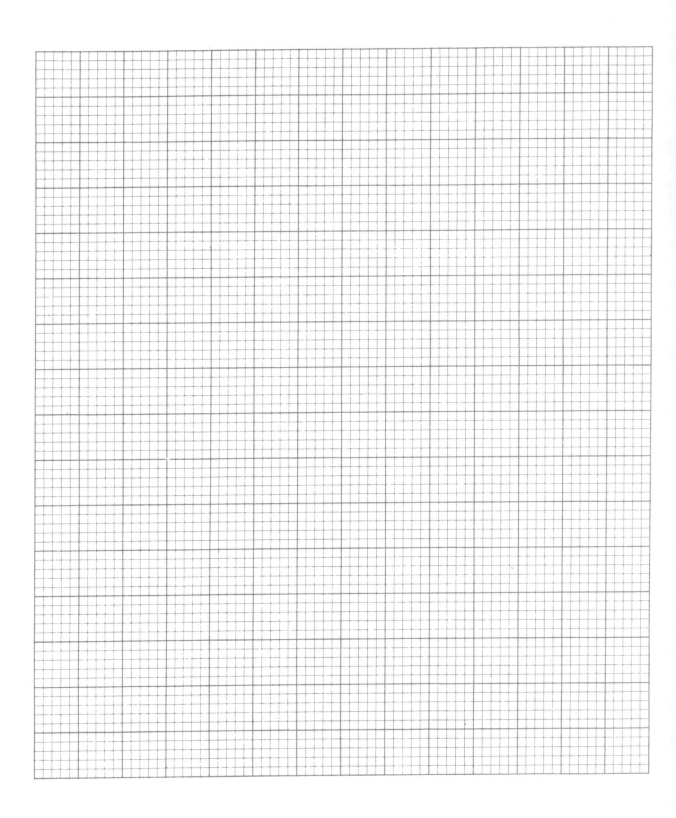

Report for Experiment 9

Name: _____ Date: _____ Class: _____

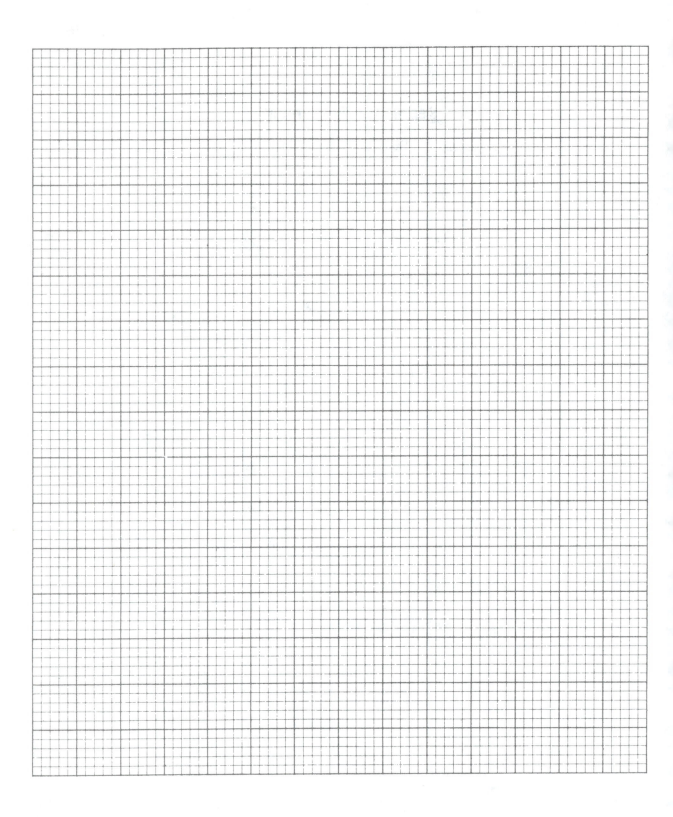

Checkup 5

The exercises in this checkup reflect information covered in Floyd's Chapter 5, "Combinational Logic," and Buchla's Experiments 8 and 9.

1. Show the logic circuit for the Boolean expressions:

   a. $X = \overline{\overline{A}} (B + \overline{C})$

   b. $X = \overline{\overline{AB}} + C\overline{\overline{D}}$

2. Develop the truth table and Karnaugh map that will indicate when at least three of four switches are closed. The switches are represented by the letters A, B, C, and D. A closed switch produces a logic 0. The output required is a logic 1 if the condition is found to be true.

3. Draw the circuit for the situation stated in Problem 2.

4. A seat-belt warning alarm for a car is needed. The front seat contains two switches, labeled D and P, which are asserted HIGH when either a driver or a passenger is seated. Two additional switches, labeled D' and P', represent the belt-fastened switches. These switches are also asserted HIGH when the belts are fastened. The alarm should sound (representing a LOW output) as soon as either a driver or passenger is seated but his or her belt is not fastened. Develop the truth table and Karnaugh map for the problem. Read the minimum sum-of-products expression from the map.

5. Develop the truth table for the circuits shown in Figure 9–2.

FIGURE 9–2

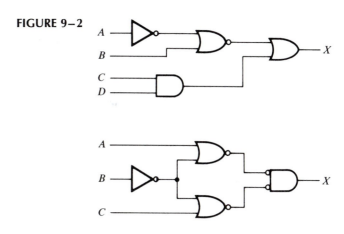

6. Show how to implement the circuits in Problem 5 using only NAND gates.

7. The inputs to a combinational logic circuit are labeled A, B, and C. The circuit has one output labeled X. The waveforms shown in Figure 9–3 are observed for the circuit on a logic analyzer. From these waveforms determine the truth table for the circuit.

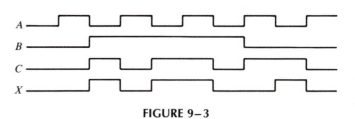

FIGURE 9–3

8. Given the circuit and input waveforms shown in Figure 9–4, sketch the output waveform.

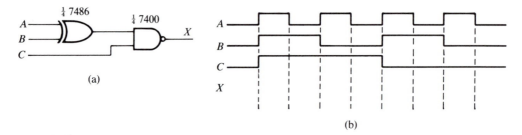

FIGURE 9–4

9. a. A common failure occurs in newly manufactured boards when an IC pin is bent under the IC, leaving it effectively open. Assume that input C of Figure 9–4 was bent under the IC (open). What effect would this have on the output waveform of the circuit?

b. Assume the bent pin actually was making contact with the other input to the NAND gate. How does this type of failure change the output of the circuit?

10. Another type of failure that occurs in newly manufactured boards is when an incorrect part is placed in a circuit board. Assume that the 7400 in Figure 9–4 was replaced with a 7486. What effect does this have on the output signal?

10

MSI Adder and Magnitude Comparator

Objectives

After completing this experiment, you will be able to:

☐ Build a binary-to-BCD code converter using a 7483A 4-bit binary adder and a 7485 magnitude comparator.

☐ Design and build a BCD-to-Excess-3 code converter.

☐ Use the 7483A to form a signed number adder with error detection.

Reference Reading

Floyd, *Digital Fundamentals*, 4th ed., Section 6–1, Adders; Section 6–2, Parallel Binary Adders; Section 6–3, Ripple Carry vs. Look-Ahead–Carry Adders; Section 6–4, Comparators

Materials Needed

7483A 4-bit binary adder
7485 4-bit magnitude comparator
7404 hex inverter
7410 triple 3-input NAND gate
Five LEDs
Four-position DIP switch
Resistors:
    Five 330 Ω
    Eight 1 kΩ

Summary of Theory

Medium-scale integration (MSI) contains more complicated functions than are available in small-scale integration (SSI). These functions, which include adders, comparators, data selectors, and decoders, are available at nominal cost—especially when their cost is compared to the cost of making the function from SSI. In this experiment, you will become familiar with two of these devices: the 4-bit adder and the 4-bit comparator.

The 7483A is a 4-bit adder with a full look-ahead–carry that is accomplished in two steps. The truth table for this device is shown in Table 10–1. To read its truth table, first use the top left diagonal of inputs (A_1, B_1, A_2, B_2, and C_0) to find the outputs Σ_1 and Σ_2 and the state of the internal carry, C_2. The condition of C_2 and the remaining inputs (A_3, B_3, A_4, and B_4) determines which of the lower diagonal output columns to read.

The 7485 magnitude comparator tests two 4-bit binary numbers (usually labeled A and B) and generates an output of 1 at one of three outputs labeled $A > B$, $A < B$, and $A = B$. Three inputs are available for cascading comparators, as explained in Floyd's text.

The circuits in the first part of this experiment are somewhat unusual applications of adders and comparators, but they should give you a good understanding of these ICs. The first circuit uses the adder and comparator to make a code converter between 4-bit binary numbers and BCD. In

TABLE 10–1

Truth table for 7483A.

		Inputs		Outputs When $C_0 = L$		When $C_2 = L$	Outputs When $C_0 = H$		When $C_2 = H$
A_1 / A_3	B_1 / B_3	A_2 / A_4	B_2 / B_4	Σ_1 / Σ_3	Σ_2 / Σ_4	C_2 / C_4	Σ_1 / Σ_3	Σ_2 / Σ_4	C_2 / C_4
L	L	L	L	L	L	L	H	L	L
H	L	L	L	H	L	L	L	H	L
L	H	L	L	H	L	L	L	H	L
H	H	L	L	L	H	L	H	H	L
L	L	H	L	L	H	L	H	H	L
H	L	H	L	H	H	L	L	L	H
L	H	H	L	H	H	L	L	L	H
H	H	H	L	L	L	H	H	L	H
L	L	L	H	L	H	L	H	H	L
H	L	L	H	H	H	L	L	L	H
L	H	L	H	H	H	L	L	L	H
H	H	L	H	L	L	H	H	L	H
L	L	H	H	L	L	H	H	L	H
H	L	H	H	H	L	H	L	H	H
L	H	H	H	H	L	H	L	H	H
H	H	H	H	L	H	H	H	H	H

H = high level, L = low level.

Note: Input conditions at A_1, B_1, A_2, B_2, and C_0 are used to determine outputs Σ_1 and Σ_2 and the value of the internal carry C_2. The values at C_2, A_3, B_3, A_4, and B_4 are then used to determine outputs Σ_3, Σ_4, and C_4.

effect, we add zero to a 4-bit binary number if it is between 0 and 9. Recall that the binary numbers from 0 to 9 are exactly the same as the BCD numbers. If we add zero to these binary numbers, the result represents the equivalent BCD number. You can convert the binary numbers from 1010 to 1111 by simply adding 0110 to them. The 7485 comparator can serve as an invalid BCD code detector (another way to test for invalid codes!). If the output is invalid, then the comparator causes 6 (0110)

TABLE 10–2

Representation of 4-bit signed numbers.

Base Ten Number	Computer Representation	
+7	0111	⎫
+6	0110	
+5	0101	
+4	0100	Numbers in
+3	0011	true form
+2	0010	
+1	0001	
0	0000	⎭
−1	1111	⎫
−2	1110	
−3	1101	
−4	1100	
−5	1011	Numbers in
−6	1010	2's complement form
−7	1001	
−8	1000	⎭

↑
Sign bit

104

to be added to the input number, thus converting it to BCD.

In the Further Investigation, a more traditional use for adders is presented: addition of signed numbers in the manner of most computers. Positive numbers typically are stored in a computer in true (noncomplement) form, and negative numbers are stored in 2's complement form. (See Table 10–2.) This technique results in simpler circuitry, and the computer does not need to distinguish between addition and subtraction. Incidentally, the easiest way to find the value of these numbers is to consider the sign bit (which is the MSB) as having a negative place value and adding the place value of all columns containing a 1. Examples are illustrated in Figure 10–1. These examples are shown for 4 bits, but the idea is applicable to any number of bits.

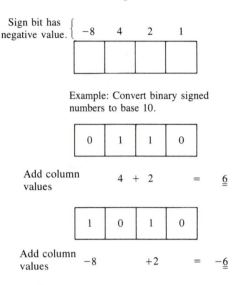

FIGURE 10–1

Procedure

Code Converters

1. Build the binary-to-BCD circuit shown in Figure 10–2. Note the unusual position of V_{CC} and ground on the 7483A. Also, be careful not to confuse the cascading inputs on the 7485 with the outputs, as they have the same labels. Complete truth Table 10–3 in the report by testing each combination of binary inputs and reading the LEDs for the outputs. A' represents a carry to the next group of 4 bits.

2. Using the basic idea in the circuit of Figure 10–2, design a new circuit that converts 4-bit BCD into Excess-3 code. (Excess-3 is described in Floyd's text, Section 2–11.) Display the Excess-3 output with LEDs. Use the 7485 to test for invalid BCD codes. If a code is invalid, indicate so with a separate LED. Draw your design in the space provided in the report.

3. Build your circuit from your design. Test all input combinations, including the invalid BCD codes. Complete truth Table 10–4 for your circuit.

For Further Investigation

Adding Signed Numbers

Fixed-point signed numbers are stored in most computers in the manner illustrated in Table 10–2. If two numbers with the same sign are added, the answer can be too large to be represented with the number of bits available. This con-

dition, called *overflow,* occurs when an addition operation causes a carry into the sign bit position. As a result, the sign bit will be in error, a condition easy to detect. When two numbers with the opposite sign are added, overflow cannot occur, so the sign bit will always be correct. Figure 10–3 illustrates overflow.

In this part of the experiment we will step through the design of a 4-bit adder for signed numbers which detects the presence of an overflow error and lights an LED when overflow occurs. We can start with the 7483A adder and a 7404 hex inverter as shown in Figure 10–4 (in the report).

1. Consider the problem of detecting an overflow error. We need consider only the sign bit for each number to be added and the sign bit for the answer. Complete truth Table 10–5 for all possible combinations of the sign bit, showing a 1 whenever an overflow error occurs.

2. Complete the Karnaugh map of the output (shown in the report as Figure 10–5) to see whether minimization is possible.

3. Write the Boolean expression for detection of an overflow error in your report.

4. Note that the signals going into the box are A_4, B_4, and $\overline{\Sigma}_4$. If you apply DeMorgan's theorem to one term of your Boolean expression, you can draw a circuit that uses only these inputs. Draw the circuit in the box in Figure 10–4. If directed by your instructor, build and test your circuit.

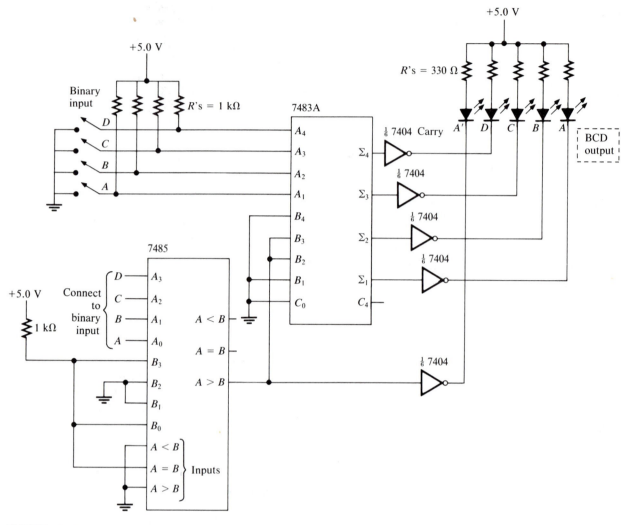

FIGURE 10–2
Binary to BCD converter.

FIGURE 10–3

Numbers with opposite signs: Overflow into sign position cannot occur.

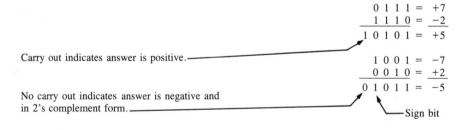

```
        0 1 1 1 =  +7
        1 1 1 0 =  -2
      1 0 1 0 1 =  +5
```

Carry out indicates answer is positive.

```
        1 0 0 1 =  -7
        0 0 1 0 =  +2
      0 1 0 1 1 =  -5
```

No carry out indicates answer is negative and
in 2's complement form.

Sign bit

Numbers with the same sign: Overflow into sign position can occur.

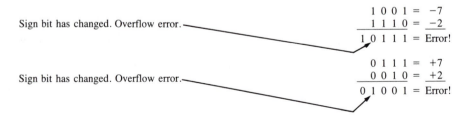

```
        1 0 0 1 =  -7
        1 1 1 0 =  -2
      1 0 1 1 1 = Error!
```

Sign bit has changed. Overflow error.

```
        0 1 1 1 =  +7
        0 0 1 0 =  +2
      0 1 0 0 1 = Error!
```

Sign bit has changed. Overflow error.

Report for Experiment 10

Name: _____ Date: _____ Class: _____

Objectives:

Procedure:

Data:

TABLE 10–3
Truth table for Figure 10–2.

Inputs (Binary)				Outputs (BCD)					
D	C	B	A	A'		D	C	B	A
0	0	0	0						
0	0	0	1						
0	0	1	0						
0	0	1	1						
0	1	0	0						
0	1	0	1						
0	1	1	0						
0	1	1	1						
1	0	0	0						
1	0	0	1						
1	0	1	0						
1	0	1	1						
1	1	0	0						
1	1	0	1						
1	1	1	0						
1	1	1	1						

TABLE 10–4
Truth table for binary to Excess-3 circuit (Step 3).

Inputs (BCD)				Outputs				
				Excess-3				Invalid Code
D	C	B	A	D	C	B	A	
0	0	0	0					
0	0	0	1					
0	0	1	0					
0	0	1	1					
0	1	0	0					
0	1	0	1					
0	1	1	0					
0	1	1	1					
1	0	0	0					
1	0	0	1					
1	0	1	0					
1	0	1	1					
1	1	0	0					
1	1	0	1					
1	1	1	0					
1	1	1	1					

Step 2. Schematic of a circuit that will convert binary to Excess-3 code:

Results and Conclusion:

Further Investigation Results:

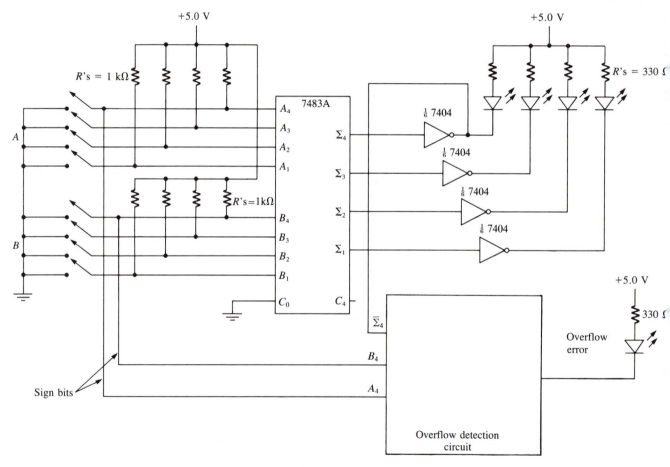

FIGURE 10–4
Signed number adder.

TABLE 10–5
Truth table for overflow error.

Sign Bits			Error
A_4	B_4	Σ_4	X
0	0	0	
0	0	1	
0	1	0	
0	1	1	
1	0	0	
1	0	1	
1	1	0	
1	1	1	

A_4 B_4 \ Σ_4	0	1
0 0		
0 1		
1 1		
1 0		

FIGURE 10–5
Karnaugh map for overflow error.

Boolean expression for overflow error:

$X =$ ____________

Evaluation and Review Questions

1. Assume the circuit of Figure 10–2 has an open output on the $A > B$ of the 7485.

a. What effect does this have on the A' output?

b. What voltage level would you expect to measure on the B_3 and B_2 inputs on the 7483A?

2. The circuit of Figure 10–6 should turn on the LED whenever the input number is less than 8 or greater than 12. Complete the design by showing where each of the remaining inputs is connected.

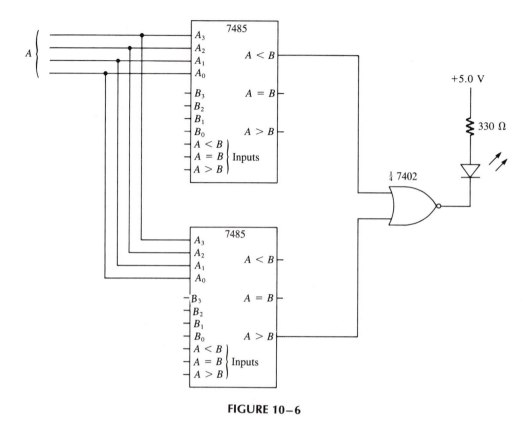

FIGURE 10–6

3. In the space below, show how two 7483A adders could be cascaded to add two 8-bit numbers.

4. What is the function of the C_0 input on the 7483 adder?

5. The circuit in Figure 10–4 is designed to add two 4-bit signed numbers. Recall that negative numbers are often stored in 2's complement form. To change the circuit into a subtracting circuit *(A-B)*, you would need to 2's complement the *B* inputs. Inverting the *B* inputs forms the 1's complement. What else must be done in order to cause the circuit to form the 2's complement of the *B* input?

11

Combinational Logic Using Multiplexers

Objectives

After completing this experiment, you will be able to:

☐ Use a multiplexer to construct and test a comparator and parity generator.

☐ Design circuits that use an *N*-input multiplexer to implement an arbitrary truth table containing 2*N* variables.

Reference Reading

Floyd, *Digital Fundamentals*, 4th ed., Section 6–5, Decoders; Section 6–6, Encoders; Section 6–7, Code Converters; Section 6–8, Multiplexers (Data Selectors); Section 6–9, Demultiplexers; Section 6–10, Parity Generators/Checkers

Materials Needed

74151A data selector/multiplexer
7404 hex inverter
One LED
Resistors:
  One 330 Ω
  Four 1 kΩ

Summary of Theory

The *multiplexer* or *data selector* is a circuit that connects any one of several inputs to a single output. The circuit that performs the opposite function, in which a single input is directed to one of several outputs, is called a *demultiplexer* or a *decoder*. These definitions are illustrated in Figure 11–1. The routing of the data is determined by additional logic signals called the *select* (or *address*) inputs. This application will be studied in Experiment 12.

Multiplexers (MUX) and demultiplexers (DMUX) have many applications in digital logic. One useful application for multiplexers is implementation of combinational logic functions directly from the truth table. For example, in Experiment 8, we needed an overflow error detection circuit with the truth table shown in Figure 11–2(a). Each output row on the truth table represents a minterm. If the output logic for that minterm is connected to the data inputs of the MUX, and if the data selected are controlled by the input variables, the truth table has been implemented directly. Figure 11–2(b) illustrates this idea conceptually.

Actually, an 8-input multiplexer is not required to implement the overflow detection logic. Any *N*-input multiplexer can generate the output function for 2*N* inputs. To illustrate, we reorganize the truth table as shown in Figure 11–3(a). The inputs labeled A_4 and B_4 on the truth table are used by the multiplexer to select a data line. Connected to that data line can be a logic 0, 1, Σ_4, or $\overline{\Sigma}_4$. For example, from the truth table, if $A_4 = 0$ and $B_4 = 1$, the D_1 input will be selected by the MUX. We decide which input to connect by checking both possible outputs for $A_4 = 0$ and $B_4 = 1$. Since both outputs are the same, in this

111

FIGURE 11–1

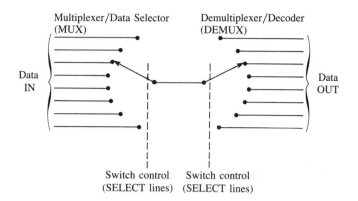

case a logic 0, then D_1 is connected to a logic 0. If the outputs were different, such as in the first and fourth rows, then the third input variable, Σ_4, would be compared with the output. Either the true (or NOTted) form of that variable then would be selected. The results are shown in Figure 11–3(b), which is equivalent to but simpler than the circuit in Figure 11–2(b).

In this experiment you will use an 8:1 MUX to implement a 4-input truth table (with 16 combinations) using the idea illustrated in Figure 11–3 and in Floyd's Example 6–18. In the first part of the experiment, you will develop the necessary circuit to implement a special comparator. In the Further Investigation the circuit is modified to make a parity generator for a 4-bit code. *Parity* is an extra bit attached to a code to check that the code has been received correctly. *Odd parity* means that the number of 1s in the code, including the parity bit, is an odd number. Odd or even parity can be generated with exclusive-OR gates, and parity generators are available in IC form. How-

ever, the implementing of an arbitrary truth table using multiplexers is the important concept.

Procedure

Special 2-bit Comparator

1. Let's assume you needed to compare two 2-bit numbers called A and B to find if A is equal to or greater than B. You could use a comparator and OR the $A > B$ and $A = B$ outputs. Another technique is to use an 8:1 MUX with the method shown in the Summary of Theory. One advantage to the MUX is that it can be adapted to any arbitrary combination of inputs. The partially completed truth table for the required comparator is shown as Table 11–1 in the report. The inputs are listed as A_2, A_1 and B_2, B_1, which represent the numbers to be compared. The A_2, A_1, and B_2 bits are to be connected to the SELECT inputs of the MUX and the B_1 bit is available to be connected as needed. It is therefore listed in a separate col-

FIGURE 11–2

Truth table for overflow error

Sign Bits			Error
A_4	B_4	Σ_4	X
0	0	0	0
0	0	1	1
0	1	0	0
0	1	1	0
1	0	0	0
1	0	1	0
1	1	0	1
1	1	1	0

MUX 8:1

D_0
D_1
D_2
D_3
D_4
D_5
D_6
D_7

Select

$\overline{C \quad B \quad A}$

X

C = MSB
A = LSB

Note: Select input variables A and B are not the same as the logic variables A_4 and B_4.

(a) Truth table

(b) Implementation

112

Truth table for overflow error

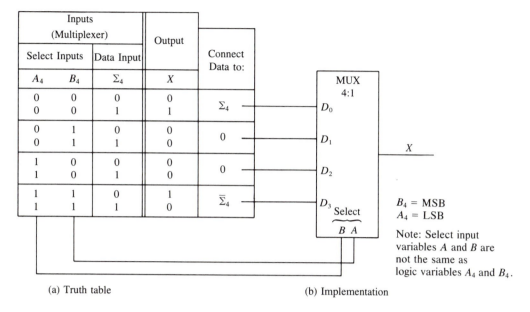

Inputs (Multiplexer)			Output	Connect Data to:
Select Inputs		Data Input		
A_4	B_4	Σ_4	X	
0	0	0	0	Σ_4
0	0	1	1	
0	1	0	0	0
0	1	1	0	
1	0	0	0	0
1	0	1	0	
1	1	0	1	$\overline{\Sigma_4}$
1	1	1	0	

(a) Truth table

B_4 = MSB
A_4 = LSB

Note: Select input variables A and B are not the same as logic variables A_4 and B_4.

(b) Implementation

FIGURE 11–3

umn. Determine the proper logic to implement a circuit in which the output represents $A \geq B$ and complete the X column of truth Table 11–1. The first two entries of the X column are completed as an example.

2. The next step in determining how to connect the MUX to implement the truth table is to look at the output X, in groups of two. The first pair of entries in X is the complement of the corresponding entries in B_1; therefore, the data should be connected to $\overline{B_1}$, as shown in the first line. Complete Table 11–1 by filling in the last column with either 0, 1, B_1, or $\overline{B_1}$.

3. Using the data from Table 11–1, complete the circuit drawing shown as Figure 11–4 in the report. From the manufacturer's specification sheet, determine how to connect the STROBE input (labeled $\overline{G}$). Construct the circuit and test its operation by checking each possible input. Demonstrate your working circuit to your instructor.

For Further Investigation

Parity Generator Using a Multiplexer

1. The technique used to implement an arbitrary function can also be used to generate either odd or even parity. The MUX can actually generate *both* odd and even parity at the same time with the choice of odd or even parity made by selecting one of the two outputs. One interesting aspect of the parity generator circuit is that any of the four inputs can turn on or off the LED in a manner similar to the way in which 3-way switches can turn on or off a light from more than one location. The truth table is set up in a similar manner to Table 11–1 and is shown in the report as Table 11–2. Four of the bits (A_3 through A_0) represent the information, and the fifth bit (X), which is the output, represents the parity bit. The requirement is for a circuit that generates both odd and even parity; however, the truth table will be set up for even parity. Even parity means that the sum of the 5 bits, *including the parity bit,* must be equal to an even number. Complete truth Table 11–2 to reflect this requirement. The first line has been completed as an example.

2. Using the truth table completed in Step 1, complete the circuit for the even parity generator. The circuit is started in Figure 11–5 of the report. Construct the circuit and demonstrate it to your instructor. Note that odd parity can be obtained from the circuit by connecting the LED to the Y output of the 74151A.

Report for Experiment 11

Name: _____ Date: _____ Class: _____

Objectives:

Procedure:

Data:

TABLE 11–1
Truth table for 2-bit comparator, $A \geq B$.

Inputs				Output	Connect
A_2	A_1	B_2	B_1	X	Data to:
0	0	0	0	1	
0	0	0	1	0	$\overline{B_1}$
0	0	1	0		
0	0	1	1		
0	1	0	0		
0	1	0	1		
0	1	1	0		
0	1	1	1		
1	0	0	0		
1	0	0	1		
1	0	1	0		
1	0	1	1		
1	1	0	0		
1	1	0	1		
1	1	1	0		
1	1	1	1		

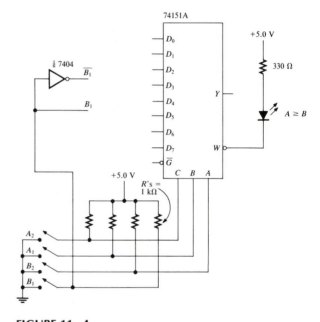

FIGURE 11–4

Results and Conclusion:

Further Investigation Results:

TABLE 11–2
Truth table for even parity generator.

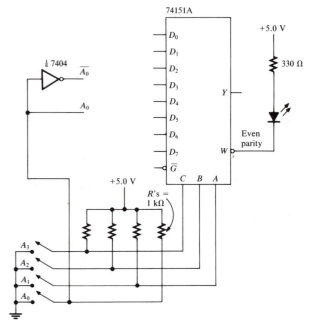

FIGURE 11–5

Inputs				Output	Connect
A_3	A_2	A_1	A_0	X	data to:
0	0	0	0	0	
0	0	0	1	1	A_0
0	0	1	0		
0	0	1	1		
0	1	0	0		
0	1	0	1		
0	1	1	0		
0	1	1	1		
1	0	0	0		
1	0	0	1		
1	0	1	0		
1	0	1	1		
1	1	0	0		
1	1	0	1		
1	1	1	0		
1	1	1	1		

Evaluation and Review Questions

1. Design an invalid BCD code detector using a 74151A. Show the connections for your design on Figure 11–6.

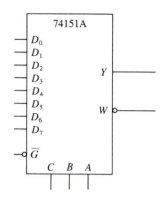

FIGURE 11–6

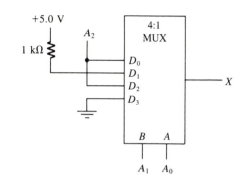

FIGURE 11–7

2. Can you reverse the procedure of this experiment? That is, given the circuit, can you find the Boolean expression? The circuit shown in Figure 11–7 uses a 4:1 MUX. The inputs are called A_2, A_1, and A_0. The first term is obtained by observing that when both select lines are LOW, A_2 is routed to the output; therefore the first minterm is written $A_2\overline{A_1}\overline{A_0}$. Using this as an example, find the remaining minterms:

$$X = \underline{\hspace{3cm}}$$

3. Assume the circuit shown in Figure 11–4 had the correct output for the first half of the truth table but had some incorrect outputs for the second half of the truth table. You decide to change ICs (not necessarily the best choice!) but the problem persists. What is the most likely cause of the problem? How would you test the circuit for your suspected problem?

4. Assume the circuit in Figure 11–4 had a short to ground on the output of the inverter. What effect would this have on the output logic? What procedure would you use to find the problem?

5. What is the function of the circuit shown in Figure 11–8? When is the output HIGH?

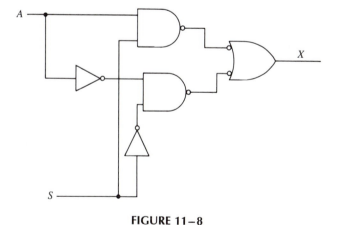

FIGURE 11–8

12

Applications of Multiplexers and Demultiplexers

Objectives

After completing this experiment, you will be able to:

☐ Construct a simple data transmission system using a multiplexer and demultiplexer.

☐ Measure the frequency of data changes using an oscilloscope or logic analyzer.

☐ Complete the design of a multiple output combinational logic circuit using a demultiplexer.

Reference Reading

Floyd, *Digital Fundamentals,* 4th ed., Section 6–5, Decoders; Section 6–6, Encoders; Section 6–7, Code Converters; Section 6–8, Multiplexers (Data Selectors); Section 6–9, Demultiplexers; Section 6–10, Parity Generators/Checkers

Materials Needed

7408 quad AND gate
Two 7493A 4-bit binary counters
74LS139A decoder/demultiplexer (74LS138 may be substituted)
74151A data selector/multiplexer
One 4-position DIP switch
LEDs: 8 total, with at least two red, two yellow, and two green
Resistors:
   Eight 330 Ω
   Two 1 kΩ

Summary of Theory:

In Experiment 11, you saw a multiplexer (MUX) used to determine the correct output for various combinational logic problems. Multiplexers are also used as data selectors, an application that will be tested in this experiment. Likewise, demultiplexers (DMUX) can function either as data routers or as decoders. Data selecting (MUX) and routing (DMUX) are the reverse of each other. The idea behind data selecting and data routing was illustrated in Figure 11–1.

In addition to its function in data routing, the demultiplexer can serve as a decoder. The decoding function is different from data routing. A decoder takes binary information from one or more input lines and generates a unique output code for each input combination. You are already familiar with the 7447A IC, which performs only the decoding function. It converts a 4-bit binary input number to a unique code that is used to drive a seven-segment display. A demultiplexer can also be used as a decoder by providing a unique output for every combination of input variables. This type of decoding is widely used in computers for pointing to a specific location of memory.

For most demultiplexers, the selected output is LOW, whereas all others are HIGH. To implement a truth table that has a *single* output with a decoder is not very efficient and is rarely done; however, a method for doing this is shown conceptually in Figure 12–1. In this case, each line on the output represents one row on the truth ta-

119

FIGURE 12–1

Implementing a combinational logic function with an active HIGH DMUX.

Truth table for overflow error

Inputs			Output
A_4	B_4	Σ_4	X
0	0	0	0
0	0	1	1
0	1	0	0
0	1	1	0
1	0	0	0
1	0	1	0
1	1	0	1
1	1	1	0

(a) Truth table

(b) Implementation

ble. If the decoder has active HIGH outputs (such as the CD4514), the lines on the truth table that represent a 1 are ORed together, as illustrated in Figure 12–1. The output of the OR gate represents the output function. If the outputs of the decoder are active LOW (such as the 74LS139), the lines representing a 1 on the truth table are connected together with a NAND gate. This is shown in Figure 12–2.

Where a DMUX shines for implementing combinational logic is when there are several outputs for the same set of input variables. Each output line of the demultiplexer represents a line on the truth table. For active HIGH decoder outputs, OR gates are used as before, but a separate OR

gate is required for each output function. Each OR gate output represents a different output function. In the case of active LOW decoder outputs, the OR gates are replaced by NAND gates.

The first part of this experiment uses a simple data transmission system to illustrate the data-selecting and data-routing process. The technique shown also has application in time-division multiplexing of displays as described in the text. It is necessary to introduce the 7493A counter to show the process; necessary information for connecting it is given in the experiment. (Counters are covered in Floyd's Chapter 8 and in Experiments 17 through 20.) Then you will connect a demultiplexer as a decoder and observe how this IC can

FIGURE 12–2

Implementing a combinational logic function with an active LOW DMUX.

Truth table for overflow error

Inputs			Output
A_4	B_4	Σ_4	X
0	0	0	0
0	0	1	1
0	1	0	0
0	1	1	0
1	0	0	0
1	0	1	0
1	1	0	1
1	1	1	0

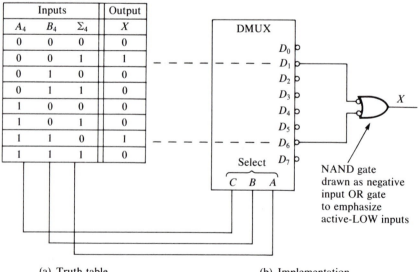

NAND gate drawn as negative input OR gate to emphasize active-LOW inputs

(a) Truth table

(b) Implementation

be used effectively when a number of outputs are required from a common set of inputs. The problem that is presented is the logic for a traffic light.

Procedure

MUX/DMUX Data Transmission

1. Connect the data transmission circuit shown in Figure 12–3. The 7493A counters are 4-bit counters connected together to form one 8-bit counter. The 8-bit counter is used for two functions. The least significant bits (CTR-1) change rapidly and change the data-select lines on both the MUX and the DMUX at the same time, causing both to select the same data line. The high-order bits (CTR-2) change at a slower rate and represent the data to be sent. CTR-2 is clocked from CTR-1, as shown.

2. Set your pulse generator to a 10 Hz TTL clock and observe the action of the circuit. The data on the transmit LEDs should appear sequentially on the receive LEDs. You can see how multiplexed data can be "time-sliced," sending only one bit at a time. Increase the generator frequency and observe that as the data change rapidly, they give the appearance of a continuous display. This technique is widely used in multiplexed displays.

3. Set the pulse generator to 10 kHz and connect channel 1 of an oscilloscope to the most significant bit (MSB) of CTR-2. Trigger the oscilloscope using channel 1 as the triggering channel. This technique, using the slowest signal for a trigger signal, assures that time relationships can be observed correctly. Use channel 2 to observe the counter outputs and the output of the MUX. Summarize your observations in the report.

4. Observe the waveforms at the receive LEDs. Measure the frequency at each LED. Record the measured frequencies in Table 12–1 of the report.

Traffic Light Decoder

5. In this step, the circuit is changed from a data router to a decoder. Disconnect the wiring, except keep CTR-1 connected (for the For Further Investigation). Remove CTR-2 and the 74151A MUX from the protoboard as they will not be needed.

6. The circuit represents the output of a state machine that controls a traffic light on a main street and a side street. Each state is represented by a different row on the truth table. There are four states, represented by the binary numbers 00, 01, 10 and 11. There are three outputs for each street: red, yellow, and green. The desired outputs for the first three states are listed in truth Table 12–2 shown in the report. A logic 0 is shown in the truth table to turn on an LED. The sequence shown in the first three rows of the truth table follows that of a traffic light. Complete the truth table by entering the required outputs for the fourth row.

7. Those outputs with more than one *zero* in a column can be connected to the appropriate LED through an AND gate. (Conversely, we could connect the logic ones through a NAND gate, but this would make the circuit more complicated.) Only two AND gates are needed. State 0 (the first row of the truth table) will have a green light ON for the main street and a red light ON for the side street. The $1Y_0$ output of the decoder (state 0) has been connected to the green LED on the main street and the red LED on the side street as an example. Using truth Table 12–1, draw the remaining wiring on the partially completed schematic shown in Figure 12–4 of the report. Note that the AND gate in the schematic is drawn as a negative input NOR gate to emphasize the active LOW output of the decoder.

8. The 74LS139 has two data-select inputs and an enable input. Use the truth table for the 74LS139 to determine the correct logic to apply to the enable input. Show the logic for the enable input on the schematic of Figure 12–4.

9. After you have completed the schematic, wire the circuit and test the four input states. If the outputs are in accordance with the truth table, you have done a good job! If not, find the problem and correct it. Show your working circuit to your instructor.

For Further Investigation

This Further Investigation is just for fun! You can now make your traffic light go through its sequence by connecting the select inputs of the decoder to the counter that you saved from the data transmission part of the experiment. Connect the output of the pulse generator directly to the A select input of the decoder and the Q_A output of the counter to the B select input. If the duty cycle of your pulse generator is relatively short, this will leave the red and green lights on for longer intervals than the yellow light. (Why?) Then slow the generator down to a frequency that prevents accidents at your intersection and watch the ants cross the street!

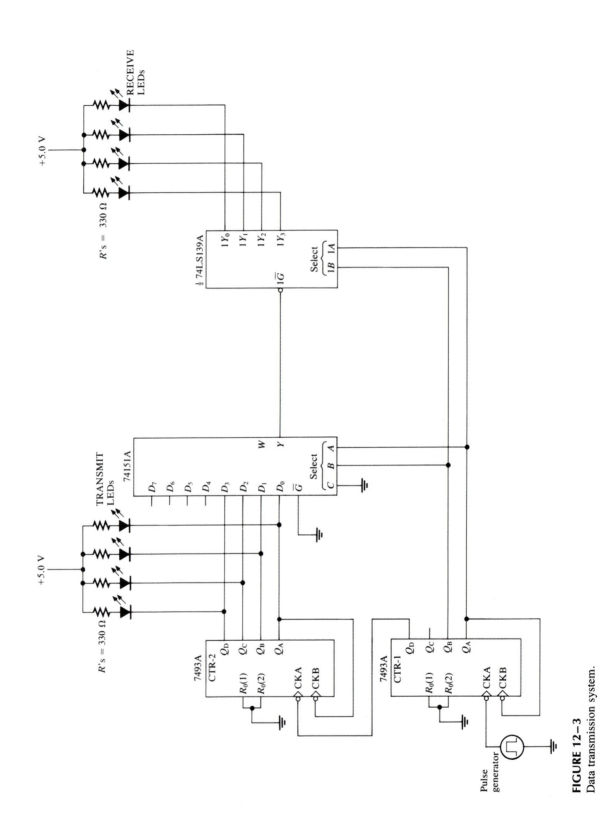

FIGURE 12–3
Data transmission system.

Report for Experiment 12

Name: _____ Date: _____ Class: _____

Objectives:

Procedure:

Data:

Step 3. Observations:

TABLE 12–1

DMUX Output	Measured Output Frequency
Y_0	
Y_1	
Y_2	
Y_3	

TABLE 12–2
Truth table for the outputs of a traffic light.

Inputs (State)		Outputs					
		Main			Side		
B	A	R	Y	G	R	Y	G
0	0	1	1	0	0	1	1
0	1	1	0	1	0	1	1
1	0	0	1	1	1	1	0
1	1						

FIGURE 12–4
Traffic light decoder.

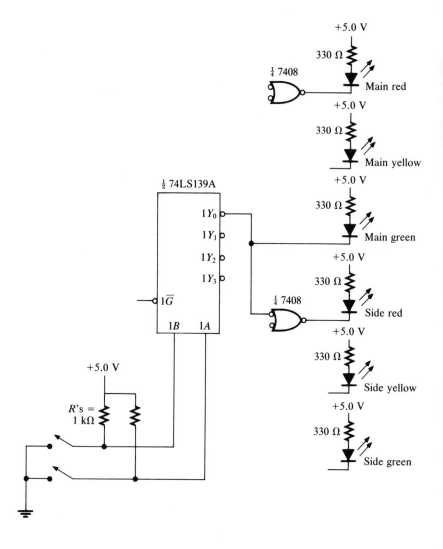

Results and Conclusion:

Further Investigation Results:

Evaluation and Review Questions

1. What changes would need to be made to the circuit in Figure 12–3 to send 8 bits instead of 4 bits?

2. What does the data transmission system you constructed in this experiment have in common with the seven-segment display multiplexer circuit shown in Floyd's text in Figure 6–66?

3. For the circuit in Figure 12–3, assume the transmit LEDs were cycling through a sequence, but on the receive side, all the LEDs were constantly ON. What could account for this? What procedure would you use to locate the fault?

4. Why were AND gates used in the circuit of Figure 12–4?

5. The circuit of Figure 12–4 could be modified by adding a state 4 to the truth table. Assume you want to turn on both yellow lights at the same time in the new state. Set up the new state by adding a switch labeled C. When switch C is opened (HIGH), the decoder is disabled and at the same time the yellow lights turn on. Show the circuit. (*Hint:* Draw a truth table showing the decoder output ($1Y1$) and switch C as the inputs and the main yellow as the output. You can accomplish this change with two 2-input gates.)

Checkup 6

The exercises in this checkup reflect information covered in Floyd's Chapter 6, "Applications of Combinational Logic," and Buchla's Experiments 10, 11, and 12.

1. Write the truth table for a half-adder. From the truth table, draw a circuit that shows how both the sum and carry bits can be implemented with only NAND gates.

2. Show how a half-adder could be implemented with a 74LS139A demultiplexer.

3. Assume you needed to add two 4-bit BCD numbers using a 7483A adder and other circuitry as necessary. The answer is to be displayed in BCD. Explain how you would accomplish this.

4. A half-subtractor circuit is very similar to a half-adder. The truth table for a half-subtractor is shown in Figure 12–5. From this truth table, draw the circuit that implements it in the fewest number of gates.

M = minuend, S = subtrahend, R = remainder, B = borrow

M	S	R	B
0	0	0	0
0	1	1	1
1	0	1	0
1	1	0	0

M
$-S$
R
(B = borrow)

FIGURE 12–5

5. The 7485 comparator has a set of inputs labeled $A < B$, $A = B$, and $A > B$. Explain the purpose of these inputs.

6. The circuit shown in Figure 12–6 is a comparator. Analyze the operation, then label the appropriate outputs for $A = B$, $A < B$, and $A > B$. Assume the outputs are asserted HIGH when true.

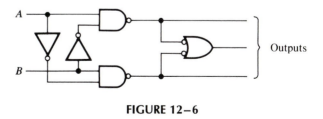

FIGURE 12–6

7. The circuit shown in Figure 12–7 can be used to decode any 4-bit word that is set on the switches and can, therefore, provide a selectable decoded output. Look over the circuit and write a short summary that explains its operation (D = most significant bit).

FIGURE 12–7

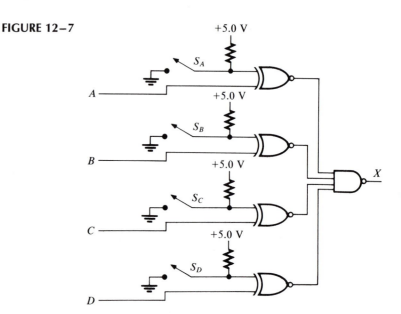

8. When a LOW appears on the output of each of the decoders shown in Figure 12–8, what is the binary code appearing on the input (D = most significant bit)?

FIGURE 12–8   (D = MSB)

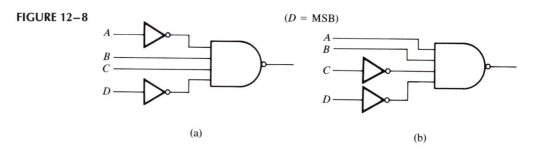

(a)   (b)

9. The output of the decoder shown in Figure 12–9 is HIGH. What is the binary code appearing on the input (D = most significant bit)?

FIGURE 12–9   (D = MSB)

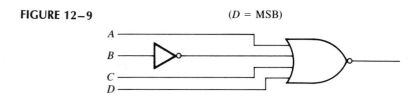

10. a. If the A input on the circuit shown in Figure 12–9 is open because of a cold solder joint, what effect will this have on the output? (Assume TTL logic.)

b. What procedure would you use to locate the problem?

128

13

The D Latch and D Flip-Flop

Objectives

After completing this experiment, you will be able to:
- Demonstrate how a latch can debounce an SPDT switch.
- Construct and test a D latch from four NAND gates and an inverter.
- Test a D flip-flop and investigate several application circuits for both the latch and the flip-flop.

Reference Reading

Floyd, Digital Fundamentals, 4th ed., Section 7–1, Latches; Section 7–2, Edge-Triggered Flip-Flops

Materials Needed

Red LED
Green LED
7486 quad XOR gate
7400 quad NAND gate
7404 hex inverter
7474 dual D flip-flop
Resistors:
  Two 330 Ω
  Two 1 kΩ

Summary of Theory

As you have seen, combinational logic circuits are circuits in which the outputs are determined fully by the current inputs. *Sequential* logic circuits contain information about previous conditions—the dial telephone, for example. The difference between combinational and sequential circuits is that sequential circuits contain *memory* and combinational circuits do not.

The most basic memory unit is the *latch*, which uses feedback to lock onto and hold data. It can be constructed from either NAND or NOR gates. The ability to remember previous conditions is easy to demonstrate with Boolean algebra. For example, Figure 13–1 shows an S-R latch made from NAND gates. This circuit is widely used for switch debouncing and is available as an integrated circuit containing four latches (the 74LS279).

A simple modification of the basic latch is the addition of steering gates and an inverter as shown in Figure 13–2. This circuit is called a gated D (for Data) latch. An enable input allows data present on the *D* input to be transferred to the output when Enable is asserted. When the enable input is not asserted, the last level—Q and $\overline{Q}$—is latched. This circuit is available in integrated circuit form as the 7475A quad D latch. Although there are four latches in this IC, there are only two shared enable signals.

Design problems are often simplified by having all transitions in a system occur synchronously

FIGURE 13–1
$\overline{S}$-$\overline{R}$ latch.

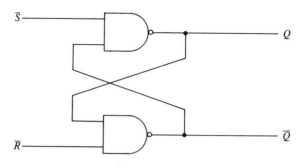

Equation for top NAND gate:

$$Q = \overline{\overline{S} \cdot \overline{Q}}$$

Applying DeMorgan's theorem:

$$Q = S + Q$$

Thus, Q appears on both sides of the equation.
If $\overline{S} = 1$, then $S = 0$ and $Q = 0 + Q$ (Q is previous state)
output is latched.

(at the same time) by using a common source of pulses to cause the change. This common pulse is called a *clock*. The output changes occur only on either the leading or the trailing edge of the clock pulse. Some ICs have inputs that directly set or re-set the output any time they are asserted. These inputs are labeled *asynchronous* inputs because no clock pulse is required. The D-type flip-flop with positive edge-triggering and asynchronous inputs is the 7474. In this experiment, you will also test this IC.

Procedure

$\overline{S}$-$\overline{R}$ Latch

1. Build the $\overline{S}$-$\overline{R}$ latch shown in Figure 13–3. We will first test this circuit and then use it as part of a new circuit. Use a wire to simulate the single-pole, double-throw (SPDT) switch. The LEDs will be used in this section as logic monitors. Note that because TTL logic is much better at sinking current than at sourcing current, the LEDs are arranged to be ON when the output is LOW. To make the LEDs read the HIGH output when

they are ON, we can connect them to the opposite output! This simple trick sometimes avoids the use of an inverter in circuits.

2. Leave the wire on the *A* terminal and note the logic shown on the LEDs. Now simulate a bouncing switch by removing the *A* end of the wire. Do NOT touch *B* yet! Instead, reconnect the wire to *A* several times.

3. Remove the *A* end of the wire and touch *B*. Simulate the switch bouncing several times by removing and reconnecting *B*. (Switches never bounce back to the opposite terminal, so you should not touch *A*.) Summarize your observations of the $\overline{S}$-$\overline{R}$ latch used as a switch debounce circuit in the report.

D Latch

4. Now modify the basic $\overline{S}$-$\overline{R}$ latch into a D latch by adding the steering gates and the inverter shown in Figure 13–4. Connect the *D* input to a TTL level pulse generator set for 1 Hz. Connect the enable input to a HIGH (through a 1 kΩ resistor). Observe the output; then change the enable to a LOW.

FIGURE 13–2
Gated D latch.

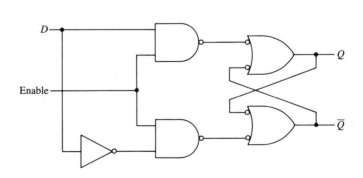

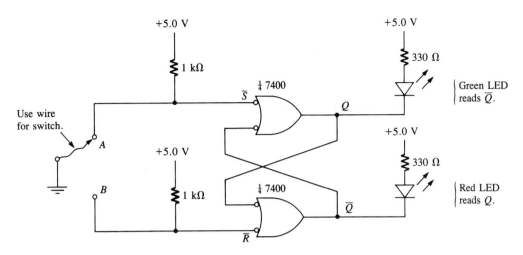

FIGURE 13–3
SPDT switch debounce.

5. Leave the enable LOW and place a momentary short to ground on first ONE output and then on the other. Summarize your observations of the gated D latch in the report.

6. Now you will make a simple burglar alarm. The circuit is shown in Figure 13–5. The data input represents switches connected to windows and doors. The enable input is pulled HIGH when the system is activated or LOW for standby. To reset the system, use a momentary ground on the Q output as shown. Build the burglar alarm and test its operation. Summarize your observations in the report.

The D Flip-Flop

7. The 7474 is a dual, positive edge-triggered D flip-flop containing two asynchronous inputs labeled $\overline{PRE}$ (preset) and $\overline{CLR}$ (clear). Construct the test circuit shown in Figure 13–6. Connect the clock through the delay circuit. The purpose of the delay is to allow setup time for the D input. Let's look at this effect first. Observe both the delayed clock signal and the Q output signal on a two-channel oscilloscope. View the delayed clock signal on channel 1, and trigger the scope from channel 1. You should observe a dc level on the output (channel 2).

8. Now remove the clock delay by connecting the clock input directly to the pulse generator. The output should have changed because there is insufficient setup time.

9. Reinstall the clock delay circuit and move the $\overline{PRE}$ input to a LOW and then a HIGH. Then put a LOW on the $\overline{CLR}$ input followed by a HIGH. Next repeat the process with the clock

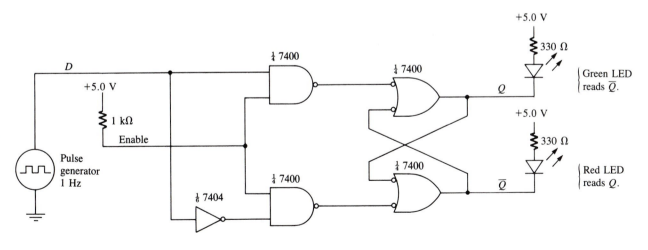

FIGURE 13–4
Gated D latch.

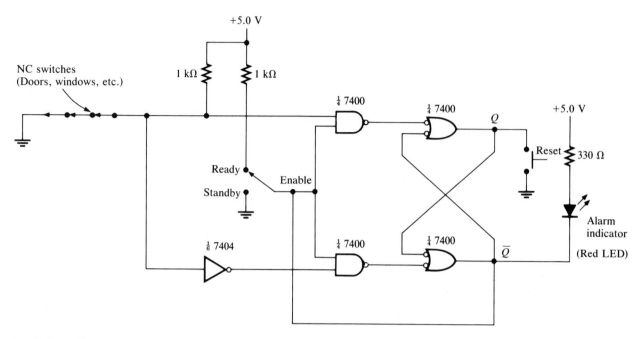

FIGURE 13–5
Simple burglar alarm.

FIGURE 13–6

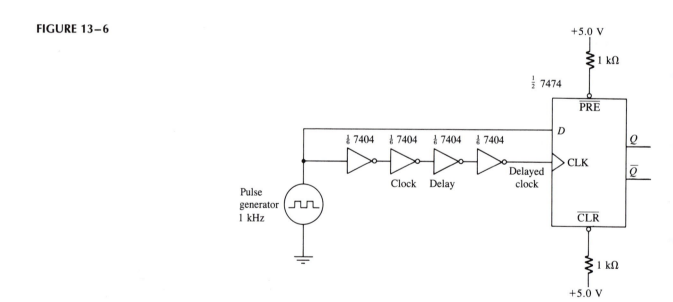

pulse disconnected. Determine if $\overline{PRE}$ and $\overline{CLR}$ are synchronous or asynchronous inputs.

10. Leave the clock delay circuit in place, but disconnect the D input. Attach a wire from $\overline{Q}$ to the D input. Observe the waveforms on a scope. Adjust the VAR HOLDOFF control on the scope and note how the output appears to change. This change is due only to the method of scope triggering, *not* to any time variations in the circuit. Normally, for relative timing measurements, you should not trigger the scope using the clock pulse.* Summarize, in the report, your observations of the D flip-flop. Discuss setup time, $\overline{PRE}$ and $\overline{CLR}$ inputs, and the effect observed in Step 10.

---

*For low-frequency timing, the CHOP mode will avoid the timing problem illustrated in step 10.

For Further Investigation

11. The circuit shown in Figure 13–7 is a practical application of a D flip-flop. It is a parity test circuit that takes serial data (bits arriving one at a time) and performs an exclusive-OR on the previous result (like a running total). The data are synchronous with the clock; that is, for every clock pulse a new data bit is tested. Construct the circuit and set the clock for 1 Hz. Move the data switch to either a HIGH or a LOW prior to the clock pulse, and observe the result. Describe your observations in the report. If a logic 1 is received, what happens to the parity? What happens when a logic 0 is received? Does the circuit have any advantage over the parity test circuit shown in Section 6–10 of Floyd's text?

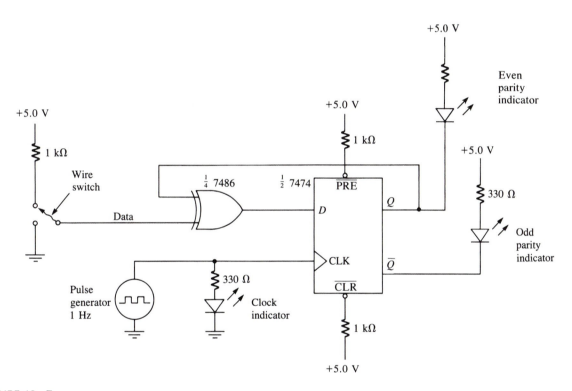

FIGURE 13–7

Report for Experiment 13

Name: _____ Date: _____ Class: _____

Objectives:

Procedure:

Data:

Step 3. Observations for SPDT switch debounce circuit:

Step 5. Observations for D latch circuit:

Step 6. Observations for the simple burgler alarm:

Step 10. Observations for the D flip-flop:

Results and Conclusions:

Further Investigation Results:

Evaluation and Review Questions:

1. Explain why the switch debounce circuit in Figure 13–3 is used only for double-throw switches.

2. If the NAND gates in Figure 13–3 were replaced with NOR gates, would the switch debounce circuit still work? Explain.

3. Show how the burglar alarm of Step 6 could be constructed with one-fourth of a 7475A D latch.

4. a. The burglar alarm can be constructed with two cross-coupled NOR gates. Draw the circuit so that it has the same functions as the alarm in Step 6 (normally closed switches, alarm, and reset).

b. What part of the circuit is essential for latching action?

5. a. Explain how the presence or absence of the clock delay circuit in Figure 13–6 affected the output.

b. What can happen to a circuit in which an inadequate setup time is given to a flip-flop?

14

The Fallen Carton Detector

Objectives

After completing this experiment, you will be able to:

☐ Design a circuit that detects the presence of a tipped-over carton for a food-processing application and rejects it before it reaches the carton-sealing machine.

☐ Decide on a troubleshooting procedure for testing the circuit if it fails.

☐ Write a formal laboratory report documenting your circuit and a simple test procedure.

Reference Reading

Floyd, *Digital Fundamentals,* 4th ed., Section 7–1, Latches; Section 7–2, Edge-Triggered Flip-Flops; Section 7–3, Pulse-Triggered (Master-Slave) Flip-Flops; Section 7–4, Data Lock-Out Flip-Flops; Section 7–5, Operating Characteristics

Materials Needed

7474 D Flip-Flop
Two each CdS photocells (Radio Shack #276–116 or equivalent)
Other materials as determined by student

Summary of Theory

A D flip-flop can be used to hold information temporarily after the initializing event has passed. In this way, the D flip-flop acts as a memory element capable of storing one bit of information. In this application, it is necessary to store information temporarily to use after the inputs have changed. The circuit can then take an action even though the originating event has passed.

The event itself can do the clocking action to assure that the flags are set each time an event occurs. The occurence of an event (carton passing a detector) is asynchronous—not related to a clock signal. Since the event will do the clocking, it is necessary to use delay in the clock signal to assure that sufficient setup time is given to the D flip-flop. (Refer to Experiment 13 to review this idea.)

Procedure

1. Design the circuit that implements the fallen carton detector described in the problem statement. Test your circuit and write a report that describes the circuit you designed. The circuit will be in operation when you are not present to help fix it in case of trouble. Your write-up should include a simple troubleshooting guide to technicians so that they can identify a circuit failure using a test procedure that you devise.

Problem Statement

A circuit is needed by a food-processing company to detect a fallen carton on a conveyer belt and activate an air solenoid to blow the carton into a reject hopper. The circuit is needed because occasionally a carton will fall and cause a jam to occur

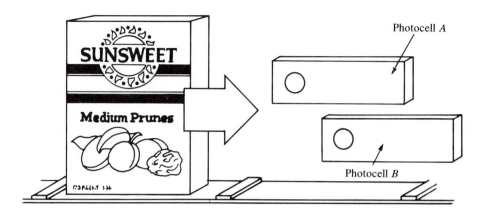

FIGURE 14-1

at the carton sealing machine. Mechanics have already installed two photocells on the line, as illustrated in Figure 14-1. Notice that the two photocells are offset from each other. The top photocell is labeled A and the lower photocell is labeled B. An upright carton will cause photocell A to be covered first and then photocell B to be covered. A fallen carton will cause only photocell B to be covered.

You can assume that if both photocells "see" the carton, it must be upright and should proceed to the sealing machine. However, if only photocell B is covered, a signal needs to be generated that will be sent to the air solenoid (an LED will simu-late the solenoid). The solenoid needs to be turned on until the next upright carton is sensed.

For this design problem, you can use the photocell circuit shown in Figure 14-2 to produce logic levels for your circuit. You will need to experiment with the value of R_1 to determine a value that gives TTL logic levels for your particular photocell and room lighting. The resistance of a photocell is lower as the light intensity increases. If the photocell is covered (high resistance), the output should be set for a logic HIGH; when it is uncovered it should be a logic LOW. If photocell A is covered, and then photocell B is covered, the circuit should *not* trip the solenoid (light the LED). On the other hand, if photocell B is covered and A remains uncovered, the circuit has detected a fallen carton, and the solenoid should be tripped (LED on). The LED should be turned on with a LOW signal. No more than two ICs can be spared for the design.

For Further Investigation

A new improved Model 2 fallen-carton detector is needed. After a single fallen carton, the air solenoid remains on, annoying the line supervisor. To avoid this, the line supervisor has requested that the solenoid be turned off by a photocell that senses the carton going into the reject hopper. Also, a reset button needs to be added to reset the circuit when it is first turned on. No more ICs can be spared for this modification.

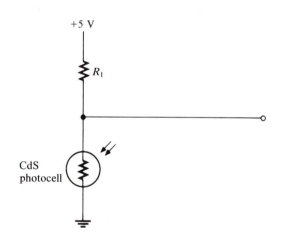

FIGURE 14-2
Simplified photocell circuit for Experiment 13.

138

Report for Experiment 14

Name: _____ Date: _____ Class: _____

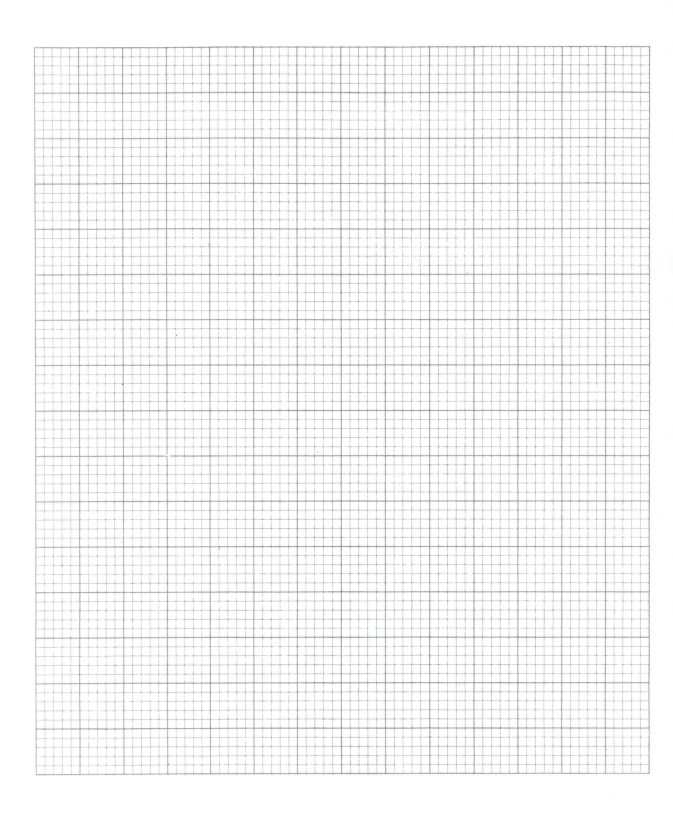

Report for Experiment 14

Name: _____ Date: _____ Class: _____

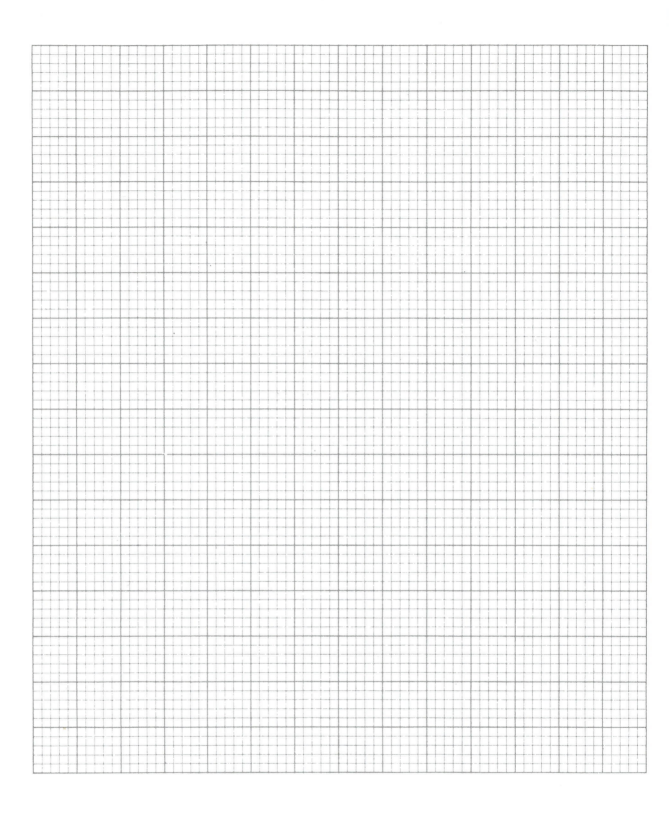

15

The J-K Flip-Flop

Objectives

After completing this experiment, you will be able to:

☐ Test various configurations for a J-K flip-flop, including the asynchronous and synchronous inputs.

☐ Compare edge-triggering with pulse-triggering.

☐ Observe frequency division characteristics of a J-K flip-flop.

☐ Measure the propagation delay for the flip-flop.

Reference Reading

Floyd, *Digital Fundamentals*, 4th ed., Section 7–2, Edge-Triggered Flip-Flops; Section 7–3, Pulse-Triggered (Master-Slave) Flip-Flops; Section 7–4, Data Lock-Out Flip-Flops; Section 7–5, Operating Characteristics; Section 7–6, Basic Flip-Flop Applications

Materials Needed

7476 dual J-K flip-flop
Three LEDs: one red, one green, one yellow
Resistors:
Three 330 Ω
Four 1 kΩ
One 4-position DIP switch

Summary of Theory

The active-LOW $\overline{S}$-$\overline{R}$ latch, constructed with cross-coupled NAND gates, and its counterpart, the active-HIGH S-R latch, constructed with cross-coupled NOR gates, are the most basic forms of a memory device. Both types of latches have two inputs that are used to set or reset the output and two complementary outputs, Q and $\overline{Q}$. Modification of the basic $\overline{S}$-$\overline{R}$ latch resulted in the gated S-R latch and the widely used gated D latch, which was used in Experiment 13. The gated D latch avoided the invalid condition (both inputs = 1) that can occur in the active-HIGH S-R latch by allowing only one input, D, to control the latch whenever the enable was asserted. Experiment 13 also introduced the D flip-flop, an edge-triggered device that allows the output to change only during the active clock edge. The D flip-flop is a device widely used for temporary storage of information.

The D flip-flop can only be set and reset, a limitation for some applications. Furthermore, the D flip-flop cannot be latched unless the clock pulses are removed—a condition that limits a number of applications for this device. A solution to these problems is the J-K flip-flop, which is basically a clocked S-R flip-flop with additional logic to replace the S-R invalid output states with a new mode called *toggle*. Toggle causes the flip-flop to change to the state opposite to its present state. It is similar to the operation of an automatic garage door opener. If the button is pressed when the door is

143

FIGURE 15–1

Comparison of basic flip-flops.

S-R flip-flop

Inputs		Output
S	R	Q
0	0	Latched
0	1	0
1	0	1
1	1	Invalid

D flip-flop

Input	Output
D	Q
Not possible	
0	0
1	1
Not possible	

J-K flip-flop

Inputs		Output
J	K	Q
0	0	Latched
0	1	0
1	0	1
1	1	Toggle

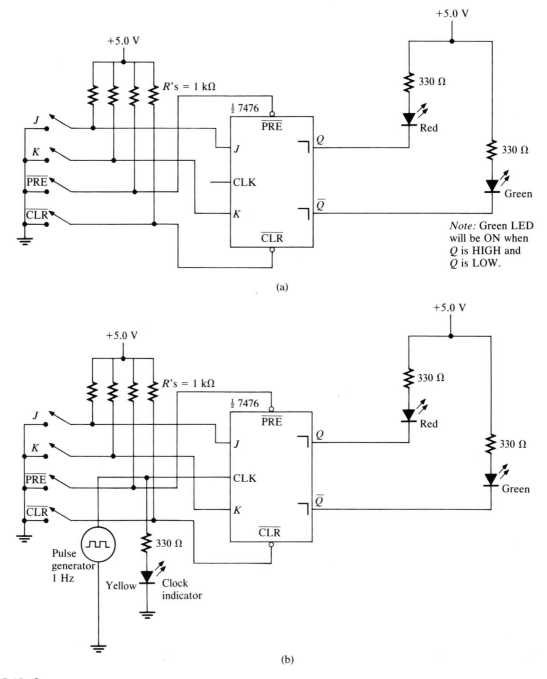

(a)

(b)

FIGURE 15–2

open, the door will close; otherwise, it will open.

The J-K flip-flop is the most versatile of the basic flip-flops. All applications for flip-flops can be accomplished with either the D or the J-K flip-flop. The clocked S-R flip-flop is seldom used; it is used mostly as an internal component of integrated circuits. (See the 74165 shift register, for example.) The truth tables for all three flip-flops are compared in Figure 15–1. The inputs are labeled *J* (the set mode) and *K* (the reset mode) to avoid confusion with the S-R flip-flop.

A certain amount of time is required for the input of a logic gate to affect the output. This time, called the *propagation delay time,* depends on the logic family. In the For Further Investigation, we investigate the propagation delay for a J-K flip-flop.

The need to assure that input data do not affect the output until they are at the correct level led to the concept of edge-triggering, investigated in the last experiment. Edge-triggering is not the only method for assuring synchronous transitions, although it is preferred. The other method is *pulse-triggered* or *master-slave* flip-flops. In these flip-flops, the data are clocked into the master on the leading edge of the clock and into the slave on the trailing edge of the clock. It is imperative that the input data not change during the time the clock pulse is HIGH or the data in the master may be changed. In principle, any flip-flop could use pulse-triggering. However, in practice D flip-flops are available only as edge-triggered devices. J-K flip-flops are available as either edge- or pulse-triggered devices. A modification called the *data-lockout flip-flop* transfers data to the master on the leading edge of the clock and into the slave on the trailing edge of the clock, eliminating the requirement to hold the data at a constant level during the clock pulse.

Procedure

The J-K Pulse-Triggered Flip-Flop

1. Construct the circuit of Figure 15–2(a). Look at the data sheet for the 7476 and determine the inactive logic required at the $\overline{PRE}$ and $\overline{CLR}$ inputs. Select the inactive level for $\overline{PRE}$ and $\overline{CLR}$. Use LEDs as logic monitors as shown in Figure 15–2(a). Select the "set" mode by connecting *J* to a logic 1 and *K* to a logic 0. With the clock LOW (not active), test the effect of $\overline{PRE}$ and $\overline{CLR}$ by putting a logic 0 on each, one at a time. Find out if the preset and clear inputs are synchronous or asynchronous.

Put $\overline{CLR}$ on LOW; then pulse the clock by putting a HIGH, then a LOW, on the clock. Observe that the $\overline{CLR}$ input overrides the *J* input.

Determine what happens if both $\overline{PRE}$ and $\overline{CLR}$ are connected to a 0 at the same time. Summarize your observations from this step in the report.

2. Put both $\overline{PRE}$ and $\overline{CLR}$ on a logic 1. Connect a TTL level pulse generator set to 1 Hz on the clock input. Add an LED clock indicator to the pulse generator as shown in Figure 15–2(b) so that you can observe the clock pulse and the outputs at the same time. Check that you fully understand the truth table (Figure 15–1) by testing the four combinations of *J* and *K* inputs while observing the LEDs.

Determine if the data are transferred to the output on the leading or the trailing edge of the clock.

Observe that the output frequency is not the same as the clock frequency in the toggle mode. Also note that the output duty cycle in the toggle mode is not the same as the clock duty cycle. This is a good way to obtain a 50% duty cycle pulse. Summarize your observations in the report. Include a discussion of the truth table for the J-K flip-flop.

3. Look at the circuit shown in Figure 15–3. Predict what it will do; then test your prediction by building it. Summarize your observations.

4. One of the disadvantages of pulse-triggered flip-flops is the requirement that the data remain constant during the clock pulse. Any glitch or noise spike that occurs during the clock pulse can cause the flip-flop to produce an incorrect output. To demonstrate, do the following:

1. Change the pulse generator to a very slow clock rate of about 0.1 Hz. Connect *J* to a HIGH and *K* to a LOW. Observe that the output remains SET after the first clock pulse, as it should.
2. When the clock indicator LED is on (indicating a HIGH pulse on the clock input), quickly switch the K input to a HIGH and back to a LOW. This simulates a noise "glitch" that occurs during the time the clock pulse is HIGH. When the clock pulse returns to LOW, observe the output. You should observe the output toggles, indicating that the noise was captured on the K input.

You can understand how this effect occurs by considering the logic diagram for the J-K flip-flop shown in Floyd's text as Figure 7–35. This illus-

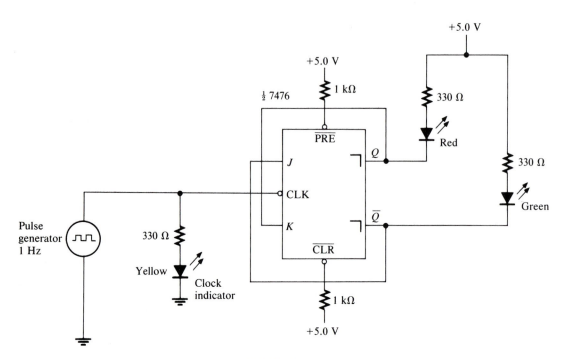

FIGURE 15–3

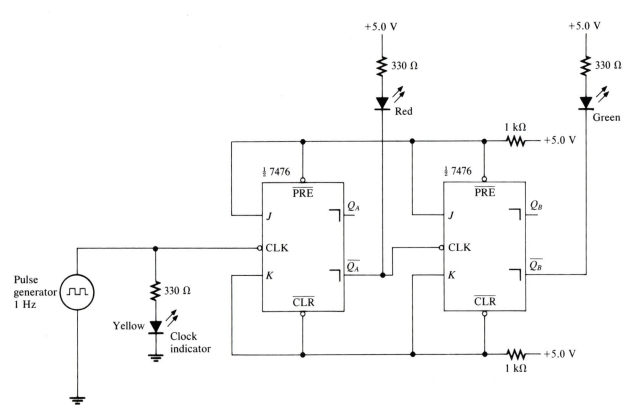

FIGURE 15–4

trates a disadvantage to the pulse-triggered flip-flop.

5. This step illustrates another application of the toggle mode. One of the most widely used applications of flip-flops is in counters. Cascaded flip-flops can be used to perform frequency division in a circuit called a *ripple counter*. Figure 15–4 illustrates one method of making a ripple counter from the two flip-flops in the 7476. Connect the circuit and sketch the LED outputs on Plot 1 in the report.

Notice that when the LEDs are ON, the output is SET. (Why?) The red and green output LEDs indicate that the pulse generator frequency has been changed by the flip-flops. Ripple counters are covered further in Experiment 17.

For Further Investigation

Measurement of t_{PLH}

1. Set up the J-K flip-flop for toggle operation. Connect a 100 kHz TTL level clock to the CLK input. View the clock signal on channel 1 and the Q output signal on channel 2 of a two-channel oscilloscope. Trigger the scope from the channel 1 signal (since it is easier to use the earlier signal when you measure the propagation time). Set the time base on the scope to 5 μs/div. At this sweep speed, you should observe that the output frequency is one-half the clock frequency.

2. The following procedure describes how to measure the propagation delay for the 7476:

1. Center the two waveforms along the center horizontal gradicule of the scope. Set the trigger slope control to negative triggering.

2. Now increase the sweep speed to 5 or 10 ns/div. You need to adjust the trigger level control to see both waveforms. You should see a falling edge of the clock and either a rising or a falling edge of the signal. If the output signal is not rising, adjust the trigger holdoff.

3. Measure the time from the 50% point of the trailing edge of the clock pulse to the 50% rising edge of the output pulse. This time is t_{PLH}. Record your measured time in the report. Compare it with the specified maximum time on the data sheet.

4. Using the basic method described, determine how to measure t_{PHL}. Make this measurement and compare it with the specified maximum time on the data sheet.

Report for Experiment 15

Name: _____ Date: _____ Class: _____

Objectives:

Procedure:

Data:

Step 1. Observations for $\overline{PRE}$ and $\overline{CLR}$ inputs:

Step 2. Observations of clocking the J-K pulse triggered flip-flop:

Step 3. Observations of test circuit:

Step 5. Ripple counter:

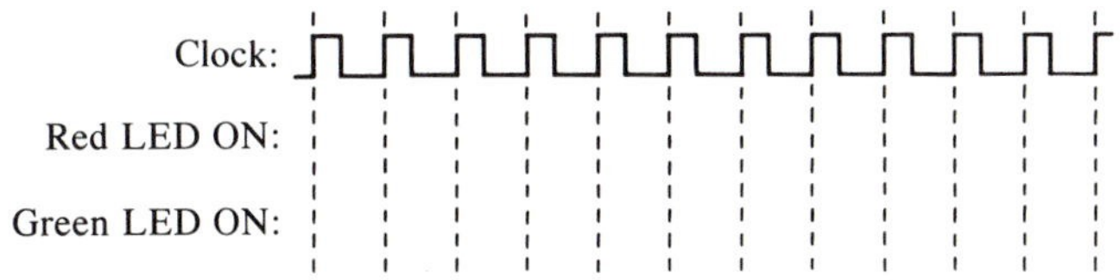

Clock:
Red LED ON:
Green LED ON:

PLOT 1

Results and Conclusion:

Further Investigation Results:

Evaluation and Review Questions:

1. **a.** What is the difference between an asynchronous and a synchronous input?

   b. What is the difference between edge-triggering and pulse-triggering?

2. Describe how you would set a J-K flip-flop asynchronously.

3. If both J and K inputs are LOW and $\overline{PRE}$ and $\overline{CLR}$ are HIGH, what effect does the clock have on the output of a J-K flip-flop?

4. Explain how a pulse-triggered J-K flip-flop can produce an incorrect output if noise is present.

5. Assume the red LED in Figure 15–3 is on steady and the green LED is off. The yellow LED is blinking. What are three possible troubles with the circuit?

16

One-Shots and Astable Multivibrators

Objectives

After completing this experiment, you will be able to:
☐ Specify the external resistor and input logic for a 74121 one-shot to produce a specific pulse and triggering mode.
☐ Build and test the circuit.
☐ Determine the frequency and duty cycle of a 555 timer configured as an astable multivibrator, and test the effects of changes in the basic circuit.

Reference Reading

Floyd, *Digital Fundamentals,* 4th ed., Section 7–7, One-Shots; Section 7–8, Astable Multivibrators and Timers

Materials Needed

74121 one-shot
7474 dual flip-flop
555 timer
Two 0.01 μF capacitors
Signal diode (1N914 or equivalent)
Resistors:
   10 kΩ
   7.5 kΩ
   One to be determined

Summary of Theory

There are three types of multivibrators: the bistable, the monostable (or *one-shot*), and the astable. The name of each type refers to the number of stable states. You are already familiar with the bistable, as it is simply a latch that can be either set or reset and will remain in either state until triggered into the opposite state. The one-shot has one stable (or inactive) state and one active state, which requires an input trigger to assert. When triggered, the one-shot enters the active state for a precise length of time and returns to the stable state to await another trigger. Finally, the astable multivibrator has no stable state and alternates (or "flip-flops") back and forth between HIGH and LOW all by itself with no input signals required. It frequently functions as a clock generator, since its output is a constant stream of pulses.

Most applications for one-shots can be met with either an IC timer or an IC one-shot. A timer is a general purpose IC that can operate as an astable or as a one-shot. As a one-shot, the timer is limited to pulse widths of not less than about 10 μs or frequencies not greater than 100 kHz. For more stringent applications, the IC one-shot takes over. The 74121, for example, can provide pulses as short as 30 ns. Also, IC one-shots often have special features, such as both leading and trailing edge-triggering and multiple inputs that can allow triggering only for specific logic combinations. Some one-shots are retriggerable. That is, the output pulse can be lengthened by multiple triggers,

151

or it can have override clear which is used to shorten the pulse time.

Timers and monostable circuits are based on charging and discharging of a capacitor in an RC circuit. The user specifies the component values to control the pulse width. Monostables are subject to stray noise, so components must be mounted as close to the device pins as possible. In addition, a bypass capacitor should be installed between V_{CC} and ground near each device.

You will begin this experiment by examining the 74121 non-retriggerable one-shot. The logic circuit and function diagram are shown in Figure 16–1. The circuit is triggered by a rising pulse on the output of the Schmitt AND gate. The purpose of the Schmitt AND gate is to allow slow rise-time signals to trigger the one-shot. In order for B to trigger it, the input must be a rising pulse, and either A_1 or A_2 must be held LOW, as shown in the last two lines of the function table in Figure 16–1 (b). If B is held HIGH, then a trailing edge pulse on either A_1 or A_2 will trigger the one-shot. Other combinations can be used to inhibit triggering.

This experiment also includes an introduction to the 555 timer, the first and still the most popular timer. It is not a TTL device but can operate on +5.0 V (and up to +18 V), so it can be TTL- or CMOS-compatible. This timer is extremely versatile. Some applications include accurate time-delay generation, pulse generation, missing pulse detectors, and voltage-controlled oscillators (VCOs).

Procedure

Monostable Multivibrator Using the 74121

1. The 74121 contains an internal timing resistor of 2 kΩ. You can select the internal resistor for the timing resistor by connecting R_{INT} to V_{CC}, or you can select an external resistor. To use an external timing resistor, connect it as shown in Figure 16–1 with R_{INT} (pin 9) left open. The capacitor is an external component but can be eliminated for very short pulses. (See the manufacturer's data sheet.)

The equation that gives the approximate pulse width t_w is

$$t_w = 0.7 C_{EXT} R_T$$

where R_T is the appropriate timing resistor, either internal or external, and C_{EXT} is in pF, R_T is in kΩ, and t_w is in ns. Using a 0.01 μF capacitor, calculate the required timing resistor to obtain a 50 μs pulse width. Obtain a resistor near the calculated value. Measure its resistance and measure the capacitance C_{EXT}. Record the computed R_T and the measured values of R_T and C_{EXT} in Table 16–1 of the report.

2. Using the measured values of R_T and C_{EXT}, compute the expected pulse width, t_w. Record the computed value in Table 16–1.

3. Assume that you need to trigger the one-shot using a leading edge trigger from the pulse generator. Determine the required connections for A_1, A_2, and B. List the input logic levels and the

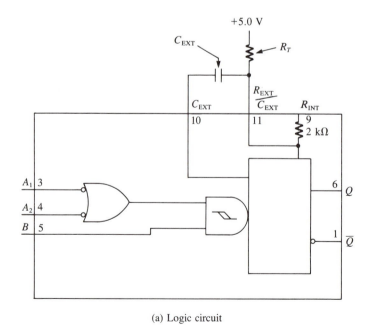

(a) Logic circuit

Inputs			Outputs	
A_1	A_2	B	Q	$\overline{Q}$
L	X	H	L	H
X	L	H	L	H
X	X	L	L	H
H	H	X	L	H
H	↓	H	⊓	⊔
↓	H	H	⊓	⊔
↓	↓	H	⊓	⊔
L	X	↑	⊓	⊔
X	L	↑	⊓	⊔

H = high logic level
L = low logic level
X = can be either low or high
↑ = positive going transition
↓ = negative going transition
⊓ = a positive pulse
⊔ = a negative pulse

(b) Function table

FIGURE 16–1

152

generator connection in your report. Build the circuit. One-shots are susceptible to noise pickup, so you should install a 0.01 μF bypass capacitor from V_{CC} to ground as close as possible to the 74121.

4. Apply a 10 kHz TTL-compatible signal from the pulse generator to the selected trigger input. Look at the pulse from the generator on channel 1 of a two-channel oscilloscope and the Q output on channel 2. Measure the pulse width and compare it with the expected pulse width from Step 1. (You may need to adjust R.) Record the measured pulse width in Table 16–1.

5. Increase the frequency slowly to 50 kHz while viewing the output on the scope. What evidence do you see that the 74121 is not retriggerable? Describe your observations.

The 555 Timer as an Astable Multivibrator

6. One of the requirements for many circuits is a clock, a series of pulses used to synchronize the various circuit elements of a digital system. In the astable mode, a 555 timer can serve as a clock generator.

A basic astable circuit is shown in Figure 16–2. There are two timing resistors. The capacitor is charged through both but is discharged only through R_2. The duty cycle, which is the ratio of the output HIGH time t_H divided by the total time T, and the frequency f, are found by the following equations:

$$\text{Duty cycle} = \frac{t_H}{T} = \frac{R_1 + R_2}{R_1 + 2R_2}$$

$$f = \frac{1.44}{(R_1 + 2R_2)C_1}$$

Measure the value of two resistors R_1 and R_2 and capacitor C_1 with listed values as shown in Table 16–2. Record the measured values of the components in Table 16–2. Using the equations given in Step 1, compute the expected frequency and duty cycle for the 555 astable multivibrator circuit shown in Figure 16–2. Enter the computed frequency and duty cycle in Table 16–2.

7. Construct the astable multivibrator circuit shown in Figure 16–2. Using an oscilloscope, measure the frequency and duty cycle of the circuit and record it in Table 16–2.

8. With the oscilloscope, observe the waveforms across capacitor C_1 and the output waveform at the same time. Trigger the scope from channel 1. On Plot 1, sketch the observed waveforms.

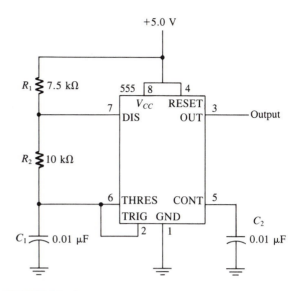

FIGURE 16–2

9. While observing the waveforms from Step 3, try placing a short across R_2. Write your observations in space provided in the report.

For Further Investigation

Obtaining a 50% Duty Cycle

1. Investigate what happens to frequency and duty cycle when a diode is placed in the charging path. Remove the short and put a diode in parallel with R_2. The cathode (line on the diode) should be connected to pin 6 of the 555, and the anode connected to pin 7. The diode bypasses R_2 during capacitor charging but does not remove it from the discharge path. Because the diode has some forward drop, the duty cycle should be near 50%. Measure the duty cycle and record it in report.

2. With the diode in place, observe the waveform across the capacitor with the oscilloscope. In Plot 2 of the report, sketch the waveform.

3. The diode helps demonstrate the effect of R_1 and R_2 in the circuit. However, the output of the circuit is dependent on the temperature primarily due to the diode temperature dependence. You can easily observe this effect by using some freeze spray on the diode while observing the output waveform. Discuss the effect on the waveform in your report.

4. The circuit just discussed illustrated that a duty cycle of 50% (or even less) can be achieved with a 555 timer. A better way to achieve a precise 50% duty cycle is to eliminate the diode and use the 555 to trigger a toggle flip-flop. Remove the diode and set up a 7474 D flip-flop in the toggle mode by connecting $\overline{Q}$ back to D. Connect the output of the 555 to the clock on the 7474. Observe the output of the 7474 and test the effect of freeze spray on this circuit. Summarize your observations.

Report for Experiment 16

Name: _____ Date: _____ Class: _____

Objectives:

Procedure:

Data:

TABLE 16-1
Data for 74121 monostable multivibrator.

Quantity	Computed Value	Measured Value
Timing Resistor, R_T		
External Capacitor, C_{EXT}	0.01 µF	
Pulse Width, t_w		

Step 3. Input logic levels and generator connection:

_____

_____

Step 5. Observations as frequency is raised to 50 kHz:

_____

_____

TABLE 16-2

Data for 555 timer as an astable multivibrator.

Quantity	Computed Value	Measured Value
Resistor, R_1	7.5 kΩ	
Resistor, R_2	10.0 kΩ	
Capacitor, C_1	0.01 μF	
Frequency		
Duty Cycle		

PLOT 1

Capacitor waveform:

Output waveform:

Step 9. Observations with a short across R_2:

_____

_____

Results and Conclusion:

Further Investigation Results:

PLOT 2

Capacitor waveform:

Observations:

Evaluation and Review Questions

1. How would you modify the circuit in Step 3 to trigger on the trailing edge of the pulse generator?

2. For the 74121 monostable multivibrator circuit, compute the value of the capacitor for a pulse width of 50 µs using the internal resistor.

3. From the data sheet for the 74121, determine the largest timing resistor and capacitor recommended by the manufacturer. What pulse width would you predict if these values were chosen for the circuit in Figure 16–1?

$$t_w = \underline{\hspace{2cm}}$$

4. Compute the duty cycle and frequency for a 555 astable multivibrator if $R_1 = 1$ kΩ, $R_2 = 170$ kΩ, and $C_1 = 0.01$ µF.

5. For the 555 astable multivibrator, determine R_1 and R_2 necessary for a period of 12 s if $C_1 = 10$ µF and the required duty cycle is 0.60.

$$R_1 = \underline{\hspace{2cm}}$$

$$R_2 = \underline{\hspace{2cm}}$$

Checkup 7

The exercises in this checkup reflect information covered in Floyd's Chapter 7, "Flip-Flops and Related Devices," and Buchla's Experiments 13, 14, 15, and 16.

1. Are the inputs to the latch shown in Figure 13–1 synchronous or asynchronous? Explain.

2. In order for a latch to retain information there must be some form of feedback. Explain where feedback is present in the gated D latch shown in Figure 13–4.

3. Explain the difference between *setup* and *hold* time for an edge-triggered D flip-flop. What happens when insufficient setup or hold time is given?

4. A D flip-flop has a setup time of 20 ns, a hold time of 5 ns, and a propagation delay of 40 ns (max).
   a. What is the minimum amount of time data must be present on the input to assure a reliable output?

   b. What minimum time before the clock pulse must the data be present at the input?

   c. Assuming the flip-flop was used in a counter in which the new data can appear at the input only after the old data have been present at the output, what is the highest frequency at which the flip-flop can be operated?

5. Compare the truth tables for a J-K and a D flip-flop.
   a. What is the advantage of a J-K flip-flop over a D flip-flop?

   b. How could you connect a J-K flip-flop to convert it into a D flip-flop?

6. A J-K flip-flop has the *J* and *K* inputs connected HIGH. A 10 kHz pulse waveform with a duty cycle of 0.33 is applied to the clock. Describe the output waveform.

7. Assume the waveforms shown in Figure 16–3 are applied to a positive edge-triggered D flip-flop. What is the *Q* output after the clock pulse has returned to zero?

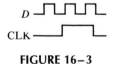

FIGURE 16–3

8. If the waveforms shown in Figure 16–3 are applied to a negative edge-triggered D flip-flop, what is the *Q* output after the clock pulse has returned to zero?

9. Look at the function table for the 74121 shown in Figure 16–1. Assume A_1 is connected to a logic HIGH. What must be done with A_2 and B to obtain a positive edge-triggered monostable multivibrator?

10. A 555 timer is set up as an astable multivibrator and used as a clock signal for a master-slave triggered 7476 J-K flip-flop, as shown in Figure 16–4. Describe the output pulse from the 555 and the signal from the flip-flop. Note that the J-K output is taken from $\overline{Q}$.

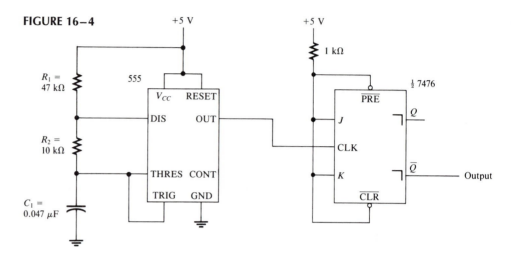

FIGURE 16–4

11. What precautions can be taken to avoid noise problems with monostable multivibrators?

12. Figure 16–5(a) shows a 7475 quad D latch connected to hold data for a seven-segment display. G1 and G2 are active-HIGH enable lines, each of which is connected to two of the latches. Given the waveforms in Figure 16–5(b), what sequence of numbers will be shown on the display?

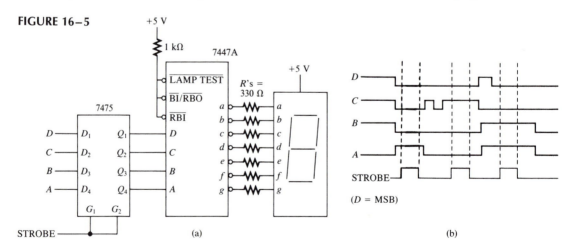

FIGURE 16–5

13. Instead of seeing the correct sequence in the seven-segment display for the circuit in Figure 16–5(a), you observe the sequence 5–4–7. What are possible reasons for the incorrect sequence? What procedure would you use to find the problem?

17

Asynchronous Counters

Objectives

After completing this experiment, you will be able to:
- [ ] Build and analyze various asynchronous up and down counters using D flip-flops.
- [ ] Change the modulus of the counter.
- [ ] Explain how the counter is a frequency divider.
- [ ] Use an IC counter and determine how to truncate its count sequence.

Reference Reading

Floyd, *Digital Fundamentals*, 4th ed., Section 8–1, Asynchronous Counters

Materials Needed

7400 quad NAND gates
7474 dual D flip-flop
7493A binary counter
Two LEDs
Resistors:
   Two 330 Ω
   Two 1 kΩ
For Further Investigation:
   7486 quad XOR gate

Summary of Theory

Digital counters are classified as either *synchronous* or *asynchronous*, depending on how they are clocked. Synchronous counters are a series of flip-flops, each clocked at the same time, causing the outputs of the stages (flip-flops) to change together. By contrast, asynchronous counters are a series of flip-flops, each clocked by the previous stage, one after the other. Since all stages of the counter are not clocked together, a "ripple" effect propagates as various flip-flops are clocked. For this reason, asynchronous counters are called *ripple counters*. You can easily make a ripple counter from D or J-K flip-flops by connecting them in a toggle mode.

The *modulus* of a counter is the number of different output states the counter may take. The counters you will test in the first four steps of this experiment can represent the numbers 0, 1, 2, and 3; therefore, they have a modulus of 4. You can change the modulus of a ripple counter by decoding any output state and using the decoded state to asynchronously preset or clear the current count. Ripple counters can be made to count either up or down. (They can be made to count both up and down, but usually it is easier to use a synchronous counter for an up/down counter.)

Two methods for changing a counter from up to down or vice versa are illustrated in this experiment. The first method involves moving the logical "true" output of the counter to the other side (as illustrated in Figures 17–2 and 17–3). The second method changes the manner in which the counter is triggered.

If we tabulate a binary count sequence, we note that the LSB (least significant bit) changes at

FIGURE 17–1

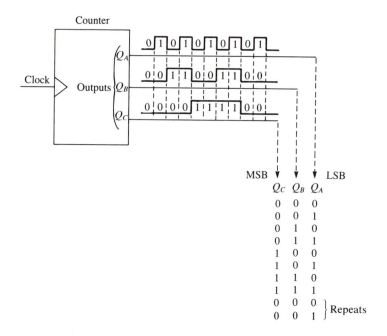

the fastest rate and the rate of change is divided by 2 as we look at succeeding columns. A typical 3-stage counter might have output waveforms as shown in Figure 17–1. For this counter, we can assign each output with a "weight" equal to the column value that would be assigned in binary counting. Output *A* has a weight of 1, output *B* has a weight of 2, and output *C* has a weight of 4. For the counter shown, the count sequence is for an up counter.

Because each stage of a ripple counter changes state at a different time, the counter has a tendency to produce "glitches"—spikes of short duration—when the outputs are decoded due to the short time delays during which the various flip-flops are changing states. Glitches are a disadvantage of ripple counters for many applications. Another disadvantage is the limited operating speed due to the cumulative delays through the counter. For some applications, however, such as digital clocks, this is not a problem.

For most applications requiring a counter, MSI counters are available. The 7493A is an example of an asynchronous counter containing four J-K flip-flops, with the *J* and *K* inputs internally wired HIGH. Three of the flip-flops are connected together as a 3-bit counter. The fourth flip-flop is separate, including its own clock input. To form a 4-bit counter, connect the output of a single J-K flip-flop to the clock input of the 3-bit counter. A common reset line goes to all flip-flops. This reset line is controlled by an internal 2-input NAND gate. You can select any count sequence up to 16 by choosing the internal counter, detecting the de-

sired count, and using it to reset the counter. In For Further Investigation, you will be introduced to an idea for changing the up/down count sequence using a control signal.

In this experiment and subsequent experiments, it is necessary to determine the time relationships between various digital signals. If your laboratory is equipped with a logic analyzer, you may want to capture the data from the counters with the logic analyzer. The logic analyzer is a versatile digital instrument that allows you to capture multiple channels of digital data, store them, manipulate them, and view them. A logic analyzer converts the input data on each channel to a series of 1s and 0s of digital information and stores them in a digital memory. The data can be stored using an internal or external clock to sample the data at specific time intervals, or the signals can be sampled using an asynchronous signal, such as might be found in an asynchronous data transmission system. After the data are sampled, they can be viewed in several modes, depending on the analyzer. The primary viewing mode is either a set of reconstructed digital waveforms or a state listing of the data in memory. This list can be presented in various formats.

There are other important features that make logic analyzers important instruments for testing and troubleshooting digital circuits. One feature is the ability to qualify a trigger for certain specific conditions and to store the data only if those conditions are met. This feature, along with the analyzer's ability to keep the data before the trigger event occurs makes it a particularly valuable tool for finding intermittent and randomly occurring faults. The cause of the trigger can then pinpoint the trouble with an intermittent failure. In addition, the analyzer can be used to trigger an oscilloscope when the conditions causing a failure occur. Because logic analyzers differ in features and capabilities, it is not possible in this summary to explain detailed operation. You should refer to the operator's manual for the analyzer you have to determine specific operating instructions.

Procedure

Two-Bit Asynchronous Counters

Note: The LED indicators in this experiment are connected through NAND inverters. Although not strictly necessary, this method enables you to more easily visualize the ideas presented in the experiment without violating the I_o specification for the 7474. Also, in this experiment, it is necessary to show the difference between the *electrical* output, Q, and the *logic* output. Accordingly, the logic output is labeled with the letter A or B. It is possible for the electrical and logic outputs to have opposite meanings, as will be seen.

1. Construct the 2-bit asynchronous counter shown in Figure 17–2. Clock flip-flop A using a 1 Hz TTL pulse from the function generator to the clock input, and watch the sequence on the LEDs. Then speed up the generator to 1 kHz, and view the A and B output waveforms on a dual-channel oscilloscope. Do not use COMP (composite) triggering. Instead, trigger the oscilloscope from

channel 1 while viewing the B signal on channel 1 and the A signal or the clock on channel 2. Triggering on the slower B signal assures there is no ambiguity in determining the timing diagram. Sketch the output timing diagram in Plot 1 of the report.

Notice that the frequency of the B output is one-half that of the A output. As explained in the Summary of Theory, the column weight of flip-flop B is twice that of flip-flop A, and thus it can be thought of as the MSB of the counter. By observation of your waveforms, determine whether this is an up counter or a down counter, and record your answer.

2. Now we will change the way we take the "true" output from the counter and see what happens. If logic "truth" is taken from the other side of each flip-flop, then we have the circuit shown in Figure 17–3. Modify your circuit and view the output waveform from each stage. Sketch the timing diagram on Plot 2 of the report.

3. Next we will change the manner in which flip-flop B is clocked. Change the circuit to that of Figure 17–4. The "true" output of the counter remains on the $\overline{Q}$ side of the flip-flops. View the outputs as before, and sketch the waveforms on Plot 3.

4. Now change the logic "true" side of the counter, but do not change the clock, as illustrated in Figure 17–5. Again, sketch the outputs of each flip-flop on Plot 4.

5. You can change the modulus of the counter by taking advantage of the asynchronous clear ($\overline{\text{CLR}}$) and asynchronous preset ($\overline{\text{PRE}}$) in-

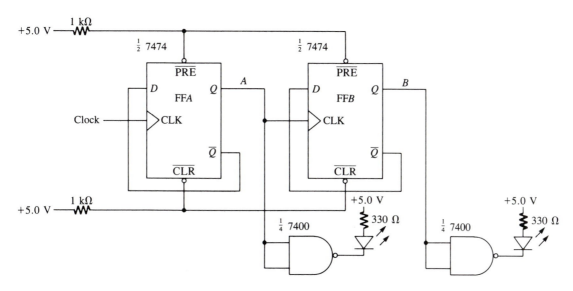

FIGURE 17–2
Ripple counter with D flip-flops.

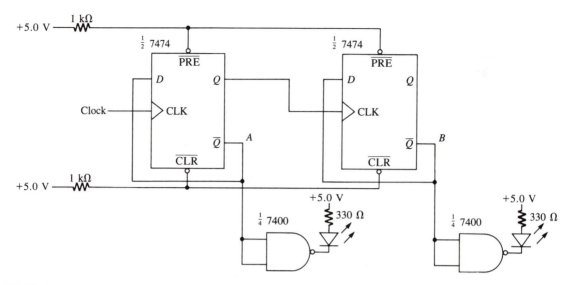

FIGURE 17–3
Ripple counter with D flip-flops. Note that the "true" output is shown on the $\overline{Q}$ output.

puts of the 7474. Look at the circuit of Figure 17–6, a modification of the circuit in Figure 17–5. Predict the behavior of this circuit, and then build the circuit. Sketch the output waveforms of each flip-flop on Plot 5. Set the generator clock frequency at 500 kHz and look for the very short signal that causes the count sequence to be truncated.

6. The very short spike, called a *glitch* (see Summary of Theory), on the *A* output is necessary to cause the counter to reset. While this signal serves a purpose, glitches in digital systems often are troublesome. Let's look at an undesired glitch

caused by two flip-flops changing states at nearly the same time.

Add a 2-input NAND gate to the circuit of Figure 17–6, which decodes state 0. (Connect the inputs of the NAND gate to $\overline{A}$ and $\overline{B}$.) Leave the generator frequency at 500 kHz. Look carefully at the output of the NAND gate. Sketch the observed waveforms on Plot 6.

The 7493A Asynchronous Counter

7. You can configure the 7493A 4-bit binary counter to count from 0 to 15 by connecting the

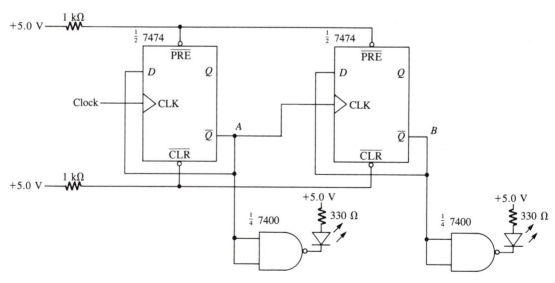

FIGURE 17–4
Ripple counter with D flip-flops. Note that the *B* counter is triggered from the $\overline{Q}$ output.

164

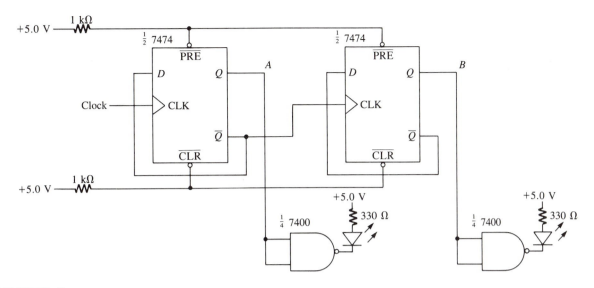

FIGURE 17–5

Ripple counter with D flip-flops. Note that the "true" output is on the Q outputs.

output of the single flip-flop (Q_A) to the clock B input. Connect the output of a TTL-level pulse from the function generator to the clock A input. From the data sheet, determine the necessary connections for the reset inputs.

8. Set the input frequency for 400 kHz. Trigger a two-channel oscilloscope from the lowest-frequency symmetrical waveform (Q_D), and observe, in turn, each output on the second channel. (If you have a logic analyzer, you can observe all four outputs together.) Sketch the timing diagram on Plot 7.

9. Figure 17–7 shows a 7493A counter configured with a truncated count sequence. Modify your previous circuit and observe the output waveforms on an oscilloscope or logic analyzer. Again, trigger the oscilloscope on the lowest-frequency symmetrical waveform, and observe each output on the second channel. Sketch the timing diagram on Plot 8.

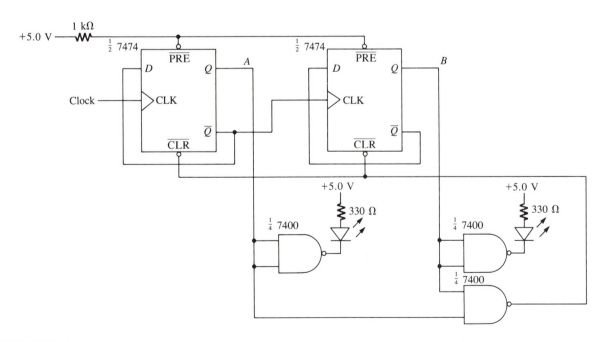

FIGURE 17–6

Ripple counter with D flip-flops and truncated count.

FIGURE 17-7
7493A with truncated count sequence.

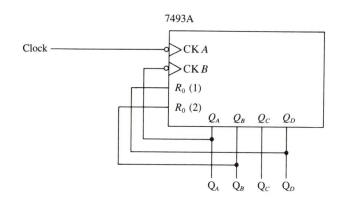

For Further Investigation

Adding the UP/DOWN Function to the 7493A

The methods you have investigated so far involve hardware changes to the circuit to change the counter function. A more useful circuit enables the up/down function to be controlled by a separate control line. The line could be controlled by a switch or even from a computer using a software command.

You have seen how reversing the bits causes the count sequence to reverse. This occurs for any nontruncated binary counting sequence, no matter how long. You can take advantage of this idea by either passing the output bits on unchanged or reversing them. The 7486 XOR gate allows you to do this. Each output from the 7493A can be connected to one input of an XOR gate. The other input is connected to an up/down control line.

Design the circuit using the 7493A as a 4-bit (0 to 15) counter. Add the up/down control using an SPST switch to select between up or down counting. Draw your circuit in the report and test its operation. Be sure and show all connections to the 7493A including the reset and clock lines. Summarize your findings in your report.

Report for Experiment 17

Name: _____ Date: _____ Class: _____

Objectives:

Procedure:

Data:

Waveforms from Step 1:

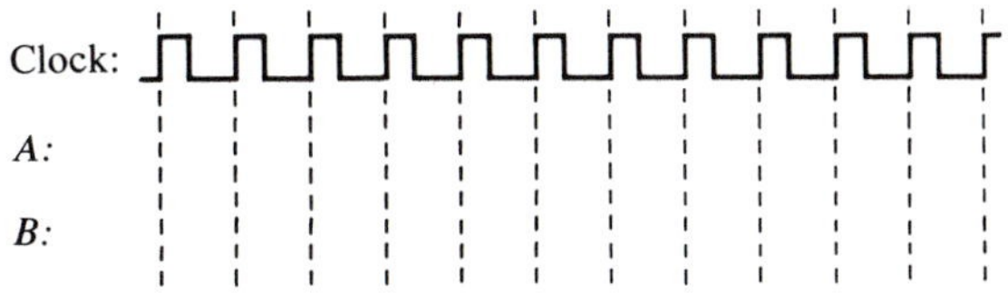

PLOT 1

Is this an up counter, or a down counter? _____

Waveforms from Step 2:

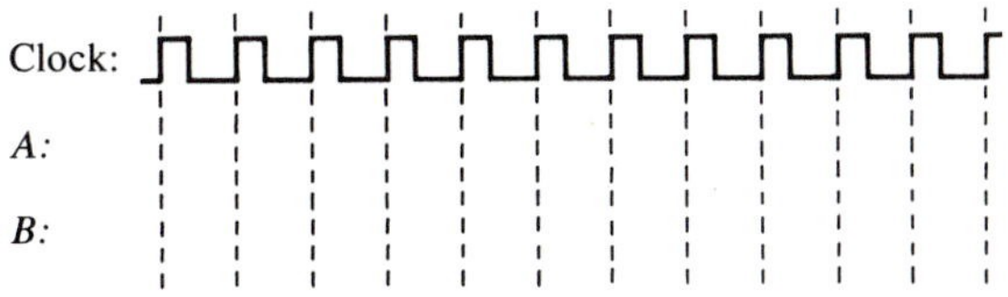

PLOT 2

Is this an up counter or a down counter? _____

Waveforms from Step 3:

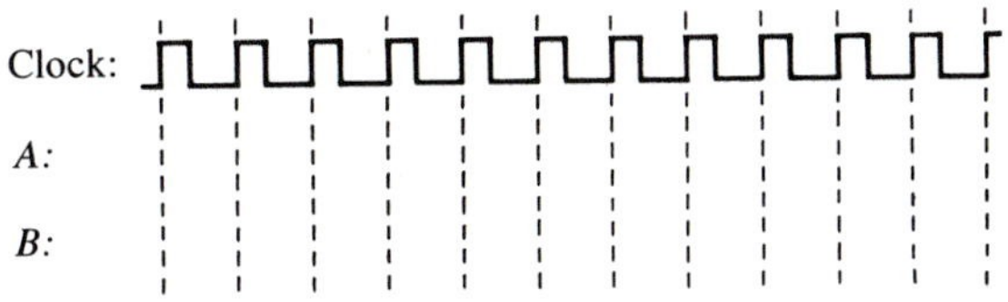

PLOT 3

Is this an up counter or a down counter? _____

167

Waveforms from Step 4:

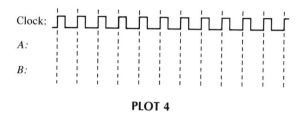

PLOT 4

Is this an up counter or a down counter? _____

Waveforms from Step 5:

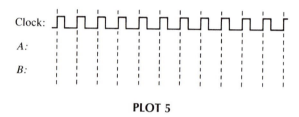

PLOT 5

What is the count sequence for this counter? _____

Waveforms from Step 6:

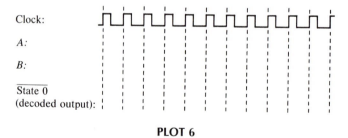

PLOT 6

Waveforms from Step 7:

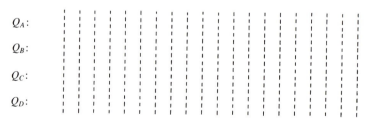

PLOT 7

Waveforms from Step 8:

Q_A:

Q_B:

Q_C:

Q_D:

PLOT 8

What is the count sequence of the counter? _____

Results and Conclusion:

Further Investigation Results:

Evaluation and Review Questions

1. Counters can be used as frequency dividers. When the clock frequency in Step 1 was 1 kHz, what was the output frequency of flip-flop A and flip-flop B?

$$f_A = \underline{\hspace{3cm}} \qquad f_B = \underline{\hspace{3cm}}$$

2. **a.** Explain how the count sequence of a ripple counter can be truncated.

   b. Why does the procedure produce a glitch?

3. Suppose that the counter in Figure 17–2 has both LEDs on all the time. The clock is checked and found to be present. What possible faults would cause this condition?

4. In Step 1, you triggered the oscilloscope on the slowest waveform. What may happen if you trigger on the clock instead?

5. **a.** Draw the circuit for a 7493A configured as a modulus-9 counter.

   b. Sketch the waveforms you would see from the circuit.

18

Analysis of Synchronous Counters with Decoding

Objectives

After completing this experiment, you will be able to:

☐ Analyze the count sequence of synchronous counters using a tabulation method.

☐ Construct and analyze a synchronous counter with decoding. Draw the state diagram.

☐ Use a two-channel oscilloscope or a logic analyzer to measure the time relationship between the flip-flops and the decoded outputs.

☐ Explain the concept of partial decoding.

Reference Reading

Floyd, *Digital Fundamentals*, 4th ed., Section 8–2, Synchronous Counters; Section 8–3, Up/Down Synchronous Counters; Section 8–5, Cascaded Counters; Section 8–6, Counter Decoding

Materials Needed

Two 7476 dual J-K flip-flops
7400 quad NAND gates
Two SPST NO pushbuttons
Four LEDs
Resistors:
   Four 330 Ω
   Two 1 kΩ
For Further Investigation:
   One MAN-72 seven-segment display
   Seven 470 Ω resistors

Summary of Theory

Synchronous counters have all clock lines tied to a common clock, causing all flip-flops to change at the same time. For this reason, the time from the clock pulse until the next count transition is much faster than in a ripple counter. This greater speed reduces the problem of glitches (short, unwanted signals due to nonsynchronous transitions) in the decoded outputs. However, glitches are not always eliminated, because stages with slightly different propagation delays can still have short intermediate states. One way to eliminate glitches is to choose a Gray code count sequence (only one flip-flop transition per clock pulse).

Decoding is the "detecting" of a specific number. A counter with full decoding has a separate output for each state in its sequence. The decoded output can be used to implement some logic that performs a task. The decoded outputs are also useful for developing counters with irregular count sequences. This experiment will also introduce you to *partial* decoding, a technique that allows you to uniquely define the output even though all bits are not used by the decoder.

There are a number of MSI counters available with features on one chip, such as synchronous and asynchronous preset or clear, up/down counting, parallel loading, display drivers, and so on. If it is possible to use an MSI counter for an application, this choice is generally the most economical. If it is not possible, then you must design the counter to meet the requirement. In this experiment you will analyze already designed synchronous counters step by step. In the next experiment, you will design a counter to meet a specific requirement. An MSI synchronous counter will be investigated in Experiment 25.

Analysis of Synchronous Counters

The method for analyzing a synchronous counter that will be illustrated is an easy-to-learn systematic tabulation technique. We will illustrate the analysis by working backward, using the counter shown in Figure 18–1. Begin by setting up Table 18–1(a). The table lists the outputs and inputs for each flip-flop in the counter. The steps are shown in the table. The first step is to determine the input Boolean equations from the schematic and write them under each input. Next the counter is placed in an arbitrary state—in this example, state 0000_2 was chosen. In the third step the equations and current state are used to determine the input present at each flip-flop. Remember, these inputs have no effect on the output until they have been clocked through the flip-flops. At clock time, the inputs determine the output based on the J-K truth table. In the fourth step, note that the D, C, and B inputs (for both J and K) are all 0 in the example,

so these flip-flops latch—in other words, they remain at 0. The A flip-flop has a 1 on J and a 0 on K so it will set after the next clock pulse. This analysis leads us to the conclusion that the next state will be 0001_2.

The analysis continues along these lines until all possible (2^N) states have been taken into account, including states that are not in the main count sequence. The completed table is shown as Table 18–1(b). Using the information from the table, the complete state diagram can then be drawn as illustrated in Figure 18–2. This completely describes the operation of the counter. This particular counter has an interesting and somewhat unusual application. It is used to develop the proper sequence of signals necessary to half-step a stepper motor.* Another method of developing these signals will be seen in the experiment on shift registers. In this experiment, you will predict and test the count sequence of synchronous counters. Because of the time required, your predictions (Tables 18–2 and 18–3) should be done before coming to the laboratory.

---

*See "How to Half-Step a Stepper Motor," by Steve Leiker, *Sky and Telescope* January 1988, p. 80, and "More on Half-Stepping a Drive Motor," by David Buchla and Bill Frandrup, *Sky and Telescope*, July 1988, p. 92.

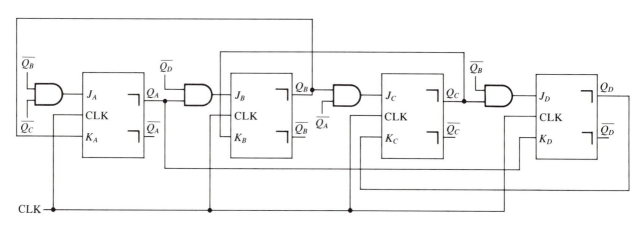

FIGURE 18–1
Synchronous counter with irregular sequence used for half-stepping a stepper motor.

TABLE 18–1(a)
Analysis of synchronous counter shown in Figure 18–1.

	Outputs				Inputs							
	Q_D	Q_C	Q_B	Q_A	$J_D = \overline{Q}_B \cdot Q_C$	$K_D = Q_A$	$J_C = \overline{Q}_A \cdot Q_B$	$K_C = Q_D$	$J_B = Q_A \cdot \overline{Q}_D$	$K_B = Q_C$	$J_A = \overline{Q}_B \cdot \overline{Q}_C$	$K_A = Q_B$
Step 2 →	0	0	0	0	0	0	0	0	0	0	1	0
Step 4	0	0	0	1								

Step 3 — Step 1

Step 1. Write the equations for J and K inputs of each counter using the schematic.

Step 2. Assume counter is in some state; in this example, it is arbitrarily placed in state 0000_2.

Step 3. Complete first row by determining each J and K input. The inputs 0000_2 are used to compute the binary value of J and K.

Step 4. Use the J-K truth table to determine the next state of each flip-flop. In this exam-

ple, $J_D = K_D = 0$ means Q_D will not change; Q_C and Q_B also will not change, but $J_A = 1$, $K_A = 0$ means that $Q_A = 1$ after next clock pulse. Write the next state under the present state that was originally assumed.

Step 5. Continue until all possible inputs are accounted for. This is done in Table 18–1(b). The sequence can now be shown on a state diagram, as in Figure 18–2.

TABLE 18–1(b)
Analysis of synchronous counter shown in Figure 18–1 (continued).

	Outputs				Inputs							
	Q_D	Q_C	Q_B	Q_A	$J_D = \overline{Q}_B \cdot Q_C$	$K_D = Q_A$	$J_C = \overline{Q}_A \cdot Q_B$	$K_C = Q_D$	$J_B = Q_A \cdot \overline{Q}_D$	$K_B = Q_C$	$J_A = \overline{Q}_B \cdot \overline{Q}_C$	$K_A = Q_B$
Main sequence	0	0	0	0	0	0	0	0	0	0	1	0
	0	0	0	1	0	1	0	0	1	0	1	0
	0	0	1	1	0	1	0	0	1	0	0	1
	0	0	1	0	0	0	1	0	0	0	0	1
	0	1	1	0	0	0	1	0	0	1	0	1
	0	1	0	0	1	0	0	0	0	1	0	0
	1	1	0	0	1	0	0	1	0	1	0	0
	1	0	0	0	0	0	0	1	0	0	1	0
	1	0	0	1	0	1	0	1	0	0	1	0
	0	0	0	1	At this step, a repeated pattern is noted.							
Account for all other states	1	1	0	1	1	1	0	1	0	1	0	0
	0	0	0	1	Returns to main sequence							
	0	1	0	1	1	1	0	0	1	1	0	0
	1	1	1	1	0	1	0	1	0	1	0	1
	0	0	0	0	Returns to previously tested state (0000)							
	0	1	1	1	0	1	0	0	1	1	0	1
	0	1	0	1	Returns to previously tested state (0101)							
	1	0	1	0	0	0	1	1	0	0	0	1
	1	1	1	0	0	0	1	1	0	1	0	1
	1	0	0	0	Returns to main sequence							
	1	0	1	1	0	1	0	1	0	0	0	1
	0	0	1	0	Returns to main sequence							

173

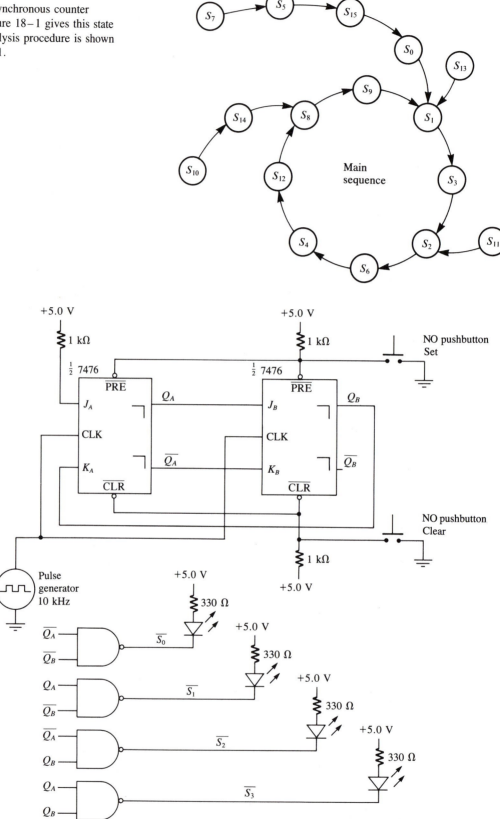

FIGURE 18-2

Analysis of synchronous counter shown in Figure 18-1 gives this state diagram. Analysis procedure is shown in Table 18-1.

FIGURE 18-3

Synchronous counter with state decoding.

174

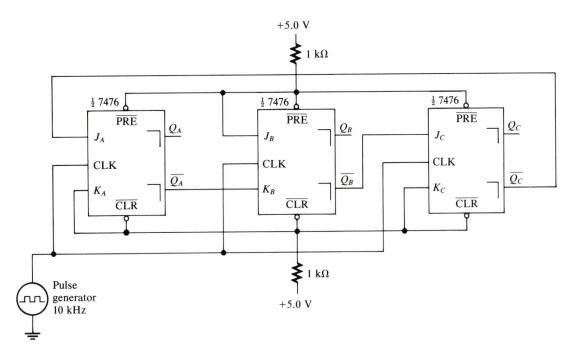

+5.0 V

1 kΩ

½ 7476

$\overline{PRE}$

J_A

CLK

K_A

$\overline{CLR}$

Q_A

$\overline{Q_A}$

½ 7476

$\overline{PRE}$

J_B

CLK

K_B

$\overline{CLR}$

Q_B

$\overline{Q_B}$

½ 7476

$\overline{PRE}$

J_C

CLK

K_C

$\overline{CLR}$

Q_C

$\overline{Q_C}$

Pulse
generator
10 kHz

1 kΩ

+5.0 V

FIGURE 18–4

Procedure

Analysis of Synchronous Counters

1. Examine the counter shown in Figure 18–3. Since there are two flip-flops, there are four possible output states. Analyze the sequence by the method illustrated in the Summary of Theory. Complete Table 18–2 in the report. From the table, draw the predicted state diagram in the space provided in the report.

2. Build the circuit. Use a TTL-level pulse generator at 10 kHz for the clock signal. The NAND gates serve as state decoders with an active-LOW output for each state. To avoid confusion, the lines from the counter to the decoders are not shown on the schematic. If you have a logic analyzer available, look at the outputs of the two flip-flops and the four decoders at the same time. If you do not have a logic analyzer, you can establish the relative time between signals using a two-channel oscilloscope. The following procedure will guide you:

1. Set up the scope to trigger on channel 1 with the Q_B signal (the slowest) viewed on that channel. Be sure that the scope is not in COMP triggering.*

2. View the pulse generator (clock) on channel 2.

Set up the sweep length using the SEC/DIV control and the VERNIER so that each clock pulse occurs on one major division of the gradicule. (Typically this will be ten.)

3. Do not change the triggering or the Q_B signal on the triggering channel. Probe the circuit while looking at channel 2. The observed signals will be in the proper time relationships to the Q_B signal.

Now on Plot 1, sketch the outputs of the flip-flops and decoders in the proper time relationship to each other.

3. Looking at the waveforms you have drawn, check that your predicted state diagram is correct. As an extra check, you can slow the clock to 1 Hz and verify the sequence with the LEDs.

4. Assume that a failure has occurred in the circuit. The wire from the Q_B output to K_A has become open. What effect does this open have on the output? Look at the signals and determine the new state diagram.

Draw the predicted state diagram in your report. Test your prediction by opening the K_A input and observing the result. You can put the counter into state 0 by pressing the clear pushbutton and into state 3 by pressing the set pushbutton.

5. Modify the circuit by adding another flip-flop and changing the inputs to J_A, K_A, and J_B, as shown in Figure 18–4. Leave the 7400 decoder circuit, but remove the set and clear switches. The decoder circuit will form an example of *partial de-*

---

*COMPOSITE triggering is shown as VERT MODE triggering on some oscilloscopes.

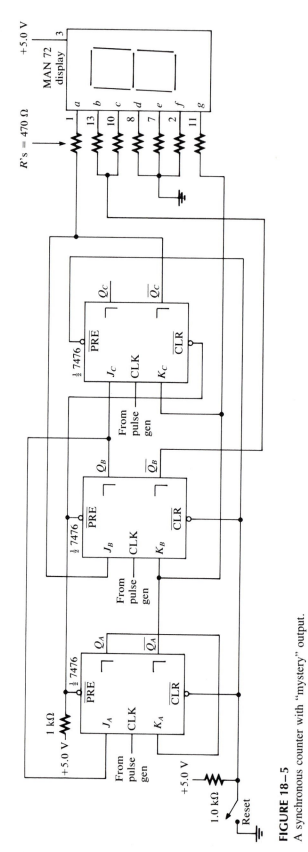

FIGURE 18–5

A synchronous counter with "mystery" output.

coding—a technique frequently employed in computers.

6. Analyze the counter by completing Table 18–3 in the report. Account for all possible states, including unused states. If you correctly account for the unused states, you will see that all unused states return to state 2. Draw the state diagram.

7. Set the pulse generator for 1 Hz and observe the LEDs connected to the state decoders. Notice that state 4 is *not* in the main sequence but state 0 *is* in the main sequence of the counter. This means that every time the state 0 LED turns ON, the counter is actually in state 0. This is an example of partial decoding; the MSB was not connected to the decoder, yet there is no ambiguity for state 0 because state 4 is not possible. Likewise, there is no ambiguity for state 0 or state 7, but partial decoding is not adequate to uniquely define states 2 and 6.

For Further Investigation

A unique circuit is shown in Figure 18–5. The output is connected in a rather unusual way directly to a seven-segment display. You are hereby challenged to figure out the sequence of letters that will be on the display. Here is your only clue: It is an English word that has something to do with detective work. (You get the other clue when you build the circuit.) If you give up, build the circuit and find the answer.

Report for Experiment 18

Name: _____ Date: _____ Class: _____

Objectives:

Procedure:

Data:

TABLE 18–2
Analysis of synchronous counter shown in Figure 18–3.

Outputs		Inputs			
Q_B Q_A	$J_B =$	$K_B =$	$J_A =$	$K_A =$	

State diagram:

Q_A:

Q_B:

$\overline{S_0}$:

$\overline{S_1}$:

$\overline{S_2}$:

$\overline{S_3}$:

PLOT 1

Step 4. State diagram:

TABLE 18–3
Analysis of synchronous counter shown in Figure 18–4.

Outputs	Inputs					
Q_C Q_B Q_A	$J_C =$	$K_C =$	$J_B =$	$K_B =$	$J_A =$	$K_A =$

Results and Conclusion:

Further Investigation Results:

Evaluation and Review Questions

1. The counter used for half-stepping a stepper motor in the example of Figure 18–1 has a state diagram sequence that is shown in Figure 18–2. Beginning with state 1, sketch the Q_D, Q_C, Q_B, and Q_A outputs. (*Hint:* An easy way to start is to write the binary number vertically where the waveforms begin. This procedure is started as an example.

$$
\begin{array}{c|c|c}
Q_A & 1 & 1 \\
Q_B & 0 & 1 \\
Q_C & 0 & 0 \\
Q_D & 0 & 0 \\
\end{array}
$$

2. How could you incorporate full decoding into the counter circuit shown in Figure 18–4?

3. Determine the sequence of the counter shown in Figure 18–6 and draw the state diagram.

FIGURE 18–6

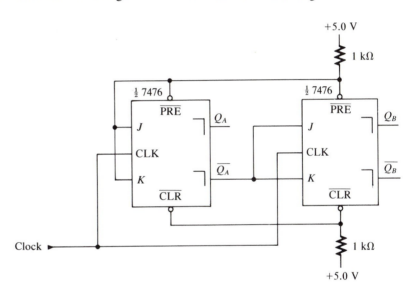

4. Explain the changes you would make to the circuit in Figure 18–4 in order to add a pushbutton that resets the counter into state 2.

5. Assume a problem exists with the counter shown in Figure 18–3. The counter is "locked-up" in state 3. What are two faults that can account for this problem?

19

Design of Synchronous Counters

Objectives

After completing this experiment, you will be able to:
- Design a synchronous counter with up to 16 states in any selected order.
- Construct and test the counter from objective 1. Determine the state diagram of the counter.

Reference Reading

Floyd, *Digital Fundamentals,* 4th ed., Section 8–4, Design of Sequential Circuits

Materials Needed

Two 7476 dual J-K flip-flops
7408 quad AND gate or other SSI IC determined
    by student
For Further Investigation:
    74139A dual 2- to 4-line decoder
    Six LEDs

Summary of Theory

The design procedure described in this summary is similar to the procedure described in the text but uses a different technique for implementing the transition table. Use whichever procedure is simplest for you.

    The design of a synchronous counter begins with a specification of the state diagram that specifies the required sequence. All states that are in the main sequence of the counter should be shown; states that are not in the main sequence should be shown only if the design requires these unused states to return to the main sequence in a specified way. If the sequence can be obtained from already existing IC, this is almost always more economical and simpler than designing a special sequence. If it is not available, then proceed with the design.

    From the state diagram, a next state table is now constructed. This procedure is illustrated with the example in Figure 19–1 for a simple counter and again in Figure 19–3 for a more complicated design. Notice in Figure 19–1 that the next state table is just another way of showing the information contained in the state diagram. The advantage of the table is that the changes required by each flip-flop in order to go from one state to the next state are clearly seen.

    The third step is to observe the transitions (changes) that are desired in each state. The required logic to force these changes will be mapped onto a Karnaugh map. In this case, the Karnaugh map takes on a different meaning than it did in combinational logic but it is read the same way.* Each square on the map represents a state of the counter. In effect, the counter sequence is just moving from square to square on the Karnaugh map at each clock pulse. To find the logic that will force the necessary change in the flip-flop outputs, look at the transition table for the J-K flip-flop,

---

*This type of Karnaugh map may be more properly termed a Karnaugh state map.

Assume you need to design a counter that counts
0–1–3–2 and stays in state 2 until a reset button is pressed.
Two flip-flops are required. Let Q_B = MSB and Q_A = LSB.
Use a J-K flip-flop.

Step 1: Draw a state diagram.

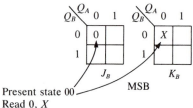

Step 2: Draw next-state table.

Present State Q_B Q_A		Next State Q_B Q_A	
0	0	0	1
0	1	1	1
1	1	1	0
1	0	1	0

Step 3: Determine inputs required for each flip-flop.
(a) Read present state 00 on next-state table.
(b) Note that Q_B does not change $0 \rightarrow 0$ (present to next state) and Q_A changes from $0 \rightarrow 1$.
(c) Read the required inputs to cause these results from transition Table 19–1.
(d) Map each input from transition table onto Karnaugh map.

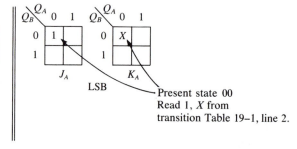

Present state 00
Read 0, X
from transition Table 19–1, line 1.

MSB   LSB

Present state 00
Read 1, X from
transition Table 19–1, line 2.

(e) Complete maps.

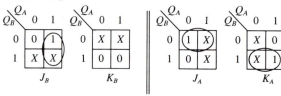

(f) Read minimum logic from each map.

$$J_B = Q_A, \quad K_B = 0, \quad J_A = \overline{Q_B}, \quad K_A = Q_B$$

Step 4: Draw circuit and check.

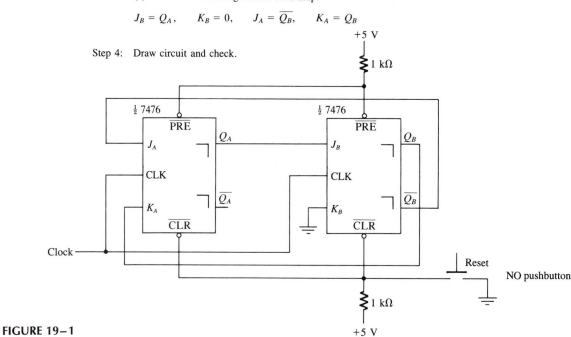

FIGURE 19–1

shown as Table 19–1. Notice that all possible output *transitions* are listed first; then the inputs that are required to cause these changes are given. The transition table contains a number of X's (don't cares) because of the versatility of the J-K flip-flop, as explained in the text. The data from the transition table are entered onto the Karnaugh maps as illustrated.

When the maps are completed, the logic can be read from the map. This logic is then used to set up the circuit as shown in Step 4. It is a good idea to check the design by completing a table such as shown in the last experiment.

The procedure just described can be extended to more complicated designs. In the last experiment, a sequential circuit was shown as an example (Figure 18–1) that generates the required waveforms for half-stepping a stepper motor. This is not the only way to obtain this sequence, but it does lead to a fairly straightforward design. Figure 19–3 illustrates the procedure for designing this circuit. Note that only the main sequence is shown in the state diagram and on the next-state table. The reason for this is that the unused states will show up as extra "don't cares" in the logic, making the design simpler. All unused states are entered on the maps as "don't cares." Although unused lock-up states are possible, and generally not desired, the design is checked afterward and corrections made as needed.

As you can see in Figure 19–3, the steps for the more complicated counter are basically the same as those used in Figure 19–1. The unused states allow the counter to be designed with a minimum of additional logic. The completed design is shown in the last experiment (Figure 18–1).

TABLE 19–1

Transition table for J-K flip-flop.

Output Transitions		Inputs	
Q_N	Q_{N+1}	J_N	K_N
0	→ 0	0	X
0	→ 1	1	X
1	→ 0	X	1
1	→ 1	X	0

Q_N = output before clock
Q_{N+1} = output after clock
J_N, K_N = inputs required to cause transition
X = don't care

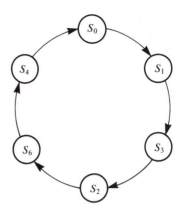

FIGURE 19–2

Procedure

1. A Gray code synchronous counter is often used in state machine design. This problem requires a six-state Gray code counter. The usual Gray code sequence is not used because the sixth state would not be "gray" when the counter returns to zero. Instead, the sequence shown in Figure 19–2 is required. There are two unused states. Complete the next-state table in the report for the main sequence shown here.

2. Using the transition table for the J-K flip-flop, complete the Karnaugh map shown in the report. The J-K transition table (Table 19–1) is repeated in the report for convenience.

3. Read the required logic expressions from the map. Check that the unused states return to the main sequence. If they do not, modify the design to assure that they do return. Then, construct and test your circuit. You can check the state sequence with an oscilloscope or a logic analyzer. Summarize the results of your test in your report.

For Further Investigation

A decoded output is needed for the counter you designed. Unfortunately, the only decoder IC that engineering has available for decoding is a 2-line to 4-line 74139A decoder. Show how you could connect this IC to obtain full decoding of the output. Then construct the circuit and put a separate LED on each output so that only one LED lights as the counter goes around. (*Hint:* Consider how you could use the enable inputs of the 74139A.)

Step 1: Draw the required state diagram. (Note that only the main sequence is shown as the unused states are not important in this problem.)

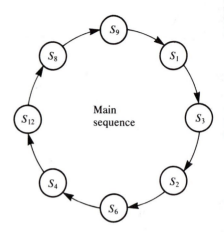

Step 2: Draw the next-state table. Four counters are required because of the number of bits used in the sequence.

Present State				Next State			
Q_D	Q_C	Q_B	Q_A	Q_D	Q_C	Q_B	Q_A
0	0	0	1	0	0	1	1
0	0	1	1	0	0	1	0
0	0	1	0	0	1	1	0
0	1	1	0	0	1	0	0
0	1	0	0	1	1	0	0
1	1	0	0	1	0	0	0
1	0	0	0	1	0	0	1
1	0	0	1	0	0	0	1

Step 3: Using the next-state and transition tables, draw the Karnaugh maps for each flip-flop. For example, in state 1, note that Q_D and Q_C do not change in going to the next state. The transition is $0 \rightarrow 0$. From the transition table, a $0 \rightarrow 0$ transistion requires $J = 0$ and $K = X$. These values are entered onto the maps for the D and C counters in the square that represents state 1. Unused states are mapped as Xs. Only the D and C maps are shown in this example.

(Note: Q_B and Q_A are positioned to make the map below easier to read.)

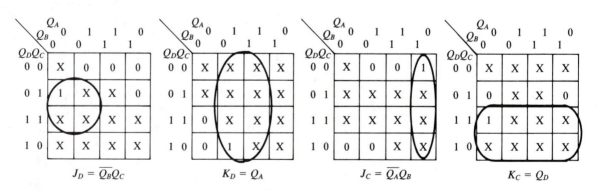

The B and A maps are left to the student as an exercise. The completed circuit can then be drawn as shown in Figure 18–1. Finally, a complete analysis should be done as described in Table 18–1(b).

FIGURE 19–3

186

Report for Experiment 19

Name: _____ Date: _____ Class: _____

Objectives:

Procedure:

Data:

Present State			Next State		
Q_C	Q_B	Q_A	Q_C	Q_B	Q_A
0	0	0			
0	0	1			
0	1	1			
0	1	0			
1	1	0			
1	0	0			

TABLE 19–1
Transition table for J-K flip-flop (repeated for reference).

Output Transitions			Inputs	
Q_N		Q_{N+1}	J_N	K_N
0	$\rightarrow$	0	0	X
0	$\rightarrow$	1	1	X
1	$\rightarrow$	0	X	1
1	$\rightarrow$	1	X	0

$Q_C Q_B$	Q_A 0	1
0 0		
0 1		
1 1		
1 0		

$J_C =$

$Q_C Q_B$	Q_A 0	1
0 0		
0 1		
1 1		
1 0		

$K_C =$

$Q_C Q_B$	Q_A 0	1
0 0		
0 1		
1 1		
1 0		

$J_B =$

$Q_C Q_B$	Q_A 0	1
0 0		
0 1		
1 1		
1 0		

$K_B =$

$Q_C Q_B$	Q_A 0	1
0 0		
0 1		
1 1		
1 0		

$J_A =$

$Q_C Q_B$	Q_A 0	1
0 0		
0 1		
1 1		
1 0		

$K_A =$

Circuit design:

Results and Conclusion:

Further Investigation Results:

Evaluation and Review Questions

1. Complete the design of the sequential counter in Figure 19–3 by constructing Karnaugh maps for the B and A flip-flops. Read the maps. As a check, you can compare your result with the circuit drawn in Figure 18–1.

2. Describe the logic necessary to add a seven-segment display to the circuit you designed in this experiment to enable the display to show the state of the counter.

3. Assume you wanted to make the sequential circuit you designed in this experiment start in state 6 if a reset pushbutton is pressed. Describe how you would modify the circuit to incorporate this feature.

4. Assume you need to change the circuit from this experiment to be able to reverse the sequence. How would you go about this?

5. Draw the transition table for a D flip-flop. Start by showing all possible output transitions (as in the J-K case) and consider what input must be placed on D in order to force the transition. You should see from this exercise why the J-K flip-flop is much more versatile for designing synchronous counters with irregular sequences.

Checkup 8

The exercises in this checkup reflect information covered in Floyd's Chapter 8, "Counters," and Buchla's Experiments 17, 18, and 19.

1. **a.** An asynchronous counter is often called a "ripple" counter. Why is this an appropriate name?

   b. What are advantages of a synchronous counter?

2. **a.** What is the minimum number of flip-flops needed to construct a counter that has 4096 different states?

   b. What is the maximum count that a counter containing 8 flip-flops can have?

3. Why is Gray code a good choice for observing the decoded outputs of a counter?

4. A 7493A is connected as shown in Figure 19–4. Determine the count sequence and draw the output waveforms.

FIGURE 19–4

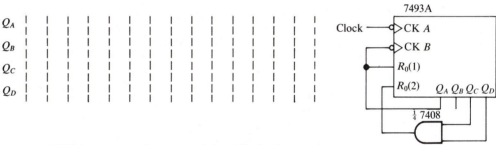

5. Show how to connect a 7493A connected as a modulus-12 ripple counter.

6. Explain the steps necessary to analyze the sequence of a synchronous counter.

7. Analyze the sequence of the counter shown in Figure 19–5.

8. Draw the output waveforms for the counter shown in Figure 19–5.

FIGURE 19–5

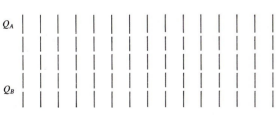

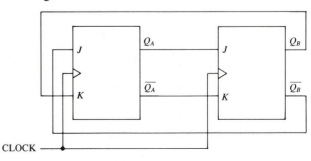

9. The circuit shown in Figure 19–6 is used to produce exactly four clock pulses when the pushbutton is momentarily pressed. Analyze the circuit by answering the following questions:

  a. Immediately after the pushbutton is pressed, what is the logic on the $R_0(1)$ and $R_0(2)$ inputs of the counter?

  b. What action occurs as a result of the logic applied on the $R_0(1)$ and $R_0(2)$ inputs?

  c. What count is decoded by the 7400?

  d. What action occurs when this count is decoded?

  e. What is the purpose of the 7474?

  f. Observe the count sequence of the 7492A in Appendix A. How does the above action cause exactly four pulses to be sent?

10. For the circuit in Figure 19–6, describe the symptoms you would expect for each of the faults listed.

  a. The wire between the Q_B output of the counter and the 7400 NAND gate is open.

  b. The output of the 7400 NAND gate is stuck HIGH.

  c. The line from Q_A to the CK B input is open.

  d. The pulse generator has stopped.

  e. The wire leading from Q_D to the 7400 NAND gate was accidentally connected to Q_C instead.

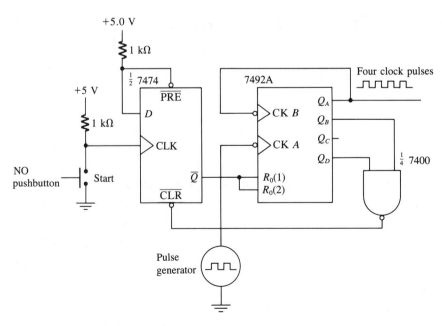

FIGURE 19–6

20

Shift Register Counters

Objectives

After completing this experiment, you will be able to:
- Test a recirculating shift register counter.
- Use the recirculating shift register counter from Objective 1 as the basis of an automated test circuit and use it to test both good and failed ICs.
- Draw the timing diagram for the circuit.
- Design two improvements to the automated test circuit.

Reference Reading

Floyd, *Digital Fundamentals*, 4th ed., Section 9–1, Shift Register Functions; Section 9–2, Serial In–Serial Out Shift Registers; Section 9–3, Serial In–Parallel Out Shift Registers; Section 9–4, Parallel In–Serial Out Shift Registers; Section 9–6, Bidirectional Shift Registers; Section 9–7, Shift Register Counters

Materials Needed

74195 4-bit shift register
7400 quad NAND gate
7493A counter
7474 D flip-flop
7486 quad exclusive-OR
Four-position DIP switch
Four LEDs
Four 330 Ω resistors
Six 1 kΩ resistors
Two N.O. pushbuttons (optional)

Summary of Theory

A *shift register* is a series of flip-flop memories connected so that data can be transferred to a neighbor each time the clock pulse is active. An example is the display on your calculator. As numbers are entered on the keyboard, the previously entered numbers are shifted to the left. Shift registers can be made to shift data to the left, or to the right, or both (bidirectional), using a control signal. They can be made from either D or J-K flip-flops. An example of a simple shift register made from D flip-flops is shown in Figure 20–1(a). The data are entered serially at the left and may be removed in either parallel or serial fashion. With some additional logic, the data may also be entered in parallel as shown in Figure 20–1(b).

Shift registers are available in a number of MSI packages with various bit lengths, loading methods, and shift directions. They are widely used to change data from serial form to parallel form, and vice versa. This is investigated further in Experiment 21.

Other applications for shift registers include arithmetic operations in computers. To multiply any number by its base, you simply move the radix point one position to the left. To multiply a binary number by 2, the number is shifted to

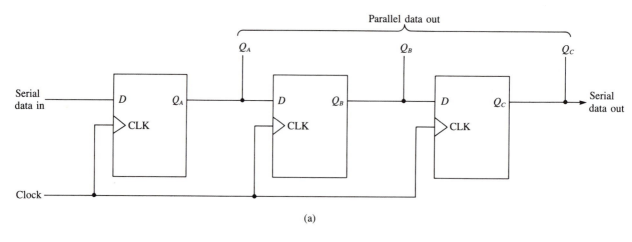

Parallel data out

(a)

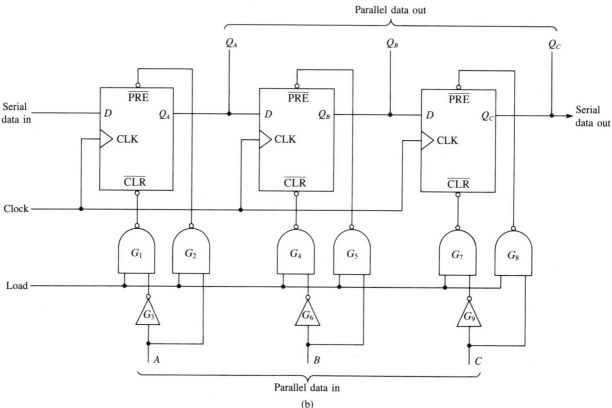

Parallel data out

Parallel data in

(b)

FIGURE 20–1
Shift registers made from D flip-flops.

the left. For example, $7 \times 2 = 14$ in binary is: $0111 \times 10 = 1110$. Note that the original number 0111 is shifted by one position to the left. Conversely, division is represented by a right shift.

Another important application of the shift register is as a digital waveform generator. Generally, a waveform generator requires feedback— that is, the output of the register is returned to the input and recirculated. Two important waveform generators are the Johnson (or "twisted-ring")

counter and the ring counter. The names can be easily associated with the correct circuit if the circuits are drawn in the manner shown in Figure 20–2. In this experiment, you will construct both a Johnson counter and a ring counter using a 74195 4-bit shift register. The ring counter will then be used to generate a bit stream that represents data for testing ICs. The concept employed in this circuit is very similar to large-scale IC testers.

194

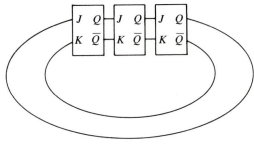

(a) Ring counter

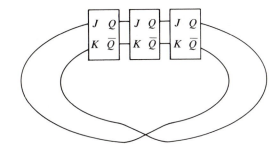

(b) Twisted-ring counter (Johnson counter)

FIGURE 20–2
Shift register counters drawn to emphasize their names. These circuits were drawn with J-K flip-flops but can be constructed from other flip-flops as well. The CLK, $\overline{PRE}$, and $\overline{CLR}$ inputs are not shown.

The 74195 function table is contained in Appendix A and is reproduced in Table 20–1 for convenience. The first input listed on the table is an asynchronous $\overline{CLEAR}$. Next is a parallel SHIFT/$\overline{LOAD}$ function on one pin. Assertion level logic is shown to define that a HIGH causes the register to SHIFT from Q_A toward Q_D at the next clock edge, and a LOW causes the register to $\overline{LOAD}$ at the next clock edge. The inputs A through D are used only when the register is loaded in parallel (also called a broadside load). Notice that the internal register portion of the 74195 is shown with S-R flip-flops, but the serial inputs to the leftmost flip-flop are labeled as J and

$\overline{K}$. These inputs function the same as the inputs to an ordinary J-K flip-flop, except the K input is inverted.

Procedure

Johnson and Ring Counters

1. The circuit shown in Figure 20–3 is a partially completed schematic for a shift register counter. It could be connected as either a Johnson (twisted-ring) or as a ring counter. Refer to Figure 20–2 and the function table for the 74195 (Table 20–1) and determine how to complete the feed-

TABLE 20–1
Function table for 74195 4-bit shift register.*

Inputs									Outputs				
			SERIAL		PARALLEL								
$\overline{CLEAR}$	SHIFT/ $\overline{LOAD}$	CLOCK	J	$\overline{K}$	A	B	C	D	Q_A	Q_B	Q_C	Q_D	$\overline{Q_D}$
L	X	X	X	X	X	X	X	X	L	L	L	L	H
H	L	↑	X	X	a	b	c	d	a	b	c	d	$\overline{d}$
H	H	L	X	X	X	X	X	X	Q_{A0}	Q_{B0}	Q_{C0}	Q_{D0}	$\overline{Q_{D0}}$
H	H	↑	L	H	X	X	X	X	Q_{A0}	Q_{A0}	Q_{Bn}	Q_{Cn}	$\overline{Q_{Cn}}$
H	H	↑	L	L	X	X	X	X	L	Q_{An}	Q_{Bn}	Q_{Cn}	$\overline{Q_{Cn}}$
H	H	↑	H	H	X	X	X	X	H	Q_{An}	Q_{Bn}	Q_{Cn}	$\overline{Q_{Cn}}$
H	H	↑	H	L	X	X	X	X	$\overline{Q_{An}}$	Q_{An}	Q_{Bn}	Q_{Cn}	$\overline{Q_{Cn}}$

H = high level (steady state)
L = low level (steady state)
X = irrelevant (any input, including transitions)
↑ = transition from low to high level
a, b, c, d = the level of steady state input at A, B, C, or D, respectively
Q_{A0}, Q_{B0}, Q_{C0}, Q_{D0} = the level of Q_A, Q_B, Q_C, or Q_D, respectively, before the indicated steady-state input conditions were established
Q_{An}, Q_{Bn}, Q_{Cn} = the level of Q_A, Q_B, or Q_C, respectively, before the most recent transition of the clock

*See Appendix A for complete description.

FIGURE 20–3
Partially completed schematic for
twisted-ring or ring counter.

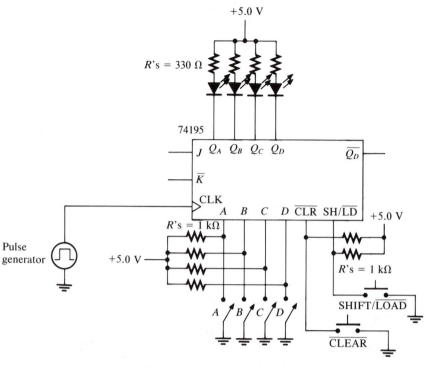

back loop for a twisted-ring counter. Show the completed schematic in your report.

2. Connect your circuit. (The $\overline{\text{CLEAR}}$ and $\overline{\text{SHIFT/LOAD}}$ pushbuttons can be made with pieces of hook-up wire.) Set the pulse generator for a TTL pulse at 1 Hz. Momentarily close the $\overline{\text{CLEAR}}$ switch. One useful feature of the counter is that when the sequence begins in state 0, it forms a Gray code sequence. Although you could load a pattern other than all zeros, this is a typical starting point for a Johnson counter.

3. Observe the pattern in the LEDs. (The LEDs are ON for a zero.) Then speed up the pulse generator to 1 kHz and develop a timing diagram for the Johnson counter outputs. Draw your timing diagram in the space provided in the report.

4. Referring to Figure 20–2 and the function table for the 74195, change the schematic to that of a ring counter. The partially completed schematic is shown in the report. A ring counter does not invert the bits that are fed back, so the desired bit pattern must be preset through the parallel load feature of the shift register. A common pattern is to have either a single 1 or a single 0 recirculate. Set the load switches for 1110 and press the $\overline{\text{SHIFT/LOAD}}$ pushbutton. From the function table, note that this is a synchronous load, so loading will take place only if a clock is present.

5. Reset the pulse generator for 1 Hz and observe the pattern in the LEDs. This pattern is es-

sentially the same pattern used in the ring counter for the keyboard encoder shown in Figure 9–38 of Floyd's text. After observing the pattern in the LEDs, speed up the pulse generator to 1 kHz and develop a timing diagram for the ring counter outputs. Draw your timing diagram in the space provided in the report.

An IC Tester

6. In this step, you will construct an automated IC test circuit. The circuit is shown in Figure 20–4. The device under test (DUT) is any 2-input combinational logic gate. The shift register is used to store the predicted data—that is, the data that are predicted if the DUT is operating correctly. The 7493A generates the input test data and synchronizes the STROBE signal and shift register clocking. Construct the circuit. You can begin with the unused 7400 NAND gate as the DUT. Set the Predict Data for the expected output column of the NAND gate's truth table; the A input to the shift register represents the last row of the truth table.

7. Set the pulse generator to 2 Hz. Start the test sequence by holding the RESET button, pressing the MANUAL CLOCK, and releasing the RESET button. Assuming the DUT output and the shift register output agree, the TEST LED will show the same sequence as the Q_D LED from

196

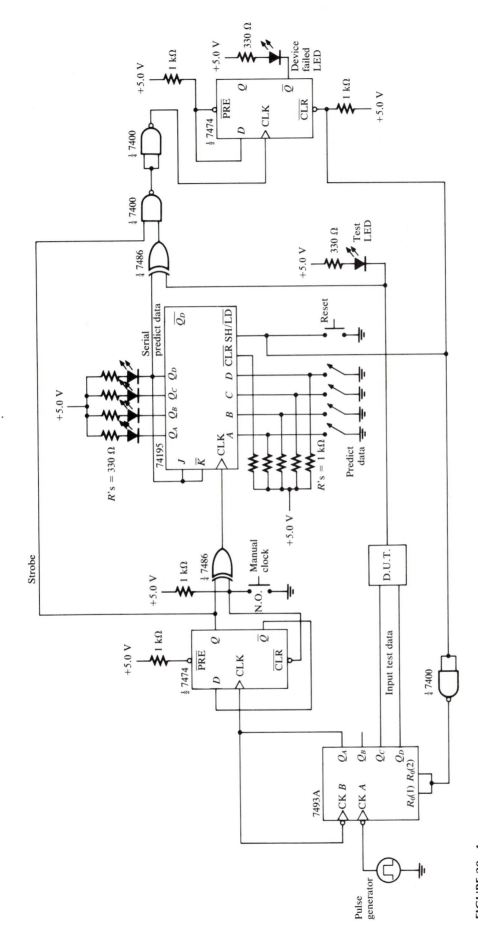

FIGURE 20–4
Automated IC tester.

the shift register. You can speed up the shift register and the tester will continue to cycle through the truth table. Try putting a fault in the data by momentarily lifting an input on the DUT; the DEVICE FAILED LED should turn on.

8. If the circuit is working, determine the time relationship between the CLOCK, INPUT TEST DATA, STROBE, and the SERIAL PREDICT DATA. A logic analyzer is a useful instrument in developing this timing diagram. If you have one available, use it to establish the relative timing of the signals; otherwise use your oscilloscope for timing. Suggestions for establishing timing with an oscilloscope are given in the first step

of Experiment 17. Show the relative timing of the signals in the space provided in the report.

For Further Investigation

The IC tester circuit continues to cycle through the test data even after a failure is detected. This is a disadvantage for finding the specific fault. A second problem with the circuit is that the operator is not alerted when all possible combinations have been tested and the DUT is found to be acceptable. Devise a circuit that (1) stops the test when a fault is detected and (2) signals the operator if the test is completed with no faults found. Summarize your circuit in the report.

Report for Experiment 20

Name: _____ Date: _____ Class: _____

Objectives:

Procedure:

Data:

Schematic for Johnson counter:

Schematic for ring counter:

N.O. pushbuttons

N.O. pushbuttons

Timing diagram for Johnson counter:

Timing diagram for ring counter loaded with 1110:

Results and Conclusions:

Further Investigation Results:

Evaluation and Review Questions

1. a. Why is the STROBE signal necessary for the automated IC tester you constructed?

b. Why couldn't the *B* output from the 7493A be used for the STROBE signal?

2. The automated IC tester was used for combinational logic gates; however, it could be used to test a sequential logic device such as a D flip-flop. Explain how you would use the input test signals to test a D flip-flop.

3. Explain why it is necessary to use an edge-triggered device for a shift register.

4. a. A 3-stage ring counter is loaded with the binary number 101. What are the next three states of the counter?

b. Repeat (a) for a Johnson counter.

5. Assume a failure has occurred on the automated IC tester. The first four serial predict data pulses are correct, but after that the SERIAL PREDICT DATA are all logic HIGH. What could account for this failure?

200

21

Design and Analysis of Shift Register Circuits

Objectives

After completing this experiment, you will be able to:

☐ Design the receiver section of an asynchronous data transfer system.

☐ Construct the data transfer system and test your circuit.

☐ Evaluate the operation of shift register circuits used for pattern generation.

Reference Reading

Floyd, *Digital Fundamentals,* 4th ed., Section 9–6, Bidirectional Shift Registers; Section 9–7, Shift Register Counters; Section 9–8, Shift Register Applications; Section 9–9, Troubleshooting; Section 9–10, Logic Symbols with Dependency Notation

Materials Needed

For the transmitter:
  7474 D flip-flop
  74195 shift register
  7400 quad 2-input NAND gate
  Four LEDs
  1.0 μF capacitor
  Resistors:
    Six 1 kΩ
    Four 330 Ω
For the receiver:
  7474 D flip-flop

  7493A ripple counter
  74195 shift register
  Four LEDs
  1.0 μF capacitor
  Other parts as determined by student

Summary of Theory

Shift registers are very versatile ICs. The last experiment showed applications for shift registers using feedback to make counters. In this experiment, shift registers are applied to another common problem in electronics—that of conversion of data from parallel form to serial form, and vice versa. One widely used system for sending data over phone lines requires that parallel data from the transmitting device be converted to serial data to be sent. In *asynchronous* transmission, the bits are sent at a constant rate, but there are varying spaces between groups of bits (words). To identify each word, a start bit is sent, which is always a 0, followed by eight data bits and two stop bits, which are always 1s. More 1s may follow, which will be ignored by the receiving equipment, until a new start bit is received. A data word is illustrated in Figure 21–1.

The preceding system is simplified in this experiment to illustrate the process of sending and receiving asynchronous data. The transmitter shown in Figure 21–2 is simply a 4-bit 74195 shift register that has been extended to 6 bits by the addition of two D flip-flops. The 74195 is first loaded with the four data bits to be sent. The D

FIGURE 21–1

Asynchronous data transmission.

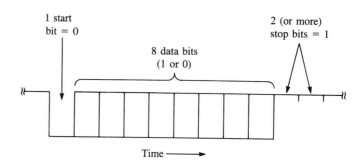

flip-flops are used for the start bit and to keep the serial data line high, as indicated. The latch is to debounce the SHIFT/LOAD line.

You will need to design a receiver for the data bits. Although the transmitter and receiver in this circuit serve to illustrate the concepts in data conversion, they will not operate properly over a distance of more than a few feet. Transmission over greater distances requires the use of special circuits called line drivers and line receivers, usually using special cable or twisted pair wiring.

In the For Further Investigation section, two small data pattern–generating circuits are presented for analysis only. Practice in tracing the logic of these circuits will increase your understanding of shift register applications.

Procedure

1. Review the asynchronous data transmitter circuit shown in Figure 21–2 and described in the Summary of Theory. Note that there are one start bit and four data bits. Be sure you understand exactly how the transmitter works. The receiver will need to detect the HIGH-to-LOW transition of the start bit from the transmitter and then accept the data bits for display in LEDs.

Design an asynchronous data receiver circuit that will clock the data bits serially into a shift register when the HIGH-to-LOW transition of the start bit is detected on the serial data line. Use a 74195 shift register for the main data storage. The receiver then clocks exactly five clock pulses into

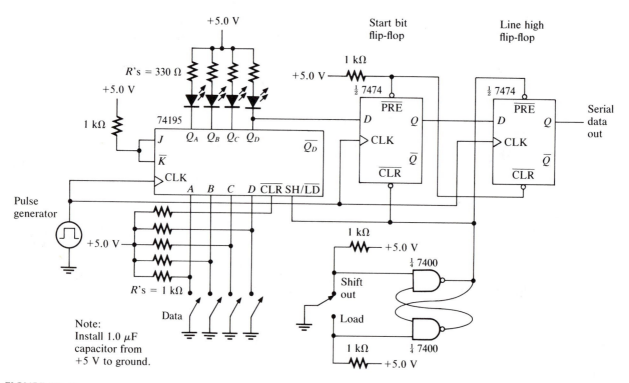

FIGURE 21–2

Asynchronous data transmitter.

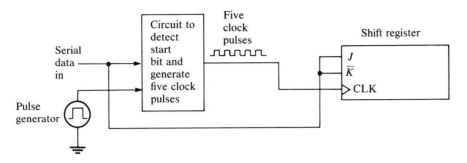

FIGURE 21–3
Block diagram of asynchronous data receiver.

the shift register. (The start bit is shifted right on through the register and is not to be displayed). The basic idea is shown in Figure 21–3. The five clock pulses can be generated with a 7493A ripple counter configured in a manner similar to the circuit, which generates exactly four pulses, as shown in Figure 19–6. Draw the complete design for your circuit in the space provided in the report. Reminder: The 7493A will divide the pulse generator frequency by 2. To keep the transmitter and receiver in step, the receiver pulse generator fre-

quency will need to be set to *twice* the transmitter frequency.

2. This step is flexible and depends on your instructor's preference. Do *one* of the four options listed.

☐ *Option A:* Construct your receiver designed in Step 1 and test it with a transmitter provided by your instructor. Set the transmitter and receiver pulse generators so that the data rates are the same (transmitter twice the re-

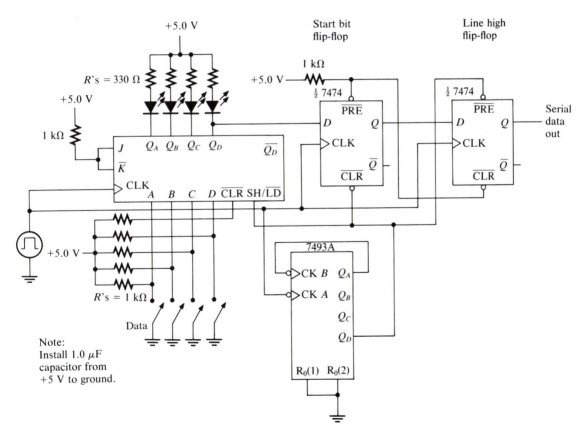

FIGURE 21–4
Circuit for Option D.

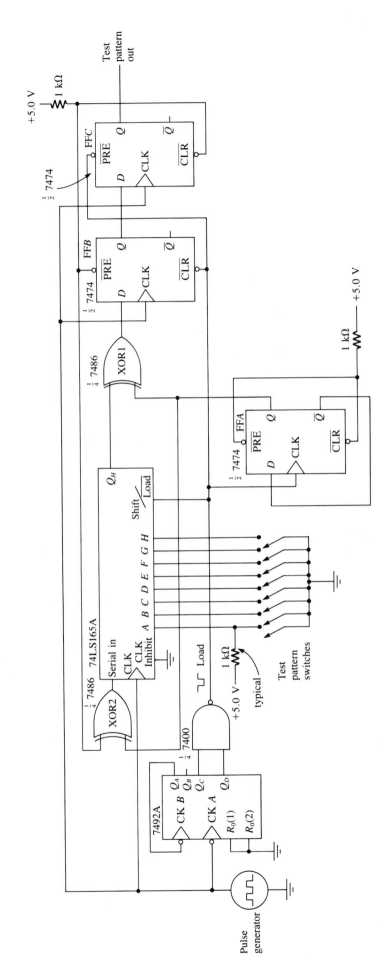

FIGURE 21–5
Test pattern generator.

ceiver frequency). Keep the line short from the pulse generators and between the transmitter and receiver. If necessary, terminate lines from the generators with a resistor equal (or a little larger than) the output impedance of the generators. In addition, install 1.0 μF capacitors across the power supply where it connects to the protoboards.

☐ *Option B:* Construct *either* the transmitter or receiver from Step 1 as assigned by your instructor. Test the data transmission system with another student who has built the remaining part of the circuit using the method described in Option A. Demonstrate your working circuit to your instructor.

☐ *Option C:* Construct *both* the transmitter and receiver from Step 1 and test them using the method described in Option A. Demonstrate your working circuit to your instructor.

☐ *Option D:* Construct a modified transmitter circuit using a 7493A ripple counter and inverter, as shown in Figure 21–4. The counter will be used to divide the basic clock by 8 in order to reload the data after eight clock pulses. Investigate the circuit and summarize its operation in the report.

For Further Investigation

Two circuits are presented for analysis. The first circuit is a test pattern generator that produces a pattern similar to the one described in Figure 9–39 of Floyd's text. The circuit is shown in Figure 21–5. The 74LS165A shift register is described in Appendix A. Analyze the operation of the circuit and write up a description of its operation in your report. You might begin by answering questions such as the following: How does the circuit load the start bit? What is the purpose of the XOR gates? How many stop bits are produced? What is the purpose of FFA?

The second circuit to analyze produces the same pattern as the main sequence of the synchronous counter illustrated in Figure 18–1. This time the sequence is generated by a shift register set up as a ring counter, as shown in Figure 21–6. (Do not worry about the transistors in the schematic. They are used to increase the drive power to a stepper motor.) Using the 74198 function table, analyze the operation of the circuit and write up a description of its operation in your report. The 74198 function table is shown in Table 21–1.

TABLE 21–1

	Inputs							Outputs				
	Mode			Serial		Parallel						
Clear	S1	S0	Clock	Left	Right	A . . . H	Q_A	Q_B	. . .	Q_G	Q_H
L	X	X	X	X	X	X	L	L	. . .	L	L
H	X	X	L	X	X	X	Q_{A0}	Q_{B0}	. . .	Q_{G0}	Q_{H0}
H	H	H	↑	X	X	a . . . h	a	b	. . .	g	h
H	L	H	↑	X	H	X	H	Q_{An}	. . .	Q_{Fn}	Q_{Gn}
H	L	H	↑	X	L	X	L	Q_{An}	. . .	Q_{Fn}	Q_{Gn}
H	H	L	↑	H	X	X	Q_{Bn}	Q_{Cn}	. . .	Q_{Hn}	H
H	H	L	↑	L	X	X	Q_{Bn}	Q_{Cn}	. . .	Q_{Hn}	L
H	L	L	X	X	X	X	Q_{A0}	Q_{B0}	. . .	Q_{G0}	Q_{H0}

Report for Experiment 21

Name: _____ Date: _____ Class: _____

Objectives:

Procedure:

Receiver Schematic:

Results and Conclusion:

Further Investigation Results:

Analysis of Figure 21–5:

Analysis of Figure 21–6:

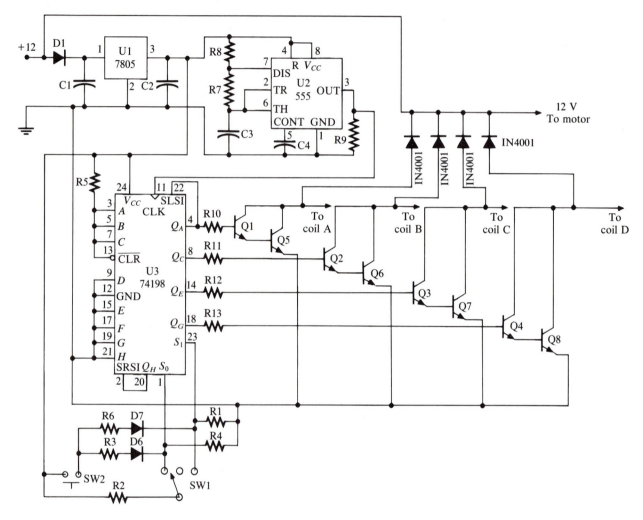

FIGURE 21–6

Evaluation and Review Questions

1. After the transmitter (Figure 21–2) has sent the data, the shift register is loaded with all 1s. Explain why this occurs.

2. What is the purpose of the 7400 latch in the transmitter circuit shown in Figure 21–2?

3. a. Figure 21–7 shows how shift registers can be connected with a single full-adder to form a serial adder. Analyze the circuit and explain how it operates.

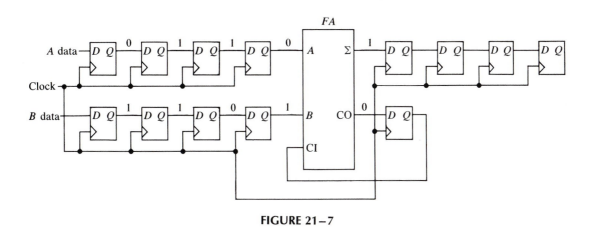

FIGURE 21–7

b. Assume the input shift registers contain the data as shown. What are the contents of the output shift register and the carry-out flip-flop after four clock pulses?

4. Using a 4-bit shift register, design a circuit that produces the two-phase clock signals shown in Figure 21–8.

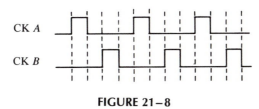

FIGURE 21–8

5. What failures could account for a transmitter that does not send a start pulse but does send the data?

22

The Baseball Scoreboard

Objectives

After completing this experiment, you will be able to:

- ☐ Using shift registers or counters, design and build a logic circuit that solves a logic problem that requires memory.
- ☐ Write a formal laboratory report describing the circuit and results of the experiment.

Reference Reading

Floyd, *Digital Fundamentals,* 4th ed., Section 9–7, Shift Register Counters; Section 9–8, Shift Register Applications; Section 9–9, Troubleshooting; Section 9–10, Logic Symbols with Dependency Notation

Materials Needed

Five LEDs (two red, three green)
Two NO pushbuttons
Other materials as determined by student

Summary of Theory

Most digital circuits contain some form of memory. Even the elementary light switch can be thought of as a memory device: It "remembers" that it has been switched on. Sequential logic circuits contain memory, whereas strictly combinational logic circuits do not. The basis of digital logic memory devices is the flip-flop, which, as in the last three experiments, is used in counters and shift registers. A counter stores the last count until the clock pulse occurs. A shift register can store several prior events, depending on the length of the register. A shift register, such as a Johnson counter, can be set with a characteristic sequence like a counter and can be used in applications requiring a counter.

In this experiment, we require two count sequences. Either sequence may be completed first. The sequence that is completed first must clear both counting devices. One approach might be to use two separate decoders, either of which can clear the counters. The method of solution is entirely up to you. The counting devices are "clocked" by manual pushbuttons. The pushbuttons will need to be debounced. One method of doing this is shown in Figure 22–1.

Procedure

The Baseball Scoreboard

1. Design a circuit that solves the baseball scoreboard problem stated next. There are two inputs, controlled by pushbutton switches (normally open contacts). There are five outputs represented by LEDs. Build the circuit. Summarize your design steps and results in a formal lab report.

Problem Statement: The Latchville Little League needs a new baseball scoreboard. (See Figure 22–2.) Your assignment is to do the logic

211

FIGURE 22–1

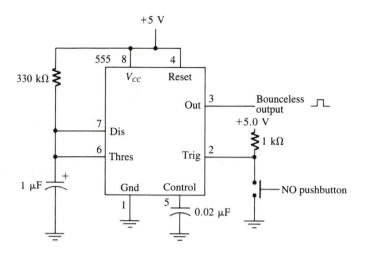

for the strikes-and-balls display. The scoreboard will have two lights (LEDs) for strikes and three lights for balls. The scoreboard operator will have two pushbuttons: one for strikes and the other for balls. Each press of the strike pushbutton turns on one more of the strike lights unless two are already on. If two are on, all lights, including strikes and balls, are cleared. (Note that the count sequence for the strike lights is a binary 0–1–3–0.) The balls pushbutton works in a similar manner. Each press causes one more light to come on unless three are already on. If three lights are already on, then all lights, including strikes, are cleared.

Design Hint: Consider using a 74175 IC for the counting device. The complete circuit can be designed to fit on a single 47-row protoboard.

For Further Investigation

Design the logic circuits needed to complete the scoreboard as illustrated in Figure 22–2. The inning is indicated by a single light (show this as an LED), which corresponds to the inning number. The inning display is controlled by a single pushbutton to advance the light. The outs display is indicated by two lights, which are controlled by a single pushbutton. When the third out is pressed, all lights on the lower row of the scoreboard are cleared.

FIGURE 22–2

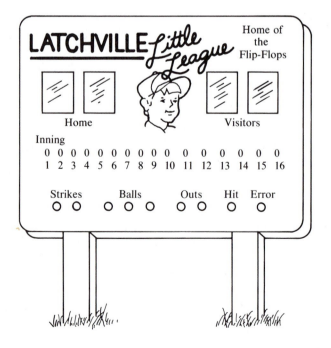

Experiment 22

Name: _____ Date: _____ Class: _____

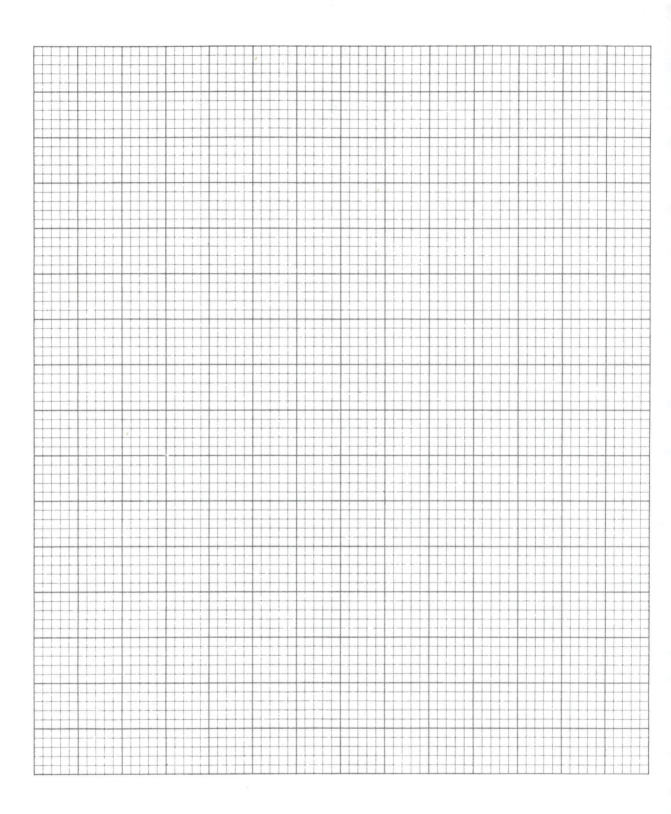

Experiment 22

Name: _____ Date: _____ Class: _____

215

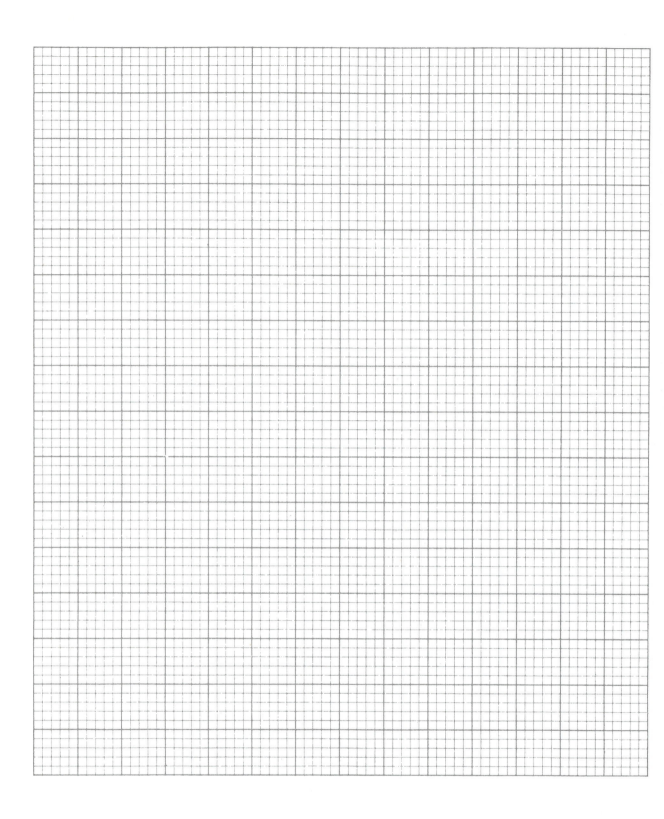

Checkup 9

The exercises in this checkup reflect information covered in Floyd's Chapter 9, "Shift Registers," and Buchla's Experiments 20, 21, and 22.

1. Compare the modulus of a five-stage ring counter with the modulus of a five-stage Johnson counter.

2. a. An eight-stage ring counter is loaded with the sequence 00000001_2. What is the output after three clock pulses?

b. How would your answer differ if the counter were a Johnson counter instead of a ring counter?

3. What are the major differences between shift register counters and synchronous counters designed with methods shown in Experiment 19?

4. Assume the inputs to the circuit shown in Figure 20–1(b) are as follows:

Load = HIGH,   A = HIGH,   B = LOW,   and   C = LOW.

a. Determine the logic level at the output of each gate (G_1 through G_8).

b. What is the logic level at each output (Q_A through Q_C)?

5. a. Figure 21–7 shows a 4-bit serial adder circuit. Is the MSB on the right side or the left side of the shift registers?

b. Assuming you needed to construct a serial magnitude comparator, which bit would you need to test first, the LSB or the MSB?

6. The 74LS165A 8-bit shift register has a clock-inhibit line. Under what conditions can this line be used as a clock line?

7. Suppose you needed to add a circuit to the transmitter in Figure 21–2 that would set a flag to a logic LOW when the last data bit has been sent (a flag is a logical indicator that a specific condition occurred). Show the circuit that would do this.

8. What is the advantage of sending data in serial form rather than parallel form? What is the primary disadvantage?

9. A 74195 has signals applied as shown in Figure 22–3. J and $\overline{K}$ are connected to a HIGH. Sketch the Q_D output.

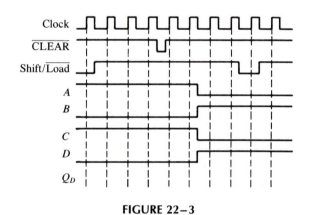

FIGURE 22–3

10. The initial contents of a 4-bit shift register are 1011. The serial input data is 0100 and the register is shifted four times to the right. List the contents of the register after each shift.

11. How could two 74LS165A shift registers be connected to form one 16-bit shift register?

12. Explain how the circuit shown in Figure 21–7 could be modified to cause the contents of B to be subtracted from the contents of A.

23

Semiconductor Memories

Objectives

After completing this experiment, you will be able to:

☐ Complete the design and construct a memory test circuit that writes certain combinations of data into each address of a small memory.

☐ Use the circuit to check the stored data and light an LED if it indicates a difference between the predict data and the stored data.

☐ Develop a partial timing diagram for the circuit using an oscilloscope or logic analyzer.

Reference Reading

Floyd, *Digital Fundamentals,* 4th ed., Chapter 10, Memories and Programmable Logic Devices

Materials Needed

7400 quad 2-input NAND gate
Two 7474 dual D flip-flops
7485 4-bit magnitude comparator
7489 64-bit R/W memory
7493A counter
330 Ω resistor; four 1 kΩ resistors
LED
N.O. pushbutton

Summary of Theory

Computers and other sequential logic systems require the ability to store instructions and data.

Semiconductor memories are a fast-access form of memory used to store the necessary information for these systems to operate. The basic semiconductor storage element is the cell, which can store one binary bit. A typical memory cell consists of a flip-flop and gates to enable the flip-flop and to control the read and write (R/W) functions, as illustrated in Floyd's text (Figure 10–26). Cells are arranged in an *X-Y* matrix of columns and rows. Figure 23–1 illustrates the arrangement for a very small memory (the 7489). Each row of this matrix stores a group of 4 binary bits called a *word,* which is treated as a single unit. Words can vary from as little as 1 bit wide to more than 32 bits. The number of rows in the matrix represents the number of words contained in the memory—in this case there are 16 rows. The memory size is shown on specification sheets as the product of the number of words times the word length. For example, a memory shown as 2K × 16 is organized into 2048 words of 16 bits per word.

Although new types of memory organization have been designed, nearly all semiconductor memories are accessed for reading or writing data by a separate set of address lines. The address represents the location of the word within the matrix. In random-access memory (RAM), each location can be independently accessed without affecting other locations. The acronym RAM is frequently applied to read/write memory, but this is something of a misnomer as other types of semiconductor memories such as ROMs (read-only memory) and PROMS (programmable read-only memory)

FIGURE 23–1

Logic diagram for a small RAM R/W memory (courtesy of Texas Instruments).

SN7489
64-BIT RANDOM-ACCESS READ/WRITE MEMORY

logic diagram

can also be accessed in a random manner. The terms RAM, read/write memory, and random-access R/W memory are generally understood to mean the same thing.

A memory is *volatile* if the contents are destroyed if power is removed. All RAM memory is volatile, although some low-power CMOS memories can appear to be nonvolatile by use of a small battery backup. Other memories, known as *dynamic* memories, are so volatile that they must be refreshed (rewritten) every few milliseconds. The other type of RAM is *static* memory, which does not require refreshing but usually is more expensive.

The access of a specific word in a memory is done by decoding the address and using the decoded output to select the proper row in memory. Depending on the organization of the matrix, column information may also be required (see Figure 10–28 in Floyd's text). In addition to the address lines, memories have one or more control lines and memory-enable lines that select the chip (chip

220

select), and the read or write option, output control, and other operations. The memory-enable lines provide for expansion of memory by allowing other identical ICs to have a different external address. An example showing how two small identical memories can be assigned a different address space is illustrated in Figure 23–2(a). Expansion of the word size is shown in Figure 23–2(b).

The outputs of memory and other devices are frequently connected to a common set of wires known as a *bus*. In order for more than one output to be connected to a bus, the outputs of each device must be either Tri-state or open-collector types. Essentially, Tri-state or open-collector outputs can be electrically disconnected from the bus when not active. Open-collector devices, such as the 7489 used in this experiment, should have a single pull-up resistor connected to each output line.

In this experiment, you will do a functional test of a very small static 16×4 RAM (the 7489). The output of this memory is the complement of the originally written data. The test circuit is designed to read and write certain combinations of binary input numbers. Such a test represents a more comprehensive functional test than merely testing that the memory can write and read all 1s or all 0s. This is because memories can be pattern sensitive—that is, certain combinations of binary numbers can actually be written and read correctly from a defective memory. Unfortunately, testing all possible combinations is not generally done since the number of combinations rises astronomically with the size of the memory. In the 7489 there are $16 \times 2^4 = 256$ combinations, but in a $2K \times 16$ memory, there are more than 134 million possibilities! Large memories have combinations that are too large for a full test to be done. Consequently, only a limited number of patterns that are likely to show errors are tested by manufacturers.

Procedure

1. Complete the circuit drawing shown in the report as Figure 23–3. The D flip-flops need to be configured as a Johnson counter that is to be cleared with the pushbutton. The outputs of the 7489 form the complement of the data that were written into the memory, so the $\overline{Q}$ outputs of the

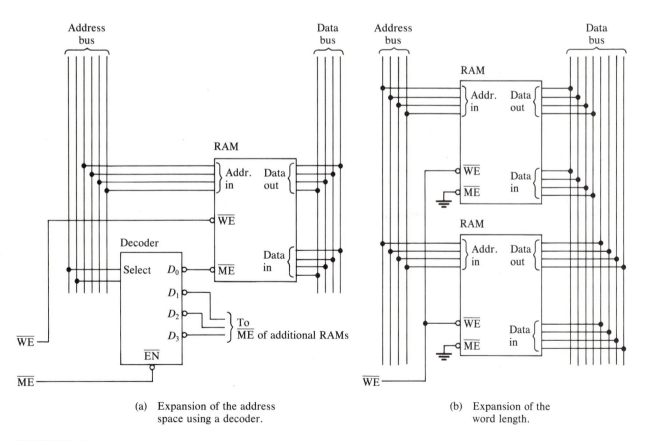

(a) Expansion of the address space using a decoder.

(b) Expansion of the word length.

FIGURE 23–2
Expansion of address space or word length with a small memory (partial schematic).

Johnson counter are shown connected to the *B* inputs of the 7485. Decide what to do with the $R_{0(1)}$ and $R_{0(2)}$ inputs on the 7493A address counter, the cascade inputs on the 7485 comparator, and the memory enable on the 7489 memory.

2. Connect the memory test circuit. Set the pulse generator for a TTL 10 kHz clock signal and start the test. The TEST FAIL light should remain off. If it does not, troubleshoot the circuit carefully and repair it.

3. Develop a partial timing diagram for the circuit using either an oscilloscope or logic analyzer. It is not necessary to draw a complete timing diagram, as it would be too extensive. Rather, choose an arbitrary time when Q_D makes a LOW-to-HIGH transition and show the timing a few clock cycles before and after this event for the address counter, Johnson counter, and memory.

(How can a scope be triggered to look before this event?)

4. Test the circuit by placing a short to ground on one of the memory outputs. The TEST FAIL light should turn on and the address counter should stop. With a logic probe you can read the specific address at which the circuit indicates a failure and the data that are found at that address.

For Further Investigation

Suppose you wanted to test *every* combination of input in the memory test circuit in Figure 23–3. You can do this by changing the Johnson counter into a ripple counter. Describe in your report the changes needed to make the D flip-flops into an up counter. Then, modify the circuit and summarize its operation.

Report for Experiment 23

Name: _____ Date: _____ Class: _____

Objectives:

Procedure:

Schematic for Memory Test:

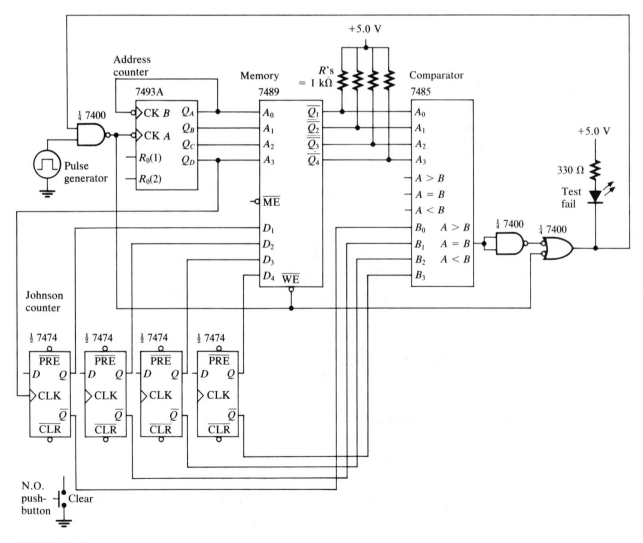

FIGURE 23–3
Partial schematic for memory test circuit.

Partial Timing Diagram:

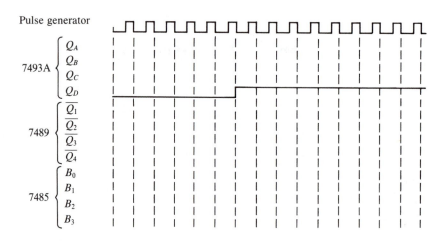

Results and Conclusion:

Further Investigation Results:

Evaluation and Review Questions

1. Assume you wanted to do a functional test on an 8K × 32 memory by checking every possible combination of inputs. There are $8192 \times 2^{32} = 3.52 \times 10^{13}$ possible combinations of the inputs. You can run the test pattern at 20 MHz (20 million tests per second). How many days would it take to complete the test?

2. Why are pull-up resistors needed on the output of the 7489?

3. The specification sheet for the 7489 indicates that it features full, on-chip decoding.
   a. What does this mean?

   b. According to the specification sheet, what is the minimum amount of time data must be available during a write operation?

4. A memory has eight address lines and ten data lines.
   a. How many different locations can be addressed?

   b. What is the word length?

5. Suppose the test fail light is on in the circuit of Figure 23–3. A check of the address counter indicates 0100 and the Johnson counter indicates 0000. The 7489 is changed and the test is repeated. The new 7489 proceeds to test positively until the same address is reached, at which point the TEST FAIL light turns on. What are possible causes of the problem? How would you go about isolating it?

24

An Electronic Lock System

Objectives

After completing this experiment, you will be able to:

☐ Build an electronic lock system.
☐ Test the circuit by injecting a test signal, and use a test procedure to develop a rational method for troubleshooting the system.
☐ Modify the design to expand the system.

Reference Reading

Floyd, *Digital Fundamentals*, 4th ed., Section 10–1, Memory Concepts; Section 10–2, Read-Only Memories (ROMs); Section 10–3, Programmable ROMs (PROMs and EPROMs); Section 10–4, Read/Write Random Access Memories (RAMs); Section 10–5, Memory Expansion

Materials Needed

7420 dual 4-input NAND gate
74121 one-shot
7489 read/write memory
7404 hex inverter
7474 dual D flip-flop
74148 priority encoder
7476 dual J-K flip-flop
7485 magnitude comparator
7402 quad NOR gates
Two LEDs
1.0 μF capacitor
Six NO pushbuttons
SPST switch
Resistors:
  Two 330 Ω
  Thirteen 1 Ω
  One 10 kΩ

Summary of Theory

Digital systems are composed of combinational and sequential circuit elements working together to perform some specific function. Small but useful systems can be constructed from the combinational and sequential circuits you have studied so far. Larger systems that can perform a variety of tasks are controlled by computers and are referred to as programmable digital systems.

The small system in this experiment uses a variety of ICs with which you have already experimented, including timers, comparators, counters, and memory circuits. As in most systems, it is necessary to store and retrieve information in a memory. The memory is the familiar 7489 used in the last experiment. It is a static memory, meaning that it does not require constant rewriting (called refresh). Although small, it has attributes of larger memories, including address and data inputs, memory and write enable inputs, and open-collector outputs to allow it to be connected directly to buses.

The protoboard construction is frequently prone to error, even in small systems like this; one of the most valuable experiences in constructing circuits like this one is the organization and troubleshooting skills you will develop as you build the circuit. It is strongly recommended that you take the time before beginning construction to develop a wire list. This list is described in the Introduction to the Student at the beginning of this lab book.

The circuit is an electronic lock that is manually controlled; hence, it normally operates at a very slow rate. This complicates troubleshooting if the circuit is not working; systems like this frequently contain a wiring error when they are first connected. A common troubleshooting technique called signal injection can be applied to this system to speed up the signal and the troubleshooting process. In addition, signal injection is a normal procedure for testing boards and small systems. Even if your system works the first time you turn it on, it is useful to test it with an injected signal, as explained in the procedure.

In this experiment you will build the electronic lock system shown in Figure 24–1. The combination is first written into the random-access memory. The stored combination is then compared with three input switches, pressed one at a time, by the user. If the stored combination agrees with the input data, then the lock will be opened (shown by an LED). If the stored combination does not agree with the input data, then an alarm will be indicated by a different LED.

To store a combination, an address counter is used to generate sequential addresses. At each address, the data representing the combination are stored. For example, to store the combination 3–0–1, begin by turning off the ALARM and pressing the CLEAR button to reset the address counter. Next press SW3, and, while it is pressed, momentarily press the WRITE switch. This causes the encoded switch value (a binary 00) to be stored in the RAM at address 0001. (The address counter has incremented by 1.) Release SW3 and repeat using SW0 and then SW1. The data stored from these operations are summarized in Table 24–1. Note that when the 7489 is read, the switch that was pressed in the WRITE mode appears in true binary form on the output.

After a combination is stored, the lock can be operated. The CLEAR pushbutton is momentarily pressed, and the ALARM switch is closed, activating the alarm. If the same three pushbuttons are now pressed in the correct order, then the LOCK OPEN indicator will turn on. If any mistake is made, the ALARM indicator will turn on.

The operation of the circuit should become clear as you follow the test procedure.

Procedure

An Electronic Lock System

1. Construct the electronic lock shown in Figure 24–1. You can fit the circuit on two protoboards by dividing it as shown. After it is built, test it, working or not, using the test procedure listed.

If it is not working, first visually check the wiring and verify that power and ground are applied to each IC. The test procedure should guide you to the problem, which you should correct before continuing.

Test Procedure

Step 1: Turn the alarm off, and connect a TTL-level pulse generator to the SW3 input of IC1(a). Set the frequency to 100 Hz. View the generator waveform on channel 1 of a two-channel oscilloscope. This is a test signal that simulates pressing SW3 100 times per second. Leave the test signal connected to channel 1 throughout the test procedure. View input B to IC3 on channel 2. Compare the waveforms to test the NAND gate operation. Press the other switches (0, 1, and 2), one at a time, to test the switches and the NAND gate operation. (Remember that any 0 on the input of a NAND gate produces a 1 on the output.)

Step 2: Calculate the expected pulse width for the monostable multivibrator (IC3). Measure the $\overline{Q}$ output pulse width, and verify that the Q output is present at the same time. Record the expected and measured pulse width in the report in Table 24–2.

Step 3: The pulse from IC3 clocks the address counter (IC4) and the alarm latch (IC9). Observe the clock inputs to each of these flip-flops. Then observe the outputs of the address counter. Compare the frequency of Q_A and Q_B with the generator frequency. Record the measured frequencies in Table 24–2.

The address counter is working properly if you can observe the toggle action of the J-K flip-flops.

Step 4: The test signal from the generator is converted by the priority encoder (IC2) to a binary number on its output. Look at a truth table for the 74148, and determine how the signal should appear on the output lines of the priority encoder. Sketch the signals on Plot 1 in the report.

You can test the effect of the other inputs to the priority encoder by moving the test signal to each input, one at a time.

Step 5: As previously stated, the pulse generator simulates SW3 being pressed 100 times per

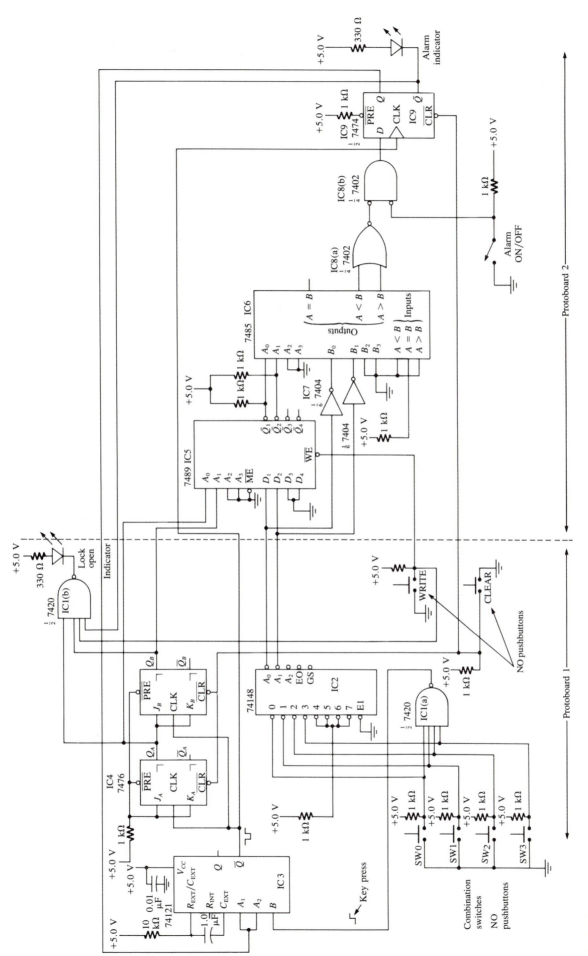

FIGURE 24–1

TABLE 24-1

Combination (Data for 3-0-1)	74148 Inputs				74148 Outputs		7476 (Address Counter)		7489 (Address Input)		7489 Outputs†	
	0	1	2	3	A_1	A_0	Q_B	Q_A	A_1	A_0	$\overline{Q}_2$	$\overline{Q}_1$
SW3	1	1	1	0	0	0	0	1*	0	1	1	1
SW0	0	1	1	1	1	1	1	0	1	0	0	0
SW1	1	0	1	1	1	0	1	1	1	1	0	1

*Data are also written at location 00.

†Outputs shown are in READ mode. Data are complemented.

second. Momentarily press the WRITE pushbutton. The priority encoder output (simulating the pressing of SW3) will be written repeatedly into four locations of memory (IC5). (However, note that only three locations are tested when operating.) When the WRITE pushbutton is released, the memory returns to the READ mode. Test the output of the memory and see that it is the complement of the data from the priority encoder. Both outputs should be HIGH; however, note that this is not a *proof* that the memory is working correctly. (How could you prove this?)

Step 6: The magnitude comparator (IC6) should have the same logic level on its A and B inputs whenever the pulse generator is LOW, because the comparator is testing the same combination that was written in Step 5. Look at the 7485 truth table and determine what each of the three output logic levels should be during this time.

Then on Plot 2 sketch the pulse generator waveform and the three comparator outputs.

2. This procedure does not test every possible fault the circuit could have; however, it should narrow the search area. Remove the pulse generator and check that the circuit operates as described in the Summary of Theory section.

For Further Investigation

Expand the electronic lock system to eight combination switches and add a 5-second delay to the alarm so that it is not set off until after the delay period has elapsed. Describe the changes to Figure 24-1 in the report.

Then, complete Table 24-3 to show the operation of the expanded lock. Assume the combination is 7-4-2 and complete the table for the WRITE mode.

Report for Experiment 24

Name: _____ Date: _____ Class: _____

Objectives:

Procedure:

Data:

TABLE 24–2

Step		Expected	Measured
2	Pulse width		
3	Frequency of Q_A		
	Frequency of Q_B		

Generator waveform:

Priority encoder outputs:

A_0:

A_1:

PLOT 1

Pulse generator waveform:

Comparator $A = B$ output:

Comparator $A < B$ output:

Comparator $A > B$ output:

PLOT 2

Results and Conclusion:

Further Investigation Results:

Description of changes to construct the expanded lock:

TABLE 24−3
Expanded electronic lock

Combi-nation (Data for 7−4−2)	74148 Input								74148 Outputs			7476 (Address Counter)		7489 (Address Input)		7489 Outputs		
	0	1	2	3	4	5	6	7	A_3	A_1	A_0	Q_B	Q_A	A_1	A_0	$\overline{Q}_3$	$\overline{Q}_2$	$\overline{Q}_1$
SW7																		
SW4																		
SW2																		

Evaluation and Review Questions

1. Why is the $\overline{Q}$ output from the one-shot (IC3) used to trigger the alarm latch (IC9)?

2. Why can't the $A = B$ output from the comparator (IC6) be used for the lock open decoder [IC1(b)] instead of the Q output from the alarm latch (IC9)?

3. What is the function of the inverters (IC7) on the B_0 and B_1 inputs to the magnitude comparator (IC6)?

232

4. Why are inputs A_1 and A_2 of the one-shot (IC3) connected to the Q output of the alarm latch (IC9)? (Look at the 74121 truth table.)

5. Explain how signal injection can be used to troubleshoot a small system such as the electronic lock.

Checkup 10

The exercises in this checkup reflect information covered in Floyd's Chapter 10, "Memories and Programmable Logic Devices," and Buchla's Experiments 23 and 24.

1. a. What is the difference between a volatile and a nonvolatile memory?

b. Is an EPROM volatile or nonvolatile?

2. a. What is the difference between a static and a dynamic memory?

b. Which type is the 7489?

c. What does a dynamic RAM use in place of a flip-flop or latch?

3. a. The electronic lock experiment (Experiment 24) used a 7489 RAM to store the combination. What disadvantage would this have in an actual combination lock?

b. What type of memory would you suggest as a better choice?

4. What is the total number of bits that can be stored in a RAM R/W memory with ten address lines and eight data lines?

5. How many address lines are needed for 16,384 locations?

6. How many 16K × 8 memory ICs are required to make a 64K × 16-bit memory?

7. How does address multiplexing reduce the pin count on RAMs?

8. Figure 23–2(a) shows how four small memories such as 7489s can be expanded to six address lines using the memory enable. Explain how you would connect eight such memories to seven address lines so that each memory occupied a unique address space.

9. Assume in the circuit shown in Figure 23–2(a) that the most significant address bit (A5) is stuck HIGH. What effect does this have on the data when the correct address should be LOW for the most significant bit?

10. What are the main advantages of CMOS RAM over TTL RAM?

11. What is a FIFO? How can it be used to change serial data rates?

12. What are tracks and sectors? To what types of memories are these terms applied?

13. **a.** What causes magnetic bubbles to form in a garnet?

   b. Are the data accesses in a serial or a random access manner?

14. Figure 24–2 shows an FPLA, which should have intact fuses as indicated by the dots. A test pattern from a counter is applied to the inputs and the outputs respond as shown. What is the likely problem with the FPLA?

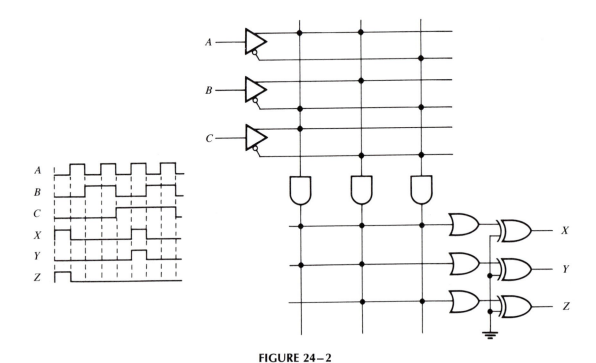

FIGURE 24–2

25

D/A and A/D Conversion

Objectives

After completing this experiment, you will be able to:

☐ Construct a circuit using a binary counter and a D/A (digital-to-analog) converter.

☐ Check the calibration of the circuit, measure its resolution in volts/step, and observe its waveforms on an oscilloscope.

☐ Modify the circuit into a tracking A/D (analog-to-digital) converter, and use it to construct a digital light meter.

Reference Reading

Floyd, *Digital Fundamentals,* 4th ed., Section 11–1, Interfacing Analog and Digital Worlds; Section 11–2, Digital-to-Analog (D/A) Converters; Section 11–3, Analog-to-Digital (A/D) Converters

Materials Needed

74191 up/down counter
MC1408 D/A converter
7447A BCD-to-seven-segment decoder/driver
MAN-72 seven-segment display
LM741 operational amplifier
3906 PNP transistor
CdS photocell (Radio Shack #276-116 or equivalent)

Resistors:
  Seven 330 Ω
  Two 1 kΩ
  Two 2.0 kΩ
  One 5.1 kΩ
  One 10 kΩ

Summary of Theory

Most quantities measured in the physical world are analog, whereas computations almost always use digital quantities. Calculated digital values frequently need to be converted back to continuous quantities for control of analog devices. The devices that accomplish this are called *converters*. A *D/A converter* inputs a digital word and produces an output voltage or current proportional to the input number. An *A/D converter* samples a continuously varying analog voltage and produces digital values of this varying voltage as its output.

D/A conversions can be done by various methods, as described in Floyd's text. For many applications, an IC D/A converter will meet the design requirements. In these cases, the performance characteristics become the important criteria, rather than the detailed circuit operation. The most important characteristics are resolution and accuracy. *Resolution* is the number of steps the full-scale signal can be divided into. It may be expressed as a percentage of full scale, as a voltage per step, or simply as the number of bits in the full-scale word. Resolution is often confused with *accuracy,* which is the percentage difference between the actual and expected outputs. Accuracy includes other possible errors, such as nonlinearity and offset error as described in Floyd's text.

In this experiment, you will use an IC D/A converter to change the binary output of a counter to an analog current. The IC chosen is a MC1408 multiplying D/A converter that multiplies the input binary number by a reference current. Figure 25–1 shows the circuit. The reference current (chosen to be nearly 1.0 mA) is set up by the 5.1 kΩ resistor connected to +5.0 V. This current scales the maximum output current as 1.0 mA, which flows through a 2.0 kΩ load resistor. The load resistor converts the output current to a voltage.

A small modification of the circuit results in a tracking A/D converter shown in Figure 25–2. The analog input is compared with the present output of the D/A converter. If the D/A converter output is less than the analog input, the counter adds a count; otherwise, it subtracts a count. In this way it follows changes on the input. We will use this circuit to construct a digital light meter in the For Further Investigation.

Procedure

Multiplying D/A Converter

1. Construct the circuit shown in Figure 25–1. The MC1408 D/A converter has 8-bit resolution, but we will use only the 4 most significant bits. Note how the input pins on the D/A converter are numbered; the MSB is the lowest number. Set the pulse generator for a TTL-level 1 Hz, and close S_1. Observe the waveforms at the output of the counter. Sketch the observed waveforms in Plot 1 of the report.

2. Open S_1. Observe the waveforms from the counter and draw them in Plot 2.

3. Apply a short to ground on the $\overline{\text{LOAD}}$ input of the counter. This parallel-loads the counter to all 1s. Now check the calibration of the D/A converter. With the short in place, measure the output voltage on pin 4 of the D/A converter. This represents the full-scale output. Determine the volts per step by dividing the full-scale output voltage by 15 (since there are 15 steps present). Record the voltage and the volts.

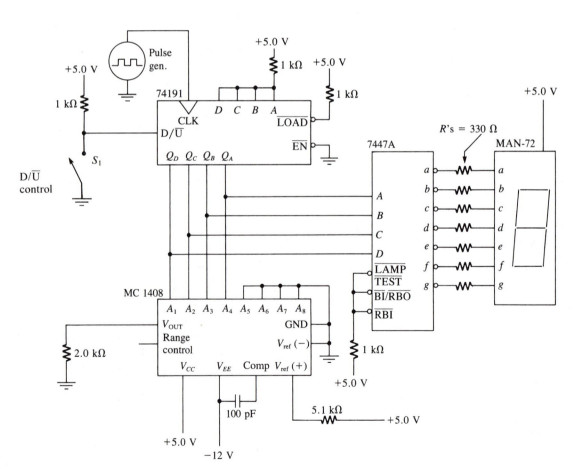

FIGURE 25–1

238

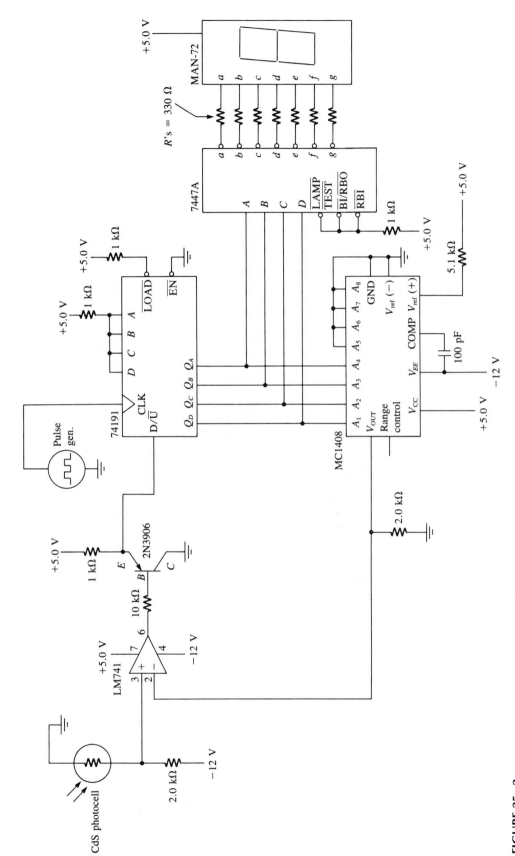

FIGURE 25–2
Simple digital light meter.

FIGURE 25-3

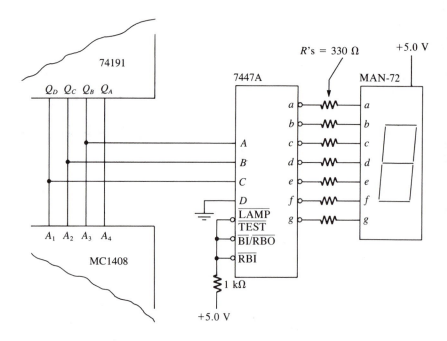

4. Disconnect the short to ground from the $\overline{\text{LOAD}}$ input of the counter. Speed the pulse generator up to 1 kHz. With an oscilloscope, observe the analog output (pin 4) from the D/A converter. On Plot 3 sketch the waveform you see. Label the voltage and time on your sketch.

5. Close S_1 and observe the analog output from the D/A converter. Sketch the observed waveform on Plot 4.

For Further Investigation

A Digital Light Meter

1. Modify the circuit into a tracking A/D converter by adding the photocell, operational amplifier (op-amp), and transistor, as shown in Figure 25-2. The circuit senses light, producing a voltage at the noninverting input (pin 3) of the op-amp. The input voltage from the photocell is compared to the output voltage from the D/A converter and causes the counter to count either up or down. The purpose of the transistor is to change the op-amp output to TTL-compatible levels for the counter.

2. Set the pulse generator for 1 Hz, and note what happens to the count in the seven-segment display as you cover the photocell with your hand. If a constant light is allowed to strike the photocell, the output still oscillates. This oscillating behavior is characteristic of the tracking A/D converter. Speed up the generator and observe the analog output of the D/A converter on the oscilloscope. Describe the signal observed on the scope as you cover the photocell.

3. The modification shown in Figure 25-3 is a simple way to remove the oscillating behavior from the seven-segment display. Note that the Q_D output of the counter is connected to the C input of the 7447A. Try it and explain how it works.

Report for Experiment 25

Name: _____ Date: _____ Class: _____

Objectives:

Procedure:

Data:

Q_A
Q_B
Q_C
Q_D

PLOT 1

Q_A
Q_B
Q_C
Q_D

PLOT 2

TABLE 25−1

Quantity	Measured Value
D/A full-scale output voltage	
Volts/step	

PLOT 3

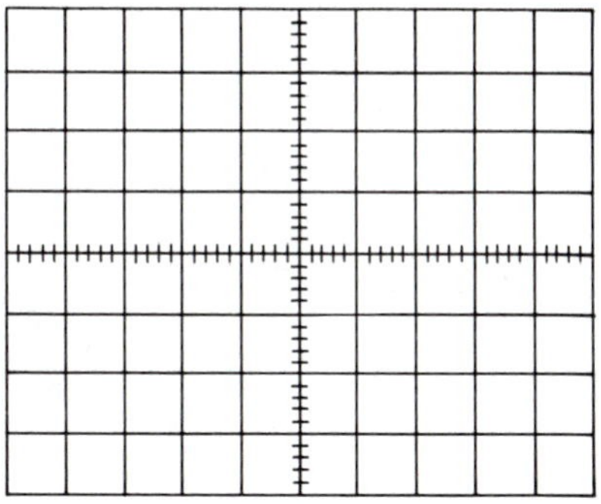

PLOT 4

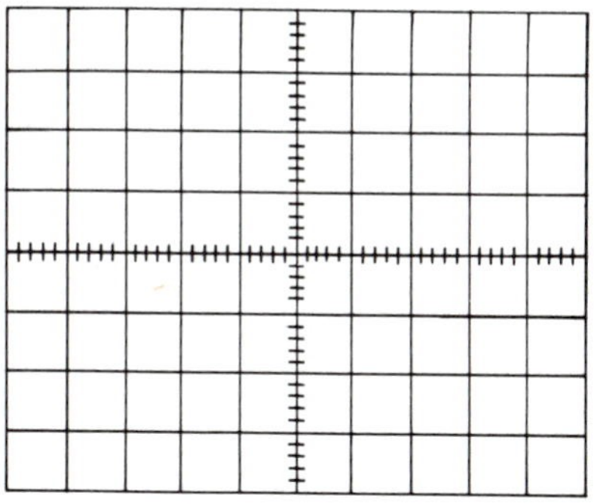

Results and Conclusions:

Further Investigation Results:

Evaluation and Review Questions

1. **a.** In Step 4, you observed the analog output from the D/A converter. What output voltage represents a binary 1010 input?

   b. What is the output frequency of the D/A converter?

2. If all eight input bits for the D/A converter were used, what would be the output resolution in volts/step?

3. **a.** What happens to the output voltage if the 5.1 kΩ resistor is made smaller?

   b. What happens to the output resolution?

4. Explain why the circuit in Figure 25–2 exhibits oscillating behavior.

5. **a.** How could you decrease the size of the voltage steps from the circuit in Figure 25–2?

   b. Would the decrease change the sensitivity of the light meter?

26

Application of Bus Systems

Objectives

After completing this experiment, you will be able to:

☐ Build a liquid-level detector and display that are interconnected with a bus system.

☐ Connect your system with that of another student. Assign each detector a unique address.

☐ Design and construct a decoder circuit that selects the desired detector and sends its data to the displays.

Reference Reading

Floyd, *Digital Fundamentals,* 4th ed., Section 11–5, Internal Device Interfacing; Section 11–6, Digital Equipment Interfacing

Materials Needed

14051B analog MUX/DMUX
14532B priority encoder
555 timer
Resistors:
  One 330 Ω
  Six 1 kΩ
  Six 27 kΩ
  One 200 kΩ
  Eight 4.7 MΩ
Capacitors:
  One 0.01 μF
  Two 0.1 μF
  One 1.0 μF

Ten DIP switches (wire jumpers may be substituted)
Four 2N3904 NPN transistors (or equivalent)
Eight LEDs
Other materials as determined by student

Summary of Theory

In many digital systems, various parts of the system must be able to exchange data with one another. These devices include computers and peripherals, memories, and electronic instruments such as voltmeters and signal generators. To interconnect each of these devices with its own set of wires for exchange of data would result in unnecessary complexity, to say the least. Instead, they are connected to a common set of wires known as a *data bus*.

In a bus system, only one device can send data at one time, although more than one device may receive data. A *protocol* (who can "talk" and who should "listen") needs to be established when the system is designed. Signals used to control the movement of data are sent over a separate bus called a *control bus*.

Another type of bus used with computers is called an *address bus*. This bus carries address information that selects a particular location or IC.

To avoid bus conflicts, logic devices that drive buses must be able to be disconnected from the bus when they are not "talking." There are two methods for achieving this. The first uses *open-collector logic* in which the upper output transistor is simply omitted from the IC. A single external pull-up resistor is attached to each bus line, which serves as the load for all open-collector devices connected to that line. For example, if several open-collector NAND gates are connected to the line, any one of them can pull the line LOW. Active command signals are usually LOW so that various devices can be added to or removed from the bus without affecting it.

The second method, which is faster and less subject to noise, uses *three-state logic* (also known as Tri-state logic, a trademark of National Semiconductor Corporation). Tri-state logic uses a separate enable line to connect the device to the bus. When it is not enabled, it is in a high-impedance or floating state. Pull-up resistors are not needed as they are in open-collector logic.

Actually, open-collector logic can be implemented with ICs that are not special open-collector types by using discrete transistors for the open-collector device. The advantage of this technique is the added drive current that can be supplied (but with additional complexity and cost). This method is illustrated in this experiment.

The circuit shown in Figure 26–1 represents a liquid-level-sensing circuit for a remote "container." The liquid-level data are sensed by a series of switches that close, one after the other, as the liquid level rises. The data are transmitted over a data bus to a display circuit, which causes an LED to indicate the level. The transistors are connected as open-collector devices using R_{17}, R_{18}, R_{19}, and R_{20} as the collector resistors. Only one collector resistor is necessary for each line on the data bus, even if more containers are added. The discrete transistors act as electronic switches. A logic LOW from the priority encoder keeps the transistors off (an open switch) and causes the bus line to be pulled HIGH by the pull-up resistor; a HIGH from the priority encoder turns the transistors on (closed switch) causing a LOW to appear on the bus line. The transistors thus invert the logic that goes to the data bus. The transistors allow added drive current for the data lines and convert the priority encoder to an open-collector device, thus allowing the addition of other sensors on the same bus. The address bus is shown with no connections other than switches; you will design a circuit to connect the address bus to the priority encoder in this experiment.

The 14051B analog MUX/DMUX chosen for the display is an interesting and versatile IC. As you can see from the data sheet, this IC functions as a set of digitally controlled switches. The common out/in line is connected on one side to all switches. One switch is closed by the control line; the remainder are left open. This process allows an analog signal to be routed from either the common side or the switch side. The circuit in Figure 26–1 makes use of this capability by sending a clock signal from the 555 timer to blink the light, which indicates the correct level.

Procedure

1. Connect the liquid-level-sensing circuit shown in Figure 26–1.* The bus wires are shown with suggested wire colors to make interfacing with another student's experiment easier. Note that the address lines are not connected in this step.

2. Test your circuit by closing switches S_0 through S_7 to simulate a rising liquid level. The LED indicators should follow the switches. If no switch is closed, all LEDs are off.

3. Test the effect of the GS line on the circuit. Temporarily, remove the connection from the GS bus line to the inhibit (pin 6) of the 14051B and tie the inhibit line to a LOW with all switches turned off. The explanation of the effect you see can be found by observing closely the second line on the 14532B truth table and the last line of the 14051B truth table. (Remember that the transistor inverts the logic). Then restore the circuit to its original condition. Summarize your observations of this step in the report.

4. In this step you will connect your bus lines with those of another student or two. Only one student should keep the address selection circuit and the pull-up resistors R_{16} through R_{20}. Other students connected to the same bus should remove these resistors and the address selection switches. Also, power and ground must be supplied from only one power supply. Select a unique address for each student's encoder on the bus and design a circuit to decode each address.† Use the E_{in} (enable input) on the 14532B as a "chip select" to place the selected encoder on the bus. Draw the schematic for your decoder and the other decoders using the common bus in the report.

5. If your circuit is working properly, you should be able to set an address on the address switches (S_8 and S_9) and be able to see the "liquid" level (switch settings) for the selected container

---

*If you need to simplify the circuit, the 555 timer can be left out. Connect +5.0 V to the left side of R_{16}.

†If you use a TTL circuit to interface to the 14532, connect a 3.3 kΩ resistor between the TTL output and +5.0 V to help pull up the voltage; do not connect any other load to the TTL output. A 7400 can be used for each decoder.

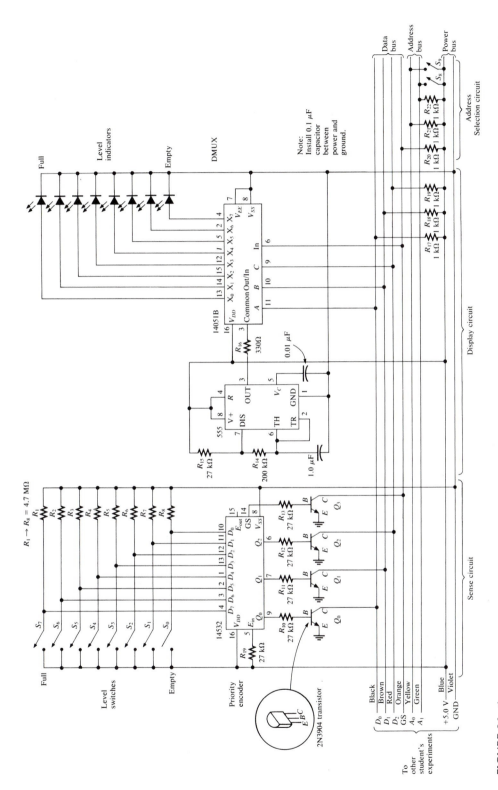

FIGURE 26–1
Remote liquid-level sensing and display circuit.

(encoder). All displays should show the same container. Demonstrate your working circuit to your instructor.

For Further Investigation

The circuit in this experiment can be cycled through the addresses you have selected by adding a counter to the address line. Design a counter that selects the four possible addresses for the address bus. The counter should indicate which address is being selected at any time in a seven-segment display. If a selected address is not used, all the level indicator LEDs should be out. Draw your schematic in your report.

Alternate Further Investigation

If you have computer experience, you can connect the address bus to an output port of a computer and program the computer to read each liquid level on an input port.

Report for Experiment 26

Name: _____ Date: _____ Class: _____

Objectives:

Procedure:

Data:

Observations from Step 3:

Decoder schematic:

Results and Conclusion:

Further Investigation Results:

Evaluation and Review Questions

1. a. For the circuit in Figure 26–1, what is the purpose of the transistors?

b. Why is it unnecessary to have a Tri-state or open-collector device on the display circuit?

2. What assures that there is no conflict on the data bus with several different priority encoders connected to the same lines?

3. The circuit in this experiment shows the 14051B connected as a DMUX. Assume you wanted to use the same IC in a circuit where you needed a MUX. Explain where you would connect the inputs and the output.

4. Assume the output from the 555 timer in Figure 26–1 is a constant HIGH.
   a. What effect would this have on the LED level indicators?

b. What is the effect on the LED level indicators if the 555 output is shorted to ground?

5. Assume that two level indicators on the same bus try to send their data to the indicator at the same time. (This is called a bus contention error). One of the indicators is trying to send a logic LOW; the other is trying to send a logic HIGH.
   a. Who wins?

b. Why?

c. How would you troubleshoot the circuit to determine which level indicator *should* be on the bus?

27

GPIB Handshake

Objectives

After performing this experiment, you will be able to:

☐ Explain the operation of a three-wire handshake circuit.

☐ Construct either the talker or listener portion of the circuit and interface your portion with another student's experiment. Troubleshoot the circuit as necessary.

☐ Using an oscilloscope or logic analyzer, construct a timing diagram for the circuit in Objective 1.

Reference Reading

Floyd, *Digital Fundamentals*, 4th ed., Section 11–6, Digital Equipment Interfacing

Materials Needed

Talker:
  Three 1 kΩ resistors
  One 0.1 µF capacitor
  ICs, one of each: 7405, 7408, 7476, 7493A, 74125
Listener:
  Resistors:
    Four 330 Ω
    Five 1 kΩ
  Capacitors:
    One 0.1 µF
    One 1.0 µF

One 100 kΩ potentiometer
ICs, one of each: 7400, 7402, 7405, 7475, 7476, 74121

Summary of Theory

The general-purpose interface bus (GPIB) standard has greatly simplified interconnection of instruments by allowing users simply to plug them into standard cabling. The interface has enabled a number of different manufacturers to produce instruments that are compatible for automated test systems. There are three kinds of devices that can be connected to the bus. There are talkers, listeners, and controllers. A talker is an instrument or device such as a DMM that can send data over the bus. A listener is a device that receives data, such as a printer. A controller is an instrument that directs the exchange of information and determines which device can talk and which device(s) must listen. A device can play more than one role.

There are three types of buses contained within the GPIB. They are the data lines, the general bus management lines, and the data transfer control lines (handshake). The active-LOW convention allows the addition or removal of instruments from the bus without affecting other instruments. It also reduces noise susceptibility in the true state. All control lines use active-LOW logic—that is, the line is low to indicate the asserted true condition. The unique three-wire handshake allows the slowest listener on the bus to control the rate that data is transferred. In this ex-

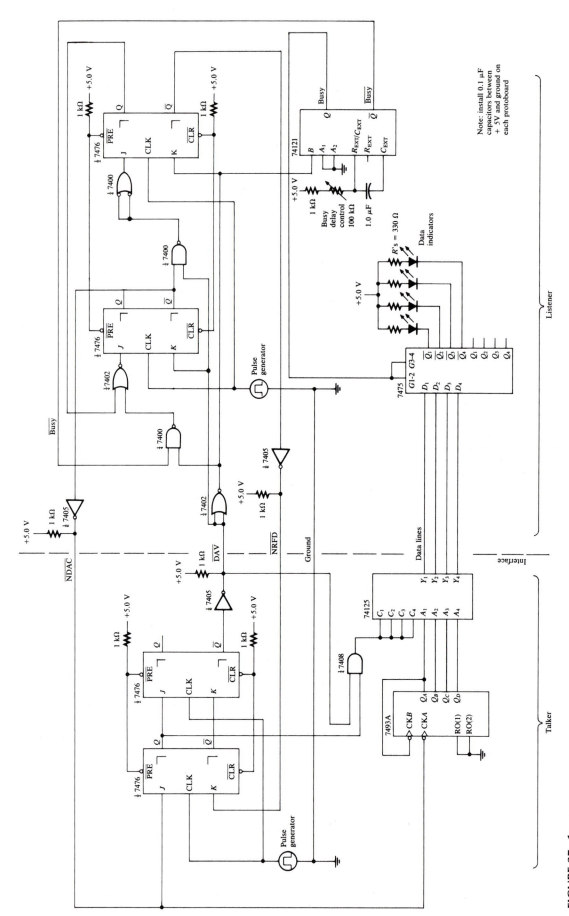

FIGURE 27–1
Simulation of GPIB handshake.

periment, a talker is connected to a listener using the basic GPIB three-wire handshake. The talker is a counter and the listener is a set of LEDs. More than one listener can be connected to the bus in order to simulate several instruments, which may run at different speeds. The experiment closely simulates an actual GPIB handshake interface except that the GPIB interface includes bidirectional bus drivers for each line. Since your circuit will have only one talker and the data will flow in only one direction, it will not be necessary to use bidirectional drivers. In other words, for this experiment only, the talker can only talk and the listener can only listen.

The three handshake lines that are simulated are as follows:

$\overline{DAV}$, data valid: This line is set LOW by the talker to indicate that valid data are present on the data lines.

$\overline{NRFD}$, not ready for data: This line is controlled by the listener(s) to indicate that it is ready for data. The line is asserted LOW when it is not ready and set HIGH when it is ready.

$\overline{NDAC}$, not data accepted: This line is asserted (LOW) by the receiver to indicate that it has not accepted data. When all listeners have accepted the data, the line goes HIGH.

In the experiment, several factors determine the rate of data transfer: the talker's clock frequency, the listener's clock frequency, the propagation delays of both the talker and listener, and the length of time for the slowest listener's busy state as indicated by the receiver's internally generated BUSY signal. (This is not a GPIB signal.)

Procedure

1. For this experiment, you should work in a small group of two or three students. One student will construct a counter along with a handshake circuit (this is the talker) and the other student(s) will construct an LED display with its handshake circuit (this is the listener). The counter will transmit a count across an interface with the data rate determined by the slowest listener. Begin by reviewing the schematic shown in Figure 27–1.

2. Construct either the talker or listener from your completed schematic. Install 0.1 μF capacitors between the power supply and the ground on each protoboard. Connect your data, ground, and handshake lines to the data, ground, and handshake lines of another student's experiment. The talker and listener should be physically close to each other to avoid noise problems. More than one listener may be connected to the bus, but for just this experiment, use only one talker. Set the pulse generators for the talker and the listener(s) to 10 kHz. Try the circuit. The talker should be able to send a continuous count sequence to the listener(s). If it doesn't work, develop a rational troubleshooting procedure to fix what is wrong. A way to get started troubleshooting is to observe the logic on the handshake lines and determine whether the problem is with the listener or the talker.

3. Vary the delay time control (BUSY signal) on a listener. This control represents the time required by the listener to process the data. The counter speed should be determined by the listener set to the longest time delay. At the slowest setting, you should be able to see the count rate change on the LEDs.

4. Set the BUSY delay time to the minimum on all listeners. Draw a timing diagram in your report for the circuit showing the transfer of a data word. Show the handshake signals, BUSY, and the four data lines on your timing diagram. Measure the actual time for the complete transfer of a data word (count) with BUSY at the minimum setting. From the timing diagram, describe the operation of the circuit in your report.

For Further Investigation

Investigate the effect on the data transfer rate as you change the receiver BUSY signal. Also observe the effect on transfer rate as the receiver's pulse generator frequency is varied. If you have more than one receiver on the line, try setting one receiver for a fast transfer rate and the other for a slow transfer rate. Summarize your findings.

Report for Experiment 27

Name: _____ Date: _____ Class: _____

Objectives:

Procedure:

Timing Diagram:

BUSY set for minimum time:

Results and Conclusion:

Further Investigation Results:

Evaluation and Review Questions

1. a. What features of the test circuit in this experiment are similar to the GPIB system?

b. What features are different?

2. Explain how the GPIB allows data to be transferred between a fast talker and a slow receiver without overloading the receiver.

3. Why was open-collector logic used for the handshake signals?

4. What advantage is there for choosing negative-true logic for the handshake signals?

5. The talker has two J-K flip-flops connected as a shift register. What effect does this have on the $\overline{\text{DAV}}$ signal?

Checkup 11

The exercises in this checkup reflect information covered in Floyd's Chapter 11, "System Interfacing," and Buchla's Experiments 25, 26, and 27.

1. a. For the op-amp circuit shown in Figure 27–2, compute the gain.

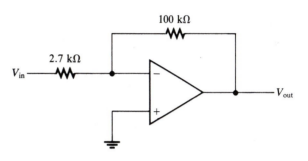

FIGURE 27–2

b. If $V_{in} = -20$ mV, compute V_{out}.

2. Compare the terms *resolution* and *accuracy* when applied to D/A converters.

3. A 3½ digit DMM has 2000 discrete steps. What is the minimum number of bits that can be used to represent a number?

4. How many comparators are needed for an 8-bit flash A/D converter?

5. a. What type of A/D converter was used in Experiment 25 for the digital light meter (Figure 25–2)?

b. Compare the advantage and disadvantage of this converter with a flash A/D converter.

6. For the circuit in Figure 25–2, assume that V_{out} from the MC1408 is -3 V and the noninverting input voltage to the comparator is -4 V. Explain what happens.

7. a. What is meant by a bidirectional bus?

  b. Is the data bus for the GPIB bidirectional?

8. Describe the GPIB handshake.

9. Explain how Tri-state logic allows you to connect several outputs together.

10. For the circuit in Figure 26–1, assume that switches S_0 through S_4 are closed and the others are open.
  a. What is the logic output $(Q_A, Q_B,$ and $Q_C)$ of the 14532B priority encoder?

  b. What data are on the data bus?

  c. Which LED should be on?

11. For the circuit in Figure 26–1, assume that switches S_0 through S_4 are closed and the others are open, yet the indicators show that the container is empty. What are likely causes of the problem?

12. The circuit shown in Figure 27–3 has two inputs, labeled A and B. Explain what each input does.

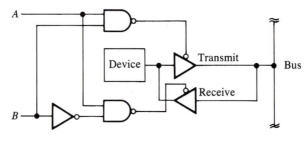

FIGURE 27–3

28

The Arithmetic Logic Unit (ALU)

Objectives

After completing this experiment, you will be able to:

□ Build a circuit containing an ALU and an accumulator, and program the ALU to perform various arithmetic and logic functions.

□ Given specific input conditions, predict the results from the ALU.

□ Use an ALU to design and build a 4-bit adder with an overflow indicator.

Reference Reading

Floyd, *Digital Fundamentals,* 4th ed., Chapter 12, Introduction to Microprocessor-Based Systems

Materials Needed

74175 quad D flip-flop
74181 arithmetic logic unit
555 timer
Six-position DIP switch
Two NO pushbuttons
Capacitors:
   1.0 μF
   0.01 μF
Five LEDs
Resistors:
   Five 330 Ω
   Seven 1 kΩ
   330 kΩ

Summary of Theory

The arithmetic logic unit (ALU) is a group of combinational logic circuits that form the heart of a computer's central processor system. The ALU is capable of performing arithmetic and logic operations on one or two words present at its data inputs. The particular operation to be performed is determined by control inputs. These operations can be arithmetic operations (such as add, subtract, and clear) or logic operations, including all of the common Boolean functions.

Figure 28–1 illustrates the role of the ALU in a typical computer or microprocessor system. (In a microprocessor, all of the blocks shown are inside the microprocessor.) The ALU has two data inputs, one connected from a special register called an *accumulator,* and the other connected through a data bus to a series of registers called the *register array.* Instructions, in the form of binary data, are fetched by the processor into an instruction register. Instructions are then decoded, and, if it is an arithmetic or logic operation, the control logic directs the ALU to perform the required operation. The results are deposited back into the accumulator. From the programmer's point of view, arithmetic and logic operations appear to be accomplished by the accumulator, as the steps described above are not seen by the programmer.

An example of an IC ALU is the 74181, which operates on either one or two 4-bit words present at its inputs. Operations are selected with four

FIGURE 28-1

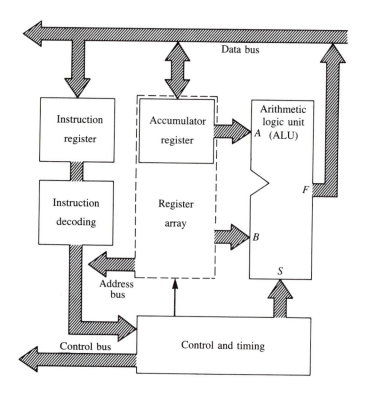

SELECT lines and a MODE input. Table 28-1 lists these operations for active-LOW data, and Table 28-2 lists the equivalent active-HIGH functions. When the MODE input is HIGH, the logic operations are selected. For example, with active-HIGH data, if the four SELECT lines are LOW and the MODE input is HIGH, the complement of the four bits appearing at the A_3—A_2—A_1—A_0 lines will appear at the output F_3—F_2—F_1—F_0. This is shown on the first line of Table 28-2. As you can see from the table, the 74181 can perform 16 logic and 16 arithmetic operations. It can be cascaded with other 74181s for more than four bits.

The circuit for this experiment uses the 74181 ALU connected to a 74175 quad D flip-flop, which will serve as our accumulator. The register array containing the second operand will be simplified to a fixed binary 0011 connected to the B side of the ALU. The instruction to be performed will be selected with switches, and timing is a debounced pushbutton. Since the instruction is selected by switches, the instruction register and decoding logic are not needed.

Procedure

The ALU

1. Connect the circuit shown in Figure 28-2. Clear the accumulator by momentarily pressing the CLEAR pushbutton. In the following steps, keep the result after each step. Do not CLEAR the accumulator unless you need to start over.

2. Add the value in the B register (0011) to the value in the accumulator (0000) with no carry input. To do so, find the SELECT code on Table 28-2 (active-HIGH logic) for arithmetic operations, and determine the correct MODE setting. (Note that the add function is shown with the word "plus," whereas the Boolean OR function is shown with the sign "+.")

The C_n input is interpreted as a $\overline{C}_n$ for active HIGH data. This is equivalent to $\overline{\text{carryin}}$ ($\overline{\text{CI}}$). Connect C_n to a HIGH to indicate no carry-input, as shown in Table 28-2.

Enter the SELECT (S_3, S_2, S_1, S_0), the CARRY IN (C_n), and MODE (M) switch settings for performing addition without carry in Table 28-3 of the report. Then press the CLOCK pushbutton and observe the results in the accumulator. You should observe 0011 if you have set up the addition correctly. Record the accumulator result and the carry-out (C_{n+4}) in Table 28-3. (Note that the C_{n+4} LED will be ON when C_{n+4} is LOW; others are ON for a HIGH output.)

3. Find the SELECT code, CARRY-IN, and MODE settings to subtract 0001 from the value in the accumulator. Set the switches for the operation and list the settings in Table 28-3. With 0011 left in the accumulator from the previous step, press

258

TABLE 28–1

Selection S3 S2 S1 S0	Active-LOW Data		
	M = H Logic Functions	M = L; Arithmetic Operations	
		$C_n = L$ (no carry)	$C_n = H$ (with carry)
L L L L	$F = \overline{A}$	$F = A$ MINUS 1	$F = A$
L L L H	$F = \overline{AB}$	$F = AB$ MINUS 1	$F = AB$
L L H L	$F = \overline{A} + B$	$F = A\overline{B}$ MINUS 1	$F = A\overline{B}$
L L H H	$F = 1$	$F = $ MINUS 1 (2's COMP.)	$F = $ ZERO
L H L L	$F = \overline{A + B}$	$F = A$ PLUS $(A + \overline{B})$	$F = A$ PLUS $(A + \overline{B})$ PLUS 1
L H L H	$F = \overline{B}$	$F = AB$ PLUS $(A + \overline{B})$	$F = AB$ PLUS $(A + \overline{B})$ PLUS 1
L H H L	$F = \overline{A \oplus B}$	$F = A$ MINUS B MINUS 1	$F = A$ MINUS B
L H H H	$F = A + \overline{B}$	$F = A + \overline{B}$	$F = (A + \overline{B})$ PLUS 1
H L L L	$F = \overline{A}B$	$F = A$ PLUS $(A + B)$	$F = A$ PLUS $(A + B)$ PLUS 1
H L L H	$F = A \oplus B$	$F = A$ PLUS B	$F = A$ PLUS B PLUS 1
H L H L	$F = B$	$F = A\overline{B}$ PLUS $(A + B)$	$F = A\overline{B}$ PLUS $(A + B)$ PLUS 1
H L H H	$F = A + B$	$F = (A + B)$	$F = (A + B)$ PLUS 1
H H L L	$F = 0$	$F = A$ PLUS A^*	$F = A$ PLUS A PLUS 1
H H L H	$F = A\overline{B}$	$F = AB$ PLUS A	$F = AB$ PLUS A PLUS 1
H H H L	$F = AB$	$F = A\overline{B}$ PLUS A	$F = A\overline{B}$ PLUS A PLUS 1
H H H H	$F = A$	$F = A$	$F = A$ PLUS 1

Source: Reprinted with permission of Texas Instruments.

*Each bit is shifted to the next more significant position.

TABLE 28–2

Selection S3 S2 S1 S0	Active-HIGH Data		
	M = H Logic Functions	M = L; Arithmetic Operations	
		$C_n = H$ (no carry)	$C_n = L$ (with carry)
L L L L	$F = \overline{A}$	$F = A$	$F = A$ PLUS 1
L L L H	$F = \overline{A + B}$	$F = A + B$	$F = (A + B)$ PLUS 1
L L H L	$F = \overline{A}B$	$F = A + \overline{B}$	$F = (A + \overline{B})$ PLUS 1
L L H H	$F = 0$	F MINUS 1 (2's COMP.)	$F = $ ZERO
L H L L	$F = \overline{AB}$	$F = A$ PLUS $A\overline{B}$	$F = A$ PLUS $A\overline{B}$ PLUS 1
L H L H	$F = \overline{B}$	$F = (A + B)$ PLUS $A\overline{B}$	$F = (A + B)$ PLUS $A\overline{B}$ PLUS 1
L H H L	$F = A \oplus B$	$F = A$ MINUS B MINUS 1	$F = A$ MINUS B
L H H H	$F = A\overline{B}$	$F = A\overline{B}$ MINUS 1	$F = A\overline{B}$
H L L L	$F = \overline{A} + B$	$F = A$ PLUS AB	$F = A$ PLUS AB PLUS 1
H L L H	$F = \overline{A \oplus B}$	$F = A$ PLUS B	$F = A$ PLUS B PLUS 1
H L H L	$F = B$	$F = (A + \overline{B})$ PLUS AB	$F = (A + \overline{B})$ PLUS AB PLUS 1
H L H H	$F = AB$	$F = AB$ MINUS 1	$F = AB$
H H L L	$F = 1$	$F = A$ PLUS A^*	$F = A$ PLUS A PLUS 1
H H L H	$F = A + \overline{B}$	$F = (A + B)$ PLUS A	$F = (A + B)$ PLUS A PLUS 1
H H H L	$F = A + B$	$F = (A + \overline{B})$ PLUS A	$F = (A + \overline{B})$ PLUS A PLUS 1
H H H H	$F = A$	$F = A$ MINUS 1	$F = A$

Source: Reprinted with permission of Texas Instruments.

*Each bit is shifted to the next more significant position.

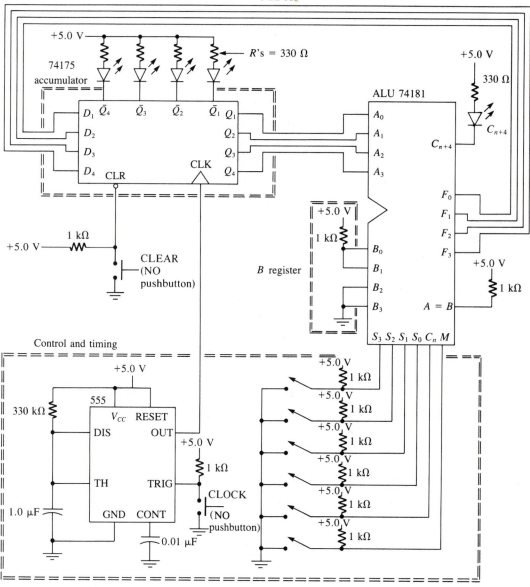

FIGURE 28-2

the CLOCK pushbutton and observe the new result in the accumulator and the carry-out (C_{n+4}). Enter the value in Table 28-3.

4. Find the SELECT code, CARRY-IN, and MODE settings to complement the accumulator result of step 3. Enter the code in Table 28-3. Set the switches for the operation and list the settings in Table 28-3. Press the CLOCK pushbutton and observe the new result in the accumulator and the carry-out. Enter the value in Table 28-3.

5. Find the SELECT code, CARRY-IN, and MODE settings to shift the result of Step 4 to the next most significant position (left shift). Enter the code in Table 28-3. (Note that this is equivalent

to multiplying by 2). Set the switches for the operation and list the settings in Table 28-3. Then press the CLOCK pushbutton as before and observe the new result in the accumulator and the carry-out. Enter the value in Table 28-3.

6. For this step set the SELECT, CARRY-IN, and MODE switches as shown in Table 28-3. From Table 28-2, predict the expected result in the accumulator and carry-out after the CLOCK. List the operation in the space on Table 28-3. Then check your prediction by pressing the CLOCK.

7. Reset the SELECT, CARRY-IN, and MODE switches as shown in Table 28-3. Again,

260

predict the expected result in the accumulator and carry out after the CLOCK and show the operation in the space on Table 28–3. Then, press the CLOCK and observe the result.

For Further Investigation

Assume you wanted to store a sequence of instructions such as those used in this experiment (the SELECT input list) in a 7489 memory. You need to be able to sequence through the list automatically. Each time the CLOCK pushbutton is pressed, a new instruction should appear at the ALU; a short time later, the accumulator should be clocked. Draw the schematic for this change in your report. If directed by your instructor, build the circuit and demonstrate that it works. You may wish to use instructions that do not require you to change the MODE or CARRY-IN inputs.

Report for Experiment 28

Name: _____ Date: _____ Class: _____

Objectives:

Procedure:

Data:

TABLE 28-3

Step	Operation	SELECT, CARRY-IN, and MODE inputs						Result in Accumulator after CLOCK				
		S_3	S_2	S_1	S_0	C_n	M	Q_4	Q_3	Q_2	Q_1	C_{n+4}
2	Addition without carry											
3	Subtract 1 from A											
4	Complement A											
5	Shift A left											
6		H	L	H	L	H	H					
7		L	H	H	L	H	H					

Results and Conclusion:

Further Investigation Results:

1. For each of the active-HIGH functions listed in Table 28–4, predict the result assuming that $A = 1001$ and $B = 0011$. Complete the table showing the predicted output. The first line is completed as an example.

TABLE 28–4

Selection S_3 S_2 S_1 S_0	$M = H$ Logic Functions	F_3	F_2	F_1	F_0
L L L L	$F = \overline{A}$	0	1	1	0
L L L H	$F = \overline{A + B}$	0	1	0	0
L L H L	$F = \overline{A}B$	0	0	1	0
L L H H	$F = 0$	0	0	0	0
L H L L	$F = \overline{AB}$	1	1	1	0
L H L H	$F = \overline{B}$	1	1	0	0
L H H L	$F = A \oplus B$	1	0	1	0
L H H H	$F = A\overline{B}$	1	0	0	0
H L L L	$F = \overline{A} + B$	0	1	1	1
H L L H	$F = \overline{A \oplus B}$	0	1	0	1
H L H L	$F = B$	0	0	1	1
H L H H	$F = AB$	0	0	0	1
H H L L	$F = 1$	1	1	1	1
H H L H	$F = A + \overline{B}$	1	1	0	1
H H H L	$F = A + B$	1	0	1	1
H H H H	$F = A$	1	0	0	1

Note: Assume $A = 1001$ (active-HIGH data) and $B = 0011$.

264

2. Show how the carry-in and carry-out are connected in order to cascade two 74181 ALUs to perform logic on two 8-bit numbers.

3. Draw a circuit that will add two 4-bit signed numbers using a 74181 ALU. Show the logic used on the SELECT, CARRY-IN, and MODE inputs. Since overflow is possible, show how to connect an LED to indicate if overflow occurs. (Review For Further Investigation of Experiment 10 for a discussion of overflow error.)

4. An edge-triggered D flip-flop was used for the accumulator in the circuit of Figure 28–2. Would a D latch work just as well? Explain your answer.

5. a. Assume that in Step 2 of the experiment the CLOCK pushbutton is pressed and the LEDs indicate 0000 instead of the expected 0011. A check of the D inputs reveals they are all HIGH. What are possible causes of the problem?

b. How would you go about isolating the problem?

Checkup 12

The exercises in this checkup reflect information covered in Floyd's Chapter 12, "Introduction to Microprocessor-Based Systems," and Buchla's Experiment 28.

1. The 8088 microprocessor contains an EU and a BIU. Explain what each section is for. Which section contains the ALU? The instruction register? The prefetch queue?

2. What is meant by memory-mapped I/O?

3. Which address lines are shared by the data lines for the 8088? How does the 8088 multiplex address and data information onto these lines?

4. How many bytes of memory can be addressed by the 8088 and 8086?

5. **a.** What is meant by *prefetching* instructions?

   b. Where are the prefetched instructions stored?

   c. What advantage does prefetching have?

6. For the 8088, what is the function of the ALE pulse?

7. **a.** What is meant by an interrupt?

   b. What information is transferred to the CPU by the PIC during an interrupt-driven I/O request?

8. Explain how a 20-bit physical address is formed in the 8088 using a 16-bit segment register and a 16-bit offset register.

9. Assume the code segment register in an 8088 microprocessor contains the address 1400_{16} and the instruction pointer contains the address $107B_{16}$. What is the physical address that is formed from the combination of these registers?

10. How does a DMA controller speed the transfer of data from RAM to a peripheral device?

11. What is the difference between an instruction and an operand?

12. a. What is a register?

   b. Which combination of registers in the 8086 points to the next instruction?

13. What determines the type of operation performed by the ALU?

14. a. What is a status flag?

   b. How is a status flag used in a program?

Appendix A

Manufacturers' Data Sheets

Guide to Bipolar Logic Device Families

Since the introduction of the first saturating logic bipolar integrated circuit family (DM54/DM74), there have been many developments in the process and manufacturing technologies as well as circuit design techniques which have produced new generations (families) of bipolar logic devices. Each generation had advantages and disadvantages over the previous generations. Today National provides six bipolar logic families.

TTL	(DM54/DM74)
Low Power	(DM54L/DM74L)
Low Power Schottky	(DM54LS/DM74LS)
Advanced Low Power Schottky	(DM54ALS/DM74ALS)
Schottky	(DM54S/DM74S)
Advanced Schottky	(DM54AS/DM74AS)

TTL LOGIC (DM54/DM74)

TTL logic was the first saturating logic integrated circuit family introduced, thus setting the standard for all the future families. It offers a combination of speed, power consumption, output source and sink capabilities suitable for most applications. This family offers the greatest variety of logic functions. The basic gate (see *Figure 1*) features a multiple-emitter input configuration for fast switching speeds, active pull-up output to provide a low driving source impedance which also improves noise margin and device speed. Typical device power dissipation is 10 mW per gate and the typical propagation delay is 10 ns when driving a 15 pF/400Ω load.

LOW POWER (DM54L/DM74L)

The low power family has essentially the same circuit configuration as the TTL devices. The resistor values, however, are increased by nearly tenfold, which results in tremendous reduction of power dissipation to less than 1/10 of the TTL family. Because of this reduction of power, the device speed is sacrificed. The propagation delays are increased threefold. These devices have a typical power dissipation of 1 mW per gate and typical propagation delay of 33 ns, making this family ideal for applications where power consumption and heat dissipation are the critical parameters.

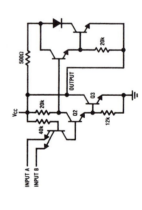

FIGURE 1. DM5400/DM7400

FIGURE 2. DM54L00/DM74L00

LOW POWER SCHOTTKY (DM54LS/DM74LS)

The low power Schottky family features a combined fivefold reduction in current and power when compared to the TTL family. Gold doping commonly used in the TTL devices reduces switching times at the expense of current gain. The LS process overcomes this limitation by using a surface barrier diode (Schottky diode) in the baker clamp configuration between the base and collector junction of the transistor. In this way, the transistor is never fully saturated and recovers quickly when base drive is interrupted. Using shallower diffusion and soft-saturating Schottky diode clamped transistors, higher current gains and faster turn-on times are obtained. The LS circuits do not use the multi-emitter inputs. They use diode-transistor inputs which are faster and give increased input breakdown voltage; the input threshold is ~0.1V lower than TTL. Another commonly used input is the vertical substrate PNP transistor. In addition to fast switching, it exhibits very high impedance at both the high and low input states, and the transistor's current gain (B) significantly reduces input loading and provides better output performance. The output structure is also modified with a Darlington transistor pair to increase speed and improve drive capability. An active pull-down transistor (Q3) is incorporated to yield a symmetrical transfer characteristic (squaring network). This family achieves circuit performance exceeding the standard TTL family at fractions of its power consumption. The typical device power dissipation is 2 mW per gate and typical propagation delay is 10 ns while driving a 15 pF/2 kΩ load.

SCHOTTKY (DM54S/DM74S)

This family features the high switching speed of unsaturated bipolar emitter-coupled logic, but consumes more power than standard TTL devices. To achieve this high speed, the Schottky barrier diode is incorporated as a clamp to divert the excess base current and to prevent the transistor from reaching deep saturation. The Schottky gate input and internal circuitry resemble the standard TTL gate except the resistor values are about one-half the TTL value. The output section has a Darlington transistor pair for pull-up and an active pull-down squaring network. This family has power dissipation of 20 mW per gate and propagation delays three times as fast as TTL devices with the average time of 3 ns while driving 15 pF/280Ω load.

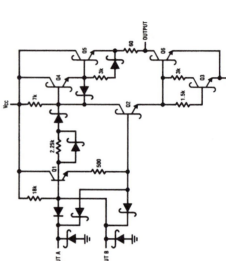

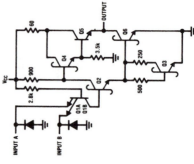

FIGURE 3. DM54LS00/DM74LS00

FIGURE 4. DM54S00/DM74S00

270

Reprinted with permission of National Semiconductor Corporation

ADVANCED LOW POWER SCHOTTKY (DM54ALS/DM74ALS)

The advanced low power Schottky family is one of the most advanced TTL families. It delivers twice the data handling efficiency and still provides up to 50% reduction in power consumption compared to the LS family. This is possible because of a new fabrication process where components are isolated by a selectively grown thick-oxide rather than the P-N junction used in conventional processes. This refined process, coupled with improved circuit design techniques, yields smaller component geometries, shallower diffusions, and lower junction capacitances. This enables the devices to have increased f_T in excess of 5 GHz and improved switching speeds by a factor of two, while offering much lower operating currents.

In addition to the pin-to-pin compatibility of the ALS family, a large number of MSI and LSI functions are introduced in the high density 24-pin 300 mil DIP. These devices offer

the designers greater cost effectiveness with the advantages of reduced component count, reduced circuit board real-estate, increased functional capabilities per device and improved speed-power performance.

The basic ALS gate schematic is quite similar to the LS gate. It consists of either the PNP transistor or the diode inputs, Darlington transistor pair pull-up and active pull-down (squaring network) at the output. Since the shallower diffusions and thinner oxides will cause ALS devices to be more susceptible to damage from electro-static discharge, additional protection via a base-emitter shorted transistor is included at the input for rapid discharge of high voltage static electricity. Furthermore, the inputs and outputs are clamped by Schottky diodes to prevent them from swinging excessively below ground level. A buried N+ guard ring around all input and output structures prevents crosstalk. The ALS family has a typical power dissipation of 1 mW per gate and typical propagation delay time of 4 ns into a 50 pF/2 kΩ load.

FIGURE 5. DM54ALS00/DM74ALS00

ADVANCED SCHOTTKY (DM54AS/DM74AS)

This family of devices is designed to meet the needs of the system designers who require the ultimate in speed. Utilizing Schottky barrier diode clamped transistors with shallower diffusions and advanced oxide-isolation fabrication techniques, the AS family achieves the fastest propagation delay that bipolar technology can offer. The AS family has virtually the same circuit configuration as the ALS family. It has PNP transistor or diode inputs with electrostatic protection base-emitter shorted transistors. The output totempole consists of a Darlington pair transistor pull-up and an active pull-down squaring network. The inputs and outputs are Schottky clamped to attenuate critical transmission line reflections. In addition, the circuit contains the "Miller Killer" network at the output section to improve output rise time and reduce power consumption during switching at high repetition rates. The AS family yields typical power dissipation of 7 mW per gate and propagation delay time of 1.5 ns when driving a 50 pF/2 kΩ load.

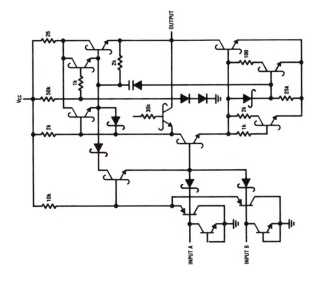

FIGURE 6. DM54AS00/DM74AS00

SELECTING A FAMILY

Two factors should be considered when choosing a logic family for application, speed and power consumption. New logic families were created to improve the speed or lower the power consumption of the previous families. The following tables rate each family.

Speed	Power Consumption
Fastest	Low
AS	L
S	ALS
ALS	LS
LS	AS
TTL	TTL
L	S
Slowest	High

Bipolar Logic Family Output Source/Sink Capability: 54/74 Families

Output			TTL	L-TTL	LS	ALS	S	AS	Units
Standard	Mil	I_{OH}	−0.4	−0.2	−0.4	−0.4	−1	−2	mA
	Com	I_{OH}	−0.4	−0.2	−0.4	−0.4	−1	−2	mA
	Mil	I_{OL}	16	2	4	4	20	20	mA
	Com	I_{OL}	16	3.6	8	8	20	20	mA
Buffered	Mil	I_{OH}	−0.8	−0.2	−0.4	−1	−1	−12	mA
	Com	I_{OH}	−0.8	−0.2	−0.4	−2.6	−1	−15	mA
	Mil	I_{OL}	16	2	4	12	20	32	mA
	Com	I_{OL}	16	3.6	8	24	20	48	mA
Bus Driver	Mil	I_{OH}	−2	N/A	−1	−12	−2	−48	mA
	Com	I_{OH}	−5.2	N/A	−2.6	−15	−6.5	−48	mA
	Mil	I_{OL}	32	N/A	12	12	20	40	mA
	Com	I_{OL}	32	N/A	24	24-48	20	48	mA

Fan-In and Fan-Out

		TTL	L-TTL	LS	ALS	S	AS	Units
Input Load:	High	1	0.25	0.5	0.5	1.25	0.5	U. L.
	Low	1	0.1125	0.225	0.125	1.25	0.3125	U. L.
Output Drive:	High	10	2.25	5	5	12.5	12.5	U. L.
	Low	10	5	10	10	25	50	U. L.

Note: UNIT LOAD (U. L.) Standard is referenced with respect to standard TTL device loading. It is defined as:
1 U. L. = 40 μA (HIGH STATE)
1 U. L. = 1.6 mA (LOW STATE)

Bipolar Logic Family Electrical Characteristics Over Operating Temperatures

		TTL	L-TTL	LS	ALS	S	AS	Units
DM5400/DM7400								
2-Input NAND	t_{PLH}*	11	35	8	4	3	2.5	ns
	t_{PHL}*	7	31	8	4	3	1.5	ns
	t_r*,	12	66	13	10	6	5	ns
	t_f*	5	30	3	6	3	3	ns
Mil/Com	I_{OH}	−400	−200	−400	−400	−1000	−2000	μA
	I_{OL}	16	2/3.6	4/8	4/8	20	20	mA
	I_{IH}	40	10	20	20	50	20	μA
	I_{IL}	−1.6	−0.18	−0.36	−0.20	−2	−0.50	mA
Min	I_{OS}	−20	−3	−20	−30	−40	−30	mA
Max	I_{OS}	−100	−15	−100	−112	−100	−112	mA
	I_{CCH}	8	0.8	1.6	0.85	16	3.2	mA
	I_{CCL}	22	2.04	4.4	3.0	36	16.1	mA
Mil	V_{OH}	2.4	2.4	2.5	$V_{CC}-2$	2.5	$V_{CC}-2$	V
Com	V_{OH}	2.4	2.4	2.7	$V_{CC}-2$	2.7	$V_{CC}-2$	V
Mil	V_{OL}	0.4	0.3	0.4	0.4	0.5	0.5	V
Com	V_{OL}	0.4	0.4	0.5	0.5	0.5	0.5	V
Mil	V_{IH}	2	2	2	2	2	2	V
	V_{IL}	0.8	0.7	0.7	0.8	0.8	0.8	V
Com	V_{IL}	0.8	0.7	0.8	0.8	0.8	0.8	V
	V_I	−1.5	N/A	−1.5	−1.5	−1.2	−1.2	V
Mil	NM-H	400	400	500	500	500	500	mV
Com	NM-H	400	400	700	700	700	700	mV
Mil	NM-L	400	400	300	400	400	300	mV
Com	NM-L	400	300	300	300	300	300	mV
Gate Power × Delay Product		100	20	20	4	60	30	pJ
DM5474/DM7474								
D Flip-Flop (CLK to Q)	t_{PLH}	14	50	17	5	8	6	ns
	t_{PHL}	20	60	22	8	9	6	ns
(PS or CLR to Q)	t_{PLH}*	14	40	17	7	6	4.5	ns
	t_{PHL}	20	60	22	10	12	6	ns
(CLK HI)	t_W	30	75	25	12	8	4	ns
(PS or CLR LOW)	t_W	30	75	20	15	9	4	ns
	t_{SET-UP}	20	50	25	15	3	3/2	ns
	t_{HOLD}	5	15	0	0	2	2/1	ns
(PS or	t_r*	13	64	9	17	4	5	ns
	t_f*	6	19	6	9	3	3	ns
	f_{MAX}*	25	11	33	34	95	125	MHz
Mil/Com	I_{OH}	−400	−200	−400	−400	−1000	−2000	μA
(CLK/D)	I_{OL}	16	2/3.6	4/8	4/8	20	20	mA
(PS/CLR)	I_{IH}	80/40	20/10	20	20	100/50	20	μA
(CLK/D)	I_{IH}	40/120	20/30	40	40	100/150	40	μA
(PS/CLR)	I_{IL}	−3.2/−1.6	−0.36/−0.18	−0.4	−0.2	−4/−2	−0.5	mA
	I_{IL}	−1.6/−3.2	−0.18/−0.36	−0.8	−0.4	−4/−6	−1.0	mA
Min	I_{OS}	−20/−18	−3	−20	−30	−40	−30	mA
Max	I_{OS}	−55	−15	−100	−112	−100	−112	mA
	I_{CC}	15	3	8	4	50	16	mA
Mil	V_{OH}	2.4	2.4	2.5	$V_{CC}-2$	2.5	$V_{CC}-2$	V
Com	V_{OH}	2.4	2.4	2.7	$V_{CC}-2$	2.7	$V_{CC}-2$	V
Mil	V_{OL}	0.4	0.3	0.4	0.4	0.5	0.5	V
Com	V_{OL}	0.4	0.4	0.5	0.5	0.5	0.5	V
Mil/Com	V_{IH}	2	2	2	2	2	2	V
	V_{IL}	0.8	0.7	0.7/0.8	0.8	0.8	0.8	V
	V_I	−1.5	N/A	−1.5	−1.5	−1.2	−1.2	V
Mil	NM-H	400	400	500	500	500	500	mV
Com	NM-H	400	400	700	700	700	700	mV
Mil	NM-L	400	400	400	400	300	300	mV
Com	NM-L	400	300	300	300	300	300	mV

Note: See Test Waveforms in this section for loading conditions. t_r and t_f are measured from 10% to 90% of waveform.
Note: NM-H is noise margin high. NM-L is noise margin low.
*Typical values. Other values are limit values.

National Semiconductor

DM5400/DM7400 Quad 2-Input NAND Gates

General Description

This device contains four independent gates each of which performs the logic NAND function.

Absolute Maximum Ratings (Note 1)

Supply Voltage	7V
Input Voltage	5.5V
Storage Temperature Range	−65°C to 150°C

Note 1: The "Absolute Maximum Ratings" are those values beyond which the safety of the device can not be guaranteed. The device should not be operated at these limits. The parametric values defined in the "Electrical Characteristics" table are not guaranteed at the absolute maximum ratings. The "Recommended Operating Conditions" table will define the conditions for actual device operation.

Connection Diagram

Dual-In-Line Package

DM5400 (J)   DM7400 (N)

TL/F/6613-1

Function Table

$Y = \overline{AB}$

Inputs		Output
A	B	Y
L	L	H
L	H	H
H	L	H
H	H	L

H = High Logic Level
L = Low Logic Level

Recommended Operating Conditions

Symbol	Parameter	DM5400			DM7400			Units
		Min	Nom	Max	Min	Nom	Max	
V_{CC}	Supply Voltage	4.5	5	5.5	4.75	5	5.25	V
V_{IH}	High Level Input Voltage	2			2			V
V_{IL}	Low Level Input Voltage			0.8			0.8	V
I_{OH}	High Level Output Current			−0.4			−0.4	mA
I_{OL}	Low Level Output Current			16			16	mA
T_A	Free Air Operating Temperature	−55		125	0		70	°C

Electrical Characteristics over recommended operating free air temperature (unless otherwise noted)

Symbol	Parameter	Conditions	Min	Typ (Note 1)	Max	Units
V_I	Input Clamp Voltage	V_{CC} = Min, I_I = −12 mA			−1.5	V
V_{OH}	High Level Output Voltage	V_{CC} = Min, I_{OH} = Max, V_{IL} = Max	2.4	3.4		V
V_{OL}	Low Level Output Voltage	V_{CC} = Min, I_{OL} = Max, V_{IH} = Min		0.2	0.4	V
I_I	Input Current @ Max Input Voltage	V_{CC} = Max, V_I = 5.5V			1	mA
I_{IH}	High Level Input Current	V_{CC} = Max, V_I = 2.4V			40	μA
I_{IL}	Low Level Input Current	V_{CC} = Max, V_I = 0.4V			−1.6	mA
I_{OS}	Short Circuit Output Current	V_{CC} = Max (Note 2) DM54 / DM74	−20 / −18		−55 / −55	mA
I_{CCH}	Supply Current With Outputs High	V_{CC} = Max		4	8	mA
I_{CCL}	Supply Current With Outputs Low	V_{CC} = Max		12	22	mA

Note 1: All typicals are at V_{CC} = 5V, T_A = 25°C.
Note 2: Not more than one output should be shorted at a time.

Switching Characteristics at V_{CC} = 5V and T_A = 25°C (See Section 1 for Test Waveforms and Output Load)

Parameter	Conditions	Min	Typ	Max	Units
	C_L = 15 pF, R_L = 400Ω				
t_{PLH} Propagation Delay Time Low to High Level Output			12	22	ns
t_{PHL} Propagation Delay Time High to Low Level Output			7	15	ns

National Semiconductor

DM5402/DM7402 Quad 2-Input NOR Gates

General Description

This device contains four independent gates each of which performs the logic NOR function.

Absolute Maximum Ratings (Note 1)

Supply Voltage	7V
Input Voltage	5.5V
Storage Temperature Range	−65°C to 150°C

Note 1: The "Absolute Maximum Ratings" are those values beyond which the safety of the device can not be guaranteed. The device should not be operated at these limits. The parametric values defined in the "Electrical Characteristics" table are not guaranteed at the absolute maximum ratings. The "Recommended Operating Conditions" table will define the conditions for actual device operation.

Function Table

$Y = \overline{A + B}$

Inputs		Output
A	B	Y
L	L	H
L	H	L
H	L	L
H	H	L

H = High Logic Level
L = Low Logic Level

Connection Diagram

Dual-In-Line Package

TL/F/6492-1

DM5402 (J)   DM7402 (N)

Recommended Operating Conditions

Symbol	Parameter	DM5401			DM7401			Units
		Min	Nom	Max	Min	Nom	Max	
V_{CC}	Supply Voltage	4.5	5	5.5	4.75	5	5.25	V
V_{IH}	High Level Input Voltage	2			2			V
V_{IL}	Low Level Input Voltage			0.8			0.8	V
V_{OH}	High Level Output Voltage			5.5			5.5	V
I_{OL}	Low Level Output Current			16			16	mA
T_A	Free Air Operating Temperature	−55		125	0		70	°C

Electrical Characteristics over recommended operating free air temperature (unless otherwise noted)

Symbol	Parameter	Conditions	Min	Typ (Note 1)	Max	Units
V_I	Input Clamp Voltage	V_{CC} = Min, I_I = −12 mA			−1.5	V
I_{CEX}	High Level Output Current	V_{CC} = Min, V_O = 5.5V, V_{IL} = Max			250	μA
V_{OL}	Low Level Output Voltage	V_{CC} = Min, I_{OL} = Max, V_{IH} = Min		0.2	0.4	V
I_I	Input Current @ Max Input Voltage	V_{CC} = Max, V_I = 5.5V			1	mA
I_{IH}	High Level Input Current	V_{CC} = Max, V_I = 2.4V			40	μA
I_{IL}	Low Level Input Current	V_{CC} = Max, V_I = 0.4V			−1.6	mA
I_{CCH}	Supply Current With Outputs High	V_{CC} = Max		4	8	mA
I_{CCL}	Supply Current With Outputs Low	V_{CC} = Max		12	22	mA

Switching Characteristics at V_{CC} = 5V and T_A = 25°C (See Section 1 for Test Waveforms and Output Load)

$C_L = 15$ pF
$R_L = 4$ kΩ (t_{PLH})
$R_L = 400$ Ω (t_{PHL})

Parameter	Conditions	Min	Typ	Max	Units
t_{PLH} Propagation Delay Time Low to High Level Output			35	45	ns
t_{PHL} Propagation Delay Time High to Low Level Output			8	15	ns

Note 1: All typicals are at V_{CC} = 5V, T_A = 25°C.

National Semiconductor

DM5404/DM7404 Hex Inverting Gates

General Description

This device contains six independent gates each of which performs the logic INVERT function.

Absolute Maximum Ratings (Note 1)

Supply Voltage	7V
Input Voltage	5.5V
Storage Temperature Range	−65°C to 150°C

Note 1: The "Absolute Maximum Ratings" are those values beyond which the safety of the device can not be guaranteed. The device should not be operated at these limits. The parametric values defined in the "Electrical Characteristics" table are not guaranteed at the absolute maximum ratings. The "Recommended Operating Conditions" table will define the conditions for actual device operation.

Connection Diagram

Dual-In-Line Package

TL/F/6494-1

DM5404 (J) DM7404 (N)

Function Table

$Y = \bar{A}$

Input	Output
A	Y
L	H
H	L

H = High Logic Level
L = Low Logic Level

Recommended Operating Conditions

		DM5403			DM7403			Units
Symbol	Parameter	Min	Nom	Max	Min	Nom	Max	
V_{CC}	Supply Voltage	4.5	5	5.5	4.75	5	5.25	V
V_{IH}	High Level Input Voltage	2			2			V
V_{IL}	Low Level Input Voltage			0.8			0.8	V
V_{OH}	High Level Output Voltage			5.5			5.5	V
I_{OL}	Low Level Output Current			16			16	mA
T_A	Free Air Operating Temperature	−55		125	0		70	°C

Electrical Characteristics over recommended operating free air temperature (unless otherwise noted)

Symbol	Parameter	Conditions	Min	Typ (Note 1)	Max	Units
V_I	Input Clamp Voltage	V_{CC} = Min, I_I = −12 mA			−1.5	V
I_{CEX}	High Level Output Current	V_{CC} = Min, V_O = 5.5V, V_{IL} = Max			250	μA
V_{OL}	Low Level Output Voltage	V_{CC} = Min, I_{OL} = Max, V_{IH} = Min		0.2	0.4	V
I_I	Input Current @ Max Input Voltage	V_{CC} = Max, V_I = 5.5V			1	mA
I_{IH}	High Level Input Current	V_{CC} = Max, V_I = 2.4V			40	μA
I_{IL}	Low Level Input Current	V_{CC} = Max, V_I = 0.4V			−1.6	mA
I_{CCH}	Supply Current With Outputs High	V_{CC} = Max.		4	8	mA
I_{CCL}	Supply Current With Outputs Low	V_{CC} = Max		12	22	mA

Switching Characteristics at V_{CC} = 5V and T_A = 25°C (See Section 1 for Test Waveforms and Output Load)

Parameter	Conditions	C_L = 15 pF R_L = 4 KΩ (t_{PLH}) R_L = 400Ω (t_{PHL})			Units
		Min	Typ	Max	
t_{PLH} Propagation Delay Time Low to High Level Output			35	45	ns
t_{PHL} Propagation Delay Time High to Low Level Output			8	15	ns

Note 1: All typicals are at V_{CC} = 5V, T_A = 25°C.

![National Semiconductor Corporation]

DM5405/DM7405 Hex Inverters with Open-Collector Outputs

General Description

This device contains six independent gates each of which performs the logic INVERT function. The open-collector outputs require external pull-up resistors for proper logical operation.

Pull-Up Resistor Equations

$$R_{MAX} = \frac{V_{CC}(Min) - V_{OH}}{N_1(I_{OH}) + N_2(I_{IH})}$$

$$R_{MIN} = \frac{V_{CC}(Max) - V_{OL}}{I_{OL} - N_3(I_{IL})}$$

Where: $N_1(I_{OH})$ = total maximum output high current for all outputs tied to pull-up resistor

$N_2(I_{IH})$ = total maximum input high current for all inputs tied to pull-up resistor

$N_3(I_{IL})$ = total maximum input low current for all inputs tied to pull-up resistor

Connection Diagram

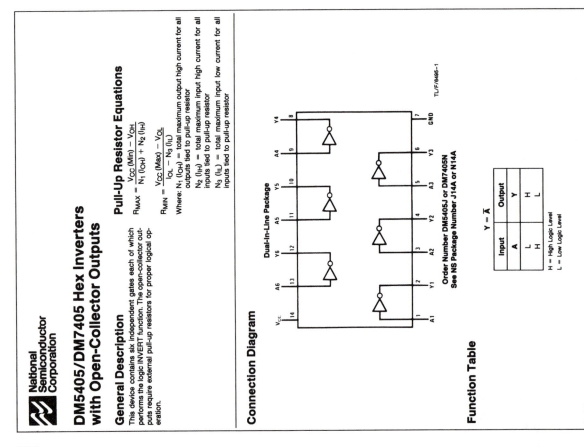

Dual-In-Line Package

Order Number DM5405J or DM7405N
See NS Package Number J14A or N14A

TL/F/6496-1

Function Table

$Y = \overline{A}$

Input	Output
A	Y
L	H
H	L

H = High Logic Level
L = Low Logic Level

Absolute Maximum Ratings (Note)

Specifications for Military/Aerospace products are not contained in this datasheet. Refer to the associated reliability electrical test specifications document.

Supply Voltage	7V
Input Voltage	5.5V
Output Voltage	7V
Operating Free Air Temperature Range	
DM54	−55°C to +125°C
DM74	0°C to +70°C
Storage Temperature Range	−65°C to +150°C

Note: The "Absolute Maximum Ratings" are those values beyond which the safety of the device cannot be guaranteed. The device should not be operated at these limits. The parametric values defined in the "Electrical Characteristics" table are not guaranteed at the absolute maximum ratings. The "Recommended Operating Conditions" table will define the conditions for actual device operation.

Recommended Operating Conditions

Symbol	Parameter	DM5405 Min	DM5405 Nom	DM5405 Max	DM7405 Min	DM7405 Nom	DM7405 Max	Units
V_{CC}	Supply Voltage	4.5	5	5.5	4.75	5	5.25	V
V_{IH}	High Level Input Voltage	2			2			V
V_{IL}	Low Level Input Voltage			0.8			0.8	V
V_{OH}	High Level Output Voltage			5.5			5.5	V
I_{OL}	Low Level Output Current			16			16	mA
T_A	Free Air Operating Temperature	−55		125	0		70	°C

Electrical Characteristics

over recommended operating free air temperature range (unless otherwise noted)

Symbol	Parameter	Conditions	Min	Typ (Note 1)	Max	Units
V_I	Input Clamp Voltage	$V_{CC} = Min, I_I = -12$ mA			−1.5	V
I_{CEX}	High Level Output Current	$V_{CC} = Min, V_O = 5.5V$ $V_{IL} = Max$			250	μA
V_{OL}	Low Level Output Voltage	$V_{CC} = Min, I_{OL} = Max$ $V_{IH} = Min$		0.2	0.4	V
I_I	Input Current @ Max Input Voltage	$V_{CC} = Max, V_I = 5.5V$			1	mA
I_{IH}	High Level Input Current	$V_{CC} = Max, V_I = 2.4V$			40	μA
I_{IL}	Low Level Input Current	$V_{CC} = Max, V_I = 0.4V$			−1.6	mA
I_{CCH}	Supply Current with Outputs High	$V_{CC} = Max$		6	12	mA
I_{CCL}	Supply Current with Outputs Low	$V_{CC} = Max$		18	33	mA

Switching Characteristics at $V_{CC} = 5V$ and $T_A = 25°C$ (See Section 1 for Test Waveforms and Output Load)

Symbol	Parameter	Conditions	Min	Max	Units
t_{PLH}	Propagation Delay Time Low to High Level Output	$C_L = 15$ pF $R_L = 4$ kΩ (t_{PLH}) $R_L = 400Ω$ (t_{PHL})		55	ns
t_{PHL}	Propagation Delay Time High to Low Level Output			15	ns

Note 1: All typicals are at $V_{CC} = 5V$, $T_A = 25°C$.

TYPES SN5408, SN54LS08, SN54S08, SN7408, SN74LS08, SN74S08
QUADRUPLE 2-INPUT POSITIVE-AND GATES

REVISED DECEMBER 1983

- **Package Options Include Both Plastic and Ceramic Chip Carriers in Addition to Plastic and Ceramic DIPs**

- **Dependable Texas Instruments Quality and Reliability**

description

These devices contain four independent 2-input AND gates.

The SN5408, SN54LS08, and SN54S08 are characterized for operation over the full military temperature range of −55°C to 125°C. The SN7408, SN74LS08 and SN74S08 are characterized for operation from 0°C to 70°C.

SN5408, SN54LS08, SN54S08 . . . J OR W PACKAGE
SN7408 . . . J OR N PACKAGE
SN74LS08, SN74S08 . . . D, J OR N PACKAGE

(TOP VIEW)

1A [1	14] V_CC
1B [2	13] 4B
1Y [3	12] 4A
2A [4	11] 4Y
2B [5	10] 3B
2Y [6	9] 3A
GND [7	8] 3Y

SN54LS08, SN54S08 . . . FK PACKAGE
SN74LS08, SN74S08 . . . FN PACKAGE

(TOP VIEW)

NC — No internal connection

FUNCTION TABLE (each gate)

INPUTS		OUTPUT
A	B	Y
H	H	H
L	X	L
X	L	L

logic diagram (each gate)

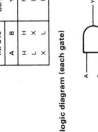

positive logic

$$Y = A \cdot B \text{ or } Y = \overline{\overline{A} + \overline{B}}$$

---

recommended operating conditions

		SN5408			SN7408			UNIT
		MIN	NOM	MAX	MIN	NOM	MAX	
V_CC	Supply voltage	4.5	5	5.5	4.75	5	5.25	V
V_IH	High-level input voltage	2			2			V
V_IL	Low-level input voltage			0.8			0.8	V
I_OH	High-level output current			−0.8			−0.8	mA
I_OL	Low-level output current			16			16	mA
T_A	Operating free-air temperature	−55		125	0		70	°C

electrical characteristics over recommended operating free-air temperature range (unless otherwise noted)

PARAMETER	TEST CONDITIONS†	SN5408			SN7408			UNIT
		MIN	TYP‡	MAX	MIN	TYP‡	MAX	
V_IK	V_CC = MIN, I_I = −12 mA			−1.5			−1.5	V
V_OH	V_CC = MIN, V_IH = 2 V, I_OH = −0.8 mA	2.4	3.4		2.4	3.4		V
V_OL	V_CC = MIN, V_IL = 0.8 V, I_OL = 16 mA		0.2	0.4		0.2	0.4	V
I_I	V_CC = MAX, V_I = 5.5 V			1			1	mA
I_IH	V_CC = MAX, V_I = 2.4 V			40			40	µA
I_IL	V_CC = MAX, V_I = 0.4 V			−1.6			−1.6	mA
I_OS§	V_CC = MAX	−20		−55	−18		−55	mA
I_CCH	V_CC = MAX, V_I = 4.5 V		11	21		11	21	mA
I_CCL	V_CC = MAX, V_I = 0 V		20	33		20	33	mA

† For conditions shown as MIN or MAX, use the appropriate value specified under recommended operating conditions.
‡ All typical values are at V_CC = 5 V, T_A = 25°C.
§ Not more than one output should be shorted at a time.

switching characteristics, V_CC = 5 V, T_A = 25°C (see note 2)

PARAMETER	FROM (INPUT)	TO (OUTPUT)	TEST CONDITIONS	MIN	TYP	MAX	UNIT
t_PLH	A or B	Y	R_L = 400 Ω, C_L = 15 pF		17.5	27	ns
t_PHL					12	19	ns

NOTE 2: See General Information Section for load circuits and voltage waveforms.

TEXAS INSTRUMENTS
POST OFFICE BOX 225012 • DALLAS, TEXAS 75265

DM5410/DM7410 Triple 3-Input NAND Gates

General Description

This device contains three independent gates each of which performs the logic NAND function.

Absolute Maximum Ratings (Note 1)

Supply Voltage	7V
Input Voltage	5.5V
Storage Temperature Range	−65°C to 150°C

Note 1: The "Absolute Maximum Ratings" are those values beyond which the safety of the device can not be guaranteed. The device should not be operated at these limits. The parametric values defined in the "Electrical Characteristics" table are not guaranteed at the absolute maximum ratings. The "Recommended Operating Conditions" table will define the conditions for actual device operation.

Connection Diagram

Dual-In-Line Package

DM5410 (J)   DM7410 (N)

TL/F/6500-1

Function Table

$Y = \overline{ABC}$

Inputs			Output
A	B	C	Y
X	X	L	H
X	L	X	H
L	X	X	H
H	H	H	L

H = High Logic Level
L = Low Logic Level
X = Either Low or High Logic Level

Recommended Operating Conditions

Symbol	Parameter	DM5409			DM7409			Units
		Min	Nom	Max	Min	Nom	Max	
V_{CC}	Supply Voltage	4.5	5	5.5	4.75	5	5.25	V
V_{IH}	High Level Input Voltage	2			2			V
V_{IL}	Low Level Input Voltage			0.8			0.8	V
V_{OH}	High Level Output Voltage			5.5			5.5	V
I_{OL}	Low Level Output Current			16			16	mA
T_A	Free Air Operating Temperature	−55		125	0		70	°C

Electrical Characteristics over recommended operating free air temperature (unless otherwise noted)

Symbol	Parameter	Conditions	Min	Typ (Note 1)	Max	Units
V_I	Input Clamp Voltage	V_{CC} = Min, I_I = −12 mA			−1.5	V
I_{CEX}	High Level Output Current	V_{CC} = Min, V_O = 5.5V, V_{IH} = Min			250	µA
V_{OL}	Low Level Output Voltage	V_{CC} = Min, I_{OL} = Max, V_{IL} = Max		0.2	0.4	V
I_I	Input Current @ Max Input Voltage	V_{CC} = Max, V_I = 5.5V			1	mA
I_{IH}	High Level Input Current	V_{CC} = Max, V_I = 2.4V			40	µA
I_{IL}	Low Level Input Current	V_{CC} = Max, V_I = 0.4V			−1.6	mA
I_{CCH}	Supply Current With Outputs High	V_{CC} = Max		11	21	mA
I_{CCL}	Supply Current With Outputs Low	V_{CC} = Max		20	33	mA

Switching Characteristics at V_{CC} = 5V and T_A = 25°C (See Section 1 for Test Waveforms and Output Load)

Parameter	Conditions	C_L = 15 pF R_L = 400Ω			Units
		Min	Typ	Max	
t_{PLH} Propagation Delay Time Low to High Level Output			21	32	ns
t_{PHL} Propagation Delay Time High to Low Level Output			16	24	ns

Note 1: All typicals are at V_{CC} = 5V, T_A = 25°C.

TYPES SN5412, SN54LS12, SN7412, SN74LS12
TRIPLE 3-INPUT POSITIVE-NAND GATES WITH OPEN-COLLECTOR OUTPUTS

REVISED DECEMBER 1983

- **Package Options Include Both Plastic and Ceramic Chip Carriers in Addition to Plastic and Ceramic DIPs**
- **Dependable Texas Instruments Quality and Reliability**

description

These devices contain three independent 3-input NAND gates with open-collector outputs. The open-collector outputs require pull-up resistors to perform correctly. They may be connected to other open-collector outputs to implement active-low wired-OR or active-high wired-AND functions. Open-collector devices are often used to generate higher V_{OH} levels.

The SN5412 and SN54LS12 are characterized for operation over the full military range of $-55°C$ to $125°C$. The SN7412 and SN74LS12 are characterized for operation from $0°C$ to $70°C$.

FUNCTION TABLE (each gate)

INPUTS A	B	C	OUTPUT Y
H	H	H	L
L	X	X	H
X	L	X	H
X	X	L	H

logic diagram (each gate)

positive logic

$$Y = \overline{A \cdot B \cdot C} \text{ or } Y = \overline{A} + \overline{B} + \overline{C}$$

SN5412, SN54LS12 . . . J OR W PACKAGE
SN7412 . . . J OR N PACKAGE
SN74LS12 . . . D, J OR N PACKAGE
(TOP VIEW)

1A	1	14 VCC
1B	2	13 1C
2A	3	12 1Y
2B	4	11 3C
2C	5	10 3B
2Y	6	9 3A
GND	7	8 3Y

SN54LS12 . . . FK PACKAGE
SN74LS12 . . . FN PACKAGE
(TOP VIEW)

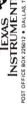

NC – No internal connection

---

recommended operating conditions

PARAMETER		SN54LS12 MIN	NOM	MAX	SN74LS12 MIN	NOM	MAX	UNIT
V_{CC}	Supply voltage	4.5	5	5.5	4.75	5	5.25	V
V_{IH}	High-level input voltage	2			2			V
V_{IL}	Low-level input voltage			0.7			0.8	V
V_{OH}	High-level output voltage			5.5			5.5	V
I_{OL}	Low-level output current			4			8	mA
T_A	Operating free-air temperature	-55		125	0		70	°C

electrical characteristics over recommended operating free-air temperature range (unless otherwise noted)

PARAMETER	TEST CONDITIONS†	SN54LS12 MIN	TYP‡	MAX	SN74LS12 MIN	TYP‡	MAX	UNIT
V_{IK}	$V_{CC} = MIN$, $I_I = -18\,mA$			-1.5			-1.5	V
I_{OH}	$V_{CC} = MIN$, $V_{IL} = MAX$, $V_{OH} = 5.5\,V$			0.1			0.1	mA
V_{OL}	$V_{CC} = MIN$, $V_{IH} = 2\,V$, $I_{OL} = 4\,mA$		0.25	0.4		0.25	0.4	V
	$V_{CC} = MIN$, $V_{IH} = 2\,V$, $I_{OL} = 8\,mA$					0.35	0.5	
I_I	$V_{CC} = MAX$, $V_I = 7\,V$			0.1			0.1	mA
I_{IH}	$V_{CC} = MAX$, $V_I = 2.7\,V$			20			20	µA
I_{IL}	$V_{CC} = MAX$, $V_I = 0.4\,V$			-0.4			-0.4	mA
I_{CCH}	$V_{CC} = MAX$, $V_I = 0\,V$		0.7	1.4		0.7	1.4	mA
I_{CCL}	$V_{CC} = MAX$, $V_I = 4.5\,V$		1.8	3.3		1.8	3.3	mA

† For conditions shown as MIN or MAX, use the appropriate value specified under recommended operating conditions.
‡ All typical values are at $V_{CC} = 5\,V$, $T_A = 25°C$.

switching characteristics, $V_{CC} = 5\,V$, $T_A = 25°C$ (see note 2)

PARAMETER	FROM (INPUT)	TO (OUTPUT)	TEST CONDITIONS	MIN	TYP	MAX	UNIT
t_{PLH}	A, B or C	Y	$R_L = 2\,k\Omega$, $C_L = 15\,pF$		17	32	ns
t_{PHL}					15	28	ns

NOTE 2: See General Information Section for load circuits and voltage waveforms.

TEXAS INSTRUMENTS
POST OFFICE BOX 225012 ● DALLAS, TEXAS 75265

Recommended Operating Conditions

Sym	Parameter	DM5417 Min	DM5417 Nom	DM5417 Max	DM7417 Min	DM7417 Nom	DM7417 Max	Units
V_{CC}	Supply Voltage	4.5	5	5.5	4.75	5	5.25	V
V_{IH}	High Level Input Voltage	2			2			V
V_{IL}	Low Level Input Voltage			0.8			0.8	V
V_{OH}	High Level Output Voltage			15			15	V
I_{OL}	Low Level Output Current			30			40	mA
T_A	Free Air Operating Temperature	-55		125	0		70	°C

Electrical Characteristics over recommended operating free air temperature (unless otherwise noted)

Sym	Parameter	Conditions	Min	Typ (Note 1)	Max	Units
V_I	Input Clamp Voltage	V_{CC} = Min, I_I = -12 mA			-1.5	V
I_{CEX}	High Level Output Current	V_{CC} = Min, V_O = 15V V_{IH} = Min			250	μA
V_{OL}	Low Level Output Voltage	V_{CC} = Min, I_{OL} = Max V_{IL} = Max			0.7	V
		I_{OL} = 16 mA V_{CC} = Min			0.4	
I_I	Input Current @ Max Input Voltage	V_{CC} = Max, V_I = 5.5V			1	mA
I_{IH}	High Level Input Current	V_{CC} = Max, V_I = 2.4V			40	μA
I_{IL}	Low Level Input Current	V_{CC} = Max, V_I = 0.4V			-1.6	mA
I_{CCH}	Supply Current With Outputs High	V_{CC} = Max		29	41	mA
I_{CCL}	Supply Current With Outputs Low	V_{CC} = Max		21	30	mA

Switching Characteristics at V_{CC} = 5V and T_A = 25°C (See Section 1 for Test Waveforms and Output Load)

Parameter	Conditions	C_L = 15 pF R_L = 110Ω Min	Typ	Max	Units
t_{PLH} Propagation Delay Time Low to High Level Output			6	10	ns
t_{PHL} Propagation Delay Time High to Low Level Output			20	30	ns

Note 1: All typicals are at V_{CC} = 5V, T_A = 25°C.

National Semiconductor

DM5420/DM7420 Dual 4-Input NAND Gates

General Description

This device contains two independent gates each of which performs the logic NAND function.

Absolute Maximum Ratings (Note 1)

Supply Voltage	7V
Input Voltage	5.5V
Storage Temperature Range	-65°C to 150°C

Note 1: The "Absolute Maximum Ratings" are those values beyond which the safety of the device can not be guaranteed. The device should not be operated at these limits. The parametric values defined in the "Electrical Characteristics" table are not guaranteed at the absolute maximum ratings. The "Recommended Operating Conditions" table will define the conditions for actual device operation.

Function Table

$$Y = \overline{ABCD}$$

Inputs A	B	C	D	Output Y
X	X	X	L	H
X	X	L	X	H
X	L	X	X	H
L	X	X	X	H
H	H	H	H	L

H = High Logic Level
L = Low Logic Level
X = Either Low or High Logic Level

Connection Diagram

Dual-In-Line Package

TL/F/6506-1

DM5420 (J) DM7420 (N)

- All Circuit Types Feature Lamp Intensity Modulation Capability

TYPE	ACTIVE LEVEL	DRIVER OUTPUTS			TYPICAL POWER DISSIPATION	PACKAGES
		OUTPUT CONFIGURATION	SINK CURRENT	MAX VOLTAGE		
SN5446A	low	open-collector	40 mA	30 V	320 mW	J, W
SN5447A	low	open-collector	40 mA	15 V	320 mW	J, W
SN5448	high	2-kΩ pull-up	6.4 mA	5.5 V	265 mW	J, W
SN5449	high	open-collector	10 mA	5.5 V	165 mW	W
SN54L46	low	open-collector	20 mA	30 V	160 mW	J
SN54L47	low	open-collector	20 mA	15 V	160 mW	J
SN54LS47	low	open-collector	12 mA	15 V	35 mW	J, W
SN54LS48	high	2-kΩ pull-up	2 mA	5.5 V	125 mW	J, W
SN54LS49	high	open-collector	4 mA	5.5 V	40 mW	J, W
SN7446A	low	open-collector	40 mA	30 V	320 mW	J, N
SN7447A	low	open-collector	40 mA	15 V	320 mW	J, N
SN7448	high	2-kΩ pull-up	6.4 mA	5.5 V	265 mW	J, N
SN74LS47	low	open-collector	24 mA	15 V	35 mW	J, N
SN74LS48	high	2-kΩ pull-up	6 mA	5.5 V	125 mW	J, N
SN74LS49	high	open-collector	8 mA	5.5 V	40 mW	J, N

logic symbols

'46, '47

'48

'49

Pin numbers shown on logic notation are for D, J or N packages.

'46A, '47A, 'L46, 'L47, 'LS47 feature

- Open-Collector Outputs Drive Indicators Directly
- Lamp-Test Provision
- Leading/Trailing Zero Suppression

'48, 'LS48 feature

- Internal Pull-Ups Eliminate Need for External Resistors
- Lamp-Test Provision
- Leading/Trailing Zero Suppression

'49, 'LS49 feature

- Open-Collector Outputs
- Blanking Input

SN54L46, SN54L47 . . . J PACKAGE
SN5446A, SN5447A, SN54LS47, SN54LS48.
SN54LS48 . . . J OR W PACKAGE
SN7446A, SN7447A,
SN7448 . . . J OR N PACKAGE
SN74LS47, SN74LS48 . . . D, J OR N PACKAGE
(TOP VIEW)

SN54LS47, SN54LS48 . . . FK PACKAGE
SN74LS47, SN74LS48 . . . FN PACKAGE
(TOP VIEW)

SN5449 . . . W PACKAGE
SN54LS49 . . . J OR W PACKAGE
SN74LS49 . . . D, J OR N PACKAGE
(TOP VIEW)

SN54LS49 . . . FK PACKAGE
SN74LS49 . . . FN PACKAGE
(TOP VIEW)

NC — No internal connection

TYPES SN5446A, '47A, '48, '49, SN54L46, 'L47, SN54LS47, 'LS48, 'LS49, SN54A, '47A, '48, SN74LS47, 'LS48, 'LS49 BCD-TO-SEVEN-SEGMENT DECODERS/DRIVERS

description

The '46A, 'L46, '47A, 'L47, and 'LS47 feature active-low outputs designed for driving common-anode VLEDs or incandescent indicators directly, and the '48, '49, 'LS48, 'LS49 feature active-high outputs for driving lamp buffers or common-cathode VLEDs. All of the circuits except '49 and 'LS49 have full ripple-blanking input/output controls and a lamp test input. The '49 and 'LS49 circuits incorporate a direct blanking input. Segment identification and resultant displays are shown below. Display patterns for BCD input counts above 9 are unique symbols to authenticate input conditions.

The '46A, '47A, '48, 'L46, 'L47, and 'LS48 circuits incorporate automatic leading and/or trailing-edge zero-blanking control (RBI and RBO). Lamp test (LT) of these types may be performed at any time when the BI/RBO node is at a high level. All types (including the '49 and 'LS49) contain an overriding blanking input (BI) which can be used to control the lamp intensity by pulsing or to inhibit the outputs. Inputs and outputs are entirely compatible for use with TTL logic outputs.

The SN54246/SN74246 through '249 and the SN54LS247/SN74LS247 through 'LS249 compose the 6 and the 9 with tails and have been designed to offer the designer a choice between two indicator fonts. The SN54249/SN74249 and SN54LS249/SN74LS249 are 16-pin versions of the 14-pin SN5449 and 'LS49. Included in the '249 circuit and 'LS249 circuits are the full functional capability for lamp test and ripple blanking, which is not available in the '49 or 'LS49 circuit.

NUMERICAL DESIGNATIONS AND RESULTANT DISPLAYS

'46A, '47A, 'L46, 'L47, 'LS47 FUNCTION TABLE

DECIMAL OR FUNCTION	INPUTS						BI/RBO†	OUTPUTS							NOTE
	LT	RBI	D	C	B	A		a	b	c	d	e	f	g	
0	H	H	L	L	L	L	H	ON	ON	ON	ON	ON	ON	OFF	
1	H	X	L	L	L	H	H	OFF	ON	ON	OFF	OFF	OFF	OFF	
2	H	X	L	L	H	L	H	ON	ON	OFF	ON	ON	OFF	ON	
3	H	X	L	L	H	H	H	ON	ON	ON	ON	OFF	OFF	ON	
4	H	X	L	H	L	L	H	OFF	ON	ON	OFF	OFF	ON	ON	
5	H	X	L	H	L	H	H	ON	OFF	ON	ON	OFF	ON	ON	
6	H	X	L	H	H	L	H	OFF	OFF	ON	ON	ON	ON	ON	
7	H	X	L	H	H	H	H	ON	ON	ON	OFF	OFF	OFF	OFF	
8	H	X	H	L	L	L	H	ON	ON	ON	ON	ON	ON	ON	
9	H	X	H	L	L	H	H	ON	ON	ON	OFF	OFF	ON	ON	
10	H	X	H	L	H	L	H	OFF	OFF	OFF	ON	ON	OFF	ON	
11	H	X	H	L	H	H	H	OFF	OFF	ON	ON	OFF	OFF	ON	
12	H	X	H	H	L	L	H	OFF	ON	OFF	OFF	OFF	ON	ON	
13	H	X	H	H	L	H	H	ON	OFF	OFF	ON	OFF	ON	ON	
14	H	X	H	H	H	L	H	OFF	OFF	OFF	ON	ON	ON	ON	
15	H	X	H	H	H	H	H	OFF	OFF	OFF	OFF	OFF	OFF	OFF	
BI	X	X	X	X	X	X	L	OFF	OFF	OFF	OFF	OFF	OFF	OFF	2
RBI	H	L	L	L	L	L	L	OFF	OFF	OFF	OFF	OFF	OFF	OFF	3
LT	L	X	X	X	X	X	H	ON	ON	ON	ON	ON	ON	ON	4

H = high level, L = low level, X = irrelevant

NOTES: 1. The blanking input (BI) must be open or held at a high logic level when output functions 0 through 15 are desired. The ripple-blanking input (RBI) must be open or high if blanking of a decimal zero is not desired.
2. When a low logic level is applied directly to the blanking input (BI), all segment outputs are off regardless of the level of any other input.
3. When ripple-blanking input (RBI) and inputs A, B, C, and D are at a low level with the lamp test input high, all segment outputs go off and the ripple-blanking output (RBO) goes to a low level (response condition).
4. When the blanking input/ripple blanking output (BI/RBO) is open or held high and a low is applied to the lamp test input, all segment outputs are on.

†BI/RBO is wire AND logic serving as blanking input (BI) and/or ripple-blanking output (RBO).

absolute maximum ratings over operating free-air temperature range (unless otherwise noted)

Supply voltage, VCC (see Note 1) . . . . 7 V
Input voltage . . . . 5.5 V
Current forced into any output in the off state . . . . 1 mA
Operating free-air temperature range: SN5446A, SN5447A . . . . −55°C to 125°C
SN7446A, SN7447A . . . . 0°C to 70°C
Storage temperature range . . . . −65°C to 150°C

NOTE 1: Voltage values are with respect to network ground terminal.

recommended operating conditions

	SN5446A			SN5447A			SN7446A			SN7447A			UNIT
	MIN	NOM	MAX	MIN	NOM	MAX	MIN	NOM	MAX	MIN	NOM	MAX	
Supply voltage, VCC	4.5	5	5.5	4.5	5	5.5	4.75	5	5.25	4.75	5	5.25	V
Off-state output voltage, VO(off) a thru g			30			15			30			15	V
On-state output current, IO(on) a thru g			40			40			40			40	mA
High-level output current, IOH BI/RBO			−200			−200			−200			−200	μA
Low-level output current, IOL BI/RBO			8			8			8			8	mA
Operating free-air temperature, TA	−55		125	−55		125	0		70	0		70	°C

electrical characteristics over recommended operating free-air temperature range (unless otherwise noted)

PARAMETER		TEST CONDITIONS†	MIN	TYP‡	MAX	UNIT
VIH	High-level input voltage		2			V
VIL	Low-level input voltage				0.8	V
VIK	Input clamp voltage	VCC = MIN, II = −12 mA			−1.5	V
VOH	High-level output voltage BI/RBO	VCC = MIN, VIH = 2 V, VIL = 0.8 V, IOH = −200 μA	2.4	3.7		V
VOL	Low-level output voltage BI/RBO	VCC = MIN, VIH = 2 V, VIL = 0.8 V, IOL = 8 mA		0.27	0.4	V
IO(off)	Off-state output current a thru g	VCC = MAX, VIH = 2 V, VIL = 0.8 V, VO(off) = MAX			250	μA
VO(on)	On-state output voltage a thru g	VCC = MIN, VIH = 2 V, VIL = 0.8 V, IO(on) = 40 mA		0.3	0.4	V
II	Input current at maximum input voltage Any input except BI/RBO	VCC = MAX, VI = 5.5 V			1	mA
IIH	High-level input current Any input except BI/RBO	VCC = MAX, VI = 2.4 V			40	μA
IIL	Low-level input current Any input except BI/RBO	VCC = MAX, VI = 0.4 V			−1.6	mA
IOS	Short-circuit output current BI/RBO	VCC = MAX			−4	mA
ICC	Supply current	VCC = MAX, See Note 2	SN54*	64	85	mA
			SN74*	64	103	

†For conditions shown as MIN or MAX, use the appropriate value specified under recommended operating conditions.
‡All typical values are at VCC = 5 V, TA = 25°C.
NOTE 2: ICC is measured with all outputs open and all inputs at 4.5 V.

switching characteristics, VCC = 5 V, TA = 25°C

PARAMETER		TEST CONDITIONS	MIN	TYP	MAX	UNIT
toff	Turn-off time from A input	CL = 15 pF, RL = 120 Ω, See Note 3			100	ns
ton	Turn-on time from A input				100	ns
toff	Turn-off time from RBI input				100	ns
ton	Turn-on time from RBI input				100	ns

NOTE 3: See General Information Section for load circuits and voltage waveforms. ; toff corresponds to tPLH, ton corresponds to tPHL.

National Semiconductor

DM5474/DM7474 Dual Positive-Edge-Triggered D Flip-Flops with Preset, Clear and Complementary Outputs

General Description

This device contains two independent positive-edge-triggered D flip-flops with complementary outputs. The information on the D input is accepted by the flip-flops on the positive going edge of the clock pulse. The triggering occurs at a voltage level and is not directly related to the transition time of the rising edge of the clock. The data on the D input may be changed while the clock is low or high without affecting the outputs as long as the data setup and hold times are not violated. A low logic level on the preset or clear inputs will set or reset the outputs regardless of the logic levels of the other inputs.

Absolute Maximum Ratings (Note 1)

Supply Voltage	7V
Input Voltage	5.5V
Storage Temperature Range	−65°C to 150°C

Note 1: The "Absolute Maximum Ratings" are those values beyond which the safety of the device can not be guaranteed. The device should not be operated at these limits. The parametric values defined in the "Electrical Characteristics" table are not guaranteed at the absolute maximum ratings. The "Recommended Operating Conditions" table will define the conditions for actual device operation.

Connection Diagram

Dual-In-Line Package

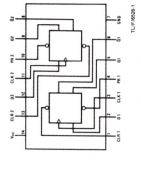

TL/F/6526-1

DM5474 (J) DM7474 (N)

Function Table

Inputs				Outputs	
PR	CLR	CLK	D	Q	Q̄
L	H	X	X	H	L
H	L	X	X	L	H*
L	L	X	X	H*	H*
H	H	↑	H	H	L
H	H	↑	L	L	H
H	H	L	X	Q₀	Q̄₀

H = High Logic Level
X = Either Low or High Logic Level
L = Low Logic Level
↑ = Positive-going transition of the clock.
* = This configuration is nonstable; that is, it will not persist when either the preset and/or clear inputs return to their inactive (high) level.
Q₀ = The output logic level of Q before the indicated input conditions were established.

Recommended Operating Conditions

Sym	Parameter		DM5474			DM7474			Units
			Min	Nom	Max	Min	Nom	Max	
V_CC	Supply Voltage		4.5	5	5.5	4.75	5	5.25	V
V_IH	High Level Input Voltage		2			2			V
V_IL	Low Level Input Voltage				0.8			0.8	V
I_OH	High Level Output Current				−0.4			−0.4	mA
I_OL	Low Level Output Current				16			16	mA
f_CLK	Clock Frequency		0		20	0		20	MHz
t_W	Pulse Width	Clock High	30			30			ns
		Clock Low	37			37			
		Clear Low	30			30			
		Preset Low	30			30			
t_SU	Input Setup Time (Note 1)		20↑			20↑			ns
t_H	Input Hold Time (Note 1)		5↑			5↑			ns
T_A	Free Air Operating Temperature		−55		125	0		70	°C

Note 1: The symbol (↑) indicates the rising edge of the clock pulse is used for reference.

National Semiconductor Corporation

DM5475/DM7475 Quad Latches

General Description

These latches are ideally suited for use as temporary storage for binary information between processing units and input/output or indicator units. Information present at a data (D) input is transferred to the Q output when the enable (G) is high, and the Q output will follow the data input as long as the enable remains high. When the enable goes low, the information (that was present at the data input at the time the transition occurred) is retained at the Q output until the enable is permitted to go high.

These latches feature complementary Q and Q̄ outputs from a 4-bit latch and are available in 16-pin packages.

Connection Diagram

Dual-In-Line Package

TL/F/6527-1

Order Number DM5475J or DM7475N
See NS Package Number J16A or N16A

Logic Diagram (Each Latch)

TL/F/6527-2

Function Table (Each Latch)

Inputs		Outputs	
D	G	Q	Q̄
L	H	L	H
H	H	H	L
X	L	Q_0	$\bar{Q}_0$

H = High Level, L = Low Level, X = Don't Care, Q_0 = The Level of Q Before the High-to-Low Transition of G

Absolute Maximum Ratings (Note)

Specifications for Military/Aerospace products are not contained in this datasheet. Refer to the associated reliability electrical test specifications document.

Supply Voltage	7V
Input Voltage	5.5V
Operating Free Air Temperature Range	
DM54	-55°C to +125°C
DM74	0°C to +70°C
Storage Temperature Range	-65°C to +150°C

Note: The "Absolute Maximum Ratings" are those values beyond which the safety of the device cannot be guaranteed. The device should not be operated at these limits. The parametric values defined in the "Electrical Characteristics" table are not guaranteed at the absolute maximum ratings. The "Recommended Operating Conditions" table will define the conditions for actual device operation.

Recommended Operating Conditions

Symbol	Parameter	DM5475			DM7475			Units
		Min	Nom	Max	Min	Nom	Max	
V_{CC}	Supply Voltage	4.5	5	5.5	4.75	5	5.25	V
V_{IH}	High Level Input Voltage	2			2			V
V_{IL}	Low Level Input Voltage			0.8			0.8	V
I_{OH}	High Level Output Current			-0.4			-0.4	mA
I_{OL}	Low Level Output Current			16			16	mA
t_W	Enable Pulse Width (Note 4)	20			20			ns
t_{SU}	Setup Time (Note 4)	20			20			ns
t_H	Hold Time (Note 4)	5			5			ns
T_A	Free Air Operating Temperature	-55		125	0		70	°C

Electrical Characteristics over recommended operating free air temperature range (unless otherwise noted)

Symbol	Parameter	Conditions	Min	Typ (Note 1)	Max	Units
V_I	Input Clamp Voltage	V_{CC} = Min, I_I = -12 mA			-1.5	V
V_{OH}	High Level Output Voltage	V_{CC} = Min, I_{OH} = Max; V_{IL} = Max, V_{IH} = Min	2.4	3.4		V
V_{OL}	Low Level Output Voltage	V_{CC} = Min, I_{OL} = Max; V_{IH} = Min, V_{IL} = Max		0.2	0.4	V
I_I	Input Current @ Max Input Voltage	V_{CC} = Max, V_I = 5.5V			1	mA
I_{IH}	High Level Input Current	V_{CC} = Max, V_I = 2.4V			80	µA
I_{IL}	Low Level Input Current	V_{CC} = Max, V_I = 0.4V			-3.2	mA
I_{OS}	Short Circuit Output Current	V_{CC} = Max (Note 2) DM54	-20		-55	mA
		DM74	-18		-55	mA
I_{CC}	Supply Current	V_{CC} = Max (Note 3) DM54		32	46	mA
		DM74		32	50	mA

Note 1: All typicals are at V_{CC} = 5V, T_A = 25°C.
Note 2: Not more than one output should be shorted at a time.
Note 3: I_{CC} is measured with all inputs grounded and all outputs open.
Note 4: T_A = 25°C and V_{CC} = 5V.

TYPES SN5476, SN54H76, SN54LS76A, SN7476, SN74H76, SN74LS76A DUAL J-K FLIP-FLOPS WITH PRESET AND CLEAR

REVISED DECEMBER 1983

- **Package Options Include Plastic and Ceramic DIPs**

- **Dependable Texas Instruments Quality and Reliability**

description

The '76 and 'H76 contain two independent J-K flip-flops with individual J-K, clock, preset, and clear inputs. The '76 and 'H76 are positive-edge-triggered flip-flops. J-K input is loaded into the master while the clock is high and transferred to the slave on the high-to-low transition. For these devices the J and K inputs must be stable while the clock is high.

The 'LS76A contain two independent negative-edge-triggered flip-flops. The J and K inputs must be stable one setup time prior to the high-to-low clock transition for predictable operation. The preset and clear are asynchronous active low inputs. When low they override the clock and data inputs forcing the outputs to the steady state levels as shown in the function table.

The SN5476, SN54H76, and the SN54LS76A are characterized for operation over the full military temperature range of −55°C to 125°C. The SN7476, SN74H76, and the SN74LS76A are characterized for operation from 0°C to 70°C.

SN5476, SN54H76, SN54LS76A . . . J OR W PACKAGE
SN7476, SN74H76 . . . J OR N PACKAGE
SN74LS76A . . . D, J OR N PACKAGE
(TOP VIEW)

1CLK	1	U	16	1K
1 PRE	2		15	1Q
1 CLR	3		14	1Q̄
1 J	4		13	GND
VCC	5		12	2K
2CLK	6		11	2Q
2 PRE	7		10	2Q̄
2 CLR	8		9	2J

'76, 'H76 FUNCTION TABLE

INPUTS					OUTPUTS	
PRE	CLR	CLK	J	K	Q	Q̄
L	H	X	X	X	H	L
H	L	X	X	X	L	H
L	L	X	X	X	H†	H†
H	H	⊓	L	L	Q_0	$\overline{Q}_0$
H	H	⊓	H	L	H	L
H	H	⊓	L	H	L	H
H	H	⊓	H	H	\multicolumn{2}{c}{TOGGLE}

'LS76A FUNCTION TABLE

INPUTS					OUTPUTS	
PRE	CLR	CLK	J	K	Q	Q̄
L	H	X	X	X	H	L
H	L	X	X	X	L	H
L	L	X	X	X	H†	H†
H	H	↓	L	L	Q_0	$\overline{Q}_0$
H	H	↓	H	L	H	L
H	H	↓	L	H	L	H
H	H	↓	H	H	\multicolumn{2}{c}{TOGGLE}
H	H	H	X	X	Q_0	$\overline{Q}_0$

† This configuration is nonstable; that is, it will not persist when either preset or clear returns to its inactive (high) level.

FOR CHIP CARRIER INFORMATION,
CONTACT THE FACTORY

logic diagrams

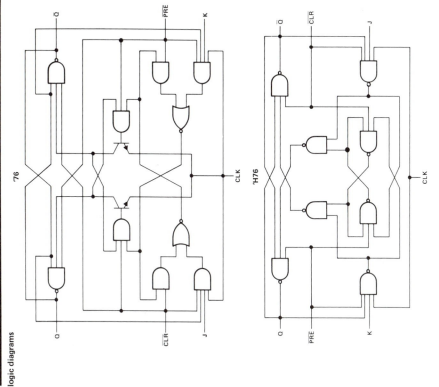

'76

'H76

TEXAS INSTRUMENTS
POST OFFICE BOX 225012 • DALLAS, TEXAS 75265

TEXAS INSTRUMENTS
POST OFFICE BOX 225012 • DALLAS, TEXAS 75265

Courtesy of Texas Instruments Incorporated

recommended operating conditions

			SN5476			SN7476			UNIT
			MIN	NOM	MAX	MIN	NOM	MAX	
V_{CC}	Supply voltage		4.5	5	5.5	4.75	5	5.25	V
V_{IH}	High-level input voltage		2			2			V
V_{IL}	Low-level input voltage				0.8			0.8	V
I_{OH}	High-level output current				−0.4			−0.4	mA
I_{OL}	Low-level output current				16			16	mA
t_w	Pulse duration	CLK high	20			20			ns
		CLK low	47			47			
		PRE or CLR low	25			25			
t_{su}	Input setup time before CLK ↑		0			0			ns
t_h	Input hold time-data after CLK ↓		0			0			ns
T_A	Operating free-air temperature		−55		125	0		70	°C

electrical characteristics over recommended operating free-air temperature range (unless otherwise noted)

PARAMETER		TEST CONDITIONS†			SN5476			SN7476			UNIT
				MIN	TYP	MAX	MIN	TYP	MAX		
V_{IK}		V_{CC} = MIN,	I_I = −12 mA				−1.5			−1.5	V
V_{OH}		V_{CC} = MIN,	V_{IH} = 2 V,	V_{IL} = 0.8 V,	2.4	3.4		2.4	3.4		V
		I_{OH} = −0.4 mA									
V_{OL}		V_{CC} = MIN,	V_{IH} = 2 V,	V_{IL} = 0.8 V,		0.2	0.4		0.2	0.4	V
		I_{OL} = 16 mA									
I_I		V_{CC} = MAX,	V_I = 5.5 V				1			1	mA
I_{IH}	J or K	V_{CC} = MAX,	V_I = 2.4 V				40			40	μA
	All other						80			80	
I_{IL}	J or K	V_{CC} = MAX,	V_I = 0.4 V				−1.6			−1.6	mA
	All other★						−3.2			−3.2	
I_{OS}§		V_{CC} = MAX			−20		−57	−18		−57	mA
I_{CC}		V_{CC} = MAX,	See Note 2			10	20		10	20	mA

† For conditions shown as MIN or MAX, use the appropriate value specified under recommended operating conditions.
‡ All typical values are at V_{CC} = 5 V, T_A = 25°C.
§ Not more than one output should be shorted at a time.
★ Clear is tested with preset high and preset is tested with clear high.
NOTE 2: With all outputs open, I_{CC} is measured with the Q and $\overline{Q}$ outputs high in turn. At the time of measurement, the clock input is grounded.

switching characteristics, V_{CC} = 5 V, T_A = 25°C (see note 3)

PARAMETER	FROM (INPUT)	TO (OUTPUT)	TEST CONDITIONS		MIN	TYP	MAX	UNIT
f_{max}					15	20		MHz
t_{PLH}	$\overline{PRE}$ or $\overline{CLR}$	Q or $\overline{Q}$	R_L = 400 Ω,	C_L = 15 pF		16	25	ns
t_{PHL}						25	40	ns
t_{PLH}	CLK	Q or $\overline{Q}$				16	25	ns
t_{PHL}						25	40	ns

NOTE 3: See General Information Section for load circuits and voltage waveforms.

---

logic diagrams (continued)

'LS76A

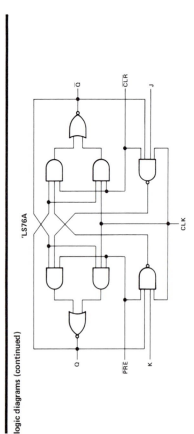

logic symbols

76, 'H76

S (2)	
1PRE (4)	
1J (1)	
1CLK (16)	
1K (3)	
1CLR (7)	
2PRE (9)	
2J (6)	
2CLK (12)	
2K (8)	

(15) 1Q
(14) 1$\overline{Q}$
(11) 2Q
(10) 2$\overline{Q}$

'LS76A

S (2)	
1PRE (4)	
1J (1) 1J	
1CLK (16) C1	
1K (3) 1K	
1CLR (7) R	
2PRE (9)	
2J (6) 2J	
2CLK (12)	
2K (8) 2K	

(15) 1Q
(14) 1$\overline{Q}$
(11) 2Q
(10) 2$\overline{Q}$

Pin numbers shown on logic notation are for D, J or N packages.

schematics of inputs and outputs

EQUIVALENT OF EACH INPUT

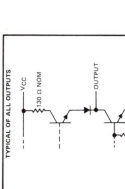

R_{eq} NOM
I_{IL} MAX   4 kΩ
−1.6 mA   2 kΩ
−3.2 mA

TYPICAL OF ALL OUTPUTS

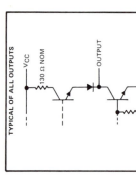

TYPES SN5483A, SN54LS83A, SN7483A, SN74LS83A
4-BIT BINARY FULL ADDERS WITH FAST CARRY

MARCH 1974—REVISED DECEMBER 1983

- Full-Carry Look-Ahead across the Four Bits

- Systems Achieve Partial Look-Ahead Performance with the Economy of Ripple Carry

- SN54283/SN74283 and SN54LS283/SN74LS283 Are Recommended For New Designs as They Feature Supply Voltage and Ground on Corner Pins to Simplify Board Layout

TYPICAL ADD TIMES

TYPE	TWO 8-BIT WORDS	TWO 16-BIT WORDS	TYPICAL POWER DISSIPATION PER 4-BIT ADDER
'83A	23 ns	43 ns	310 mW
'LS83A	25 ns	45 ns	95 mW

description

These improved full adders perform the addition of two 4-bit binary numbers. The sum (Σ) outputs are provided for each bit and the resultant carry (C4) is obtained from the fourth bit. These adders feature full internal look ahead across all four bits generating the carry term in ten nanoseconds typically. This provides the system designer with partial look-ahead performance at the economy and reduced package count of a ripple-carry implementation.

The adder logic, including the carry, is implemented in its true form meaning that the end-around carry can be accomplished without the need for logic or level inversion.

Designed for medium-speed applications, the circuits utilize transistor-transistor logic that is compatible with most other TTL families and other saturated low-level logic families.

Series 54 and 54LS circuits are characterized for operation over the full military temperature range of −55°C to 125°C, and Series 74 and 74LS circuits are characterized for operation from 0°C to 70°C.

SN5483A, SN54LS83A . . . J OR W PACKAGE
SN7483A . . . J OR N PACKAGE
SN74LS83A . . . D, J OR N PACKAGE
(TOP VIEW)

A4	1	16	B4
Σ3	2	15	Σ4
A3	3	14	C4
B3	4	13	C0
VCC	5	12	GND
Σ2	6	11	B1
B2	7	10	A1
A2	8	9	Σ1

SN54LS83A . . . FK PACKAGE
SN74LS83A . . . FN PACKAGE
(TOP VIEW)

NC - No internal connection

FUNCTION TABLE

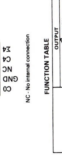

H = high level, L = low level

NOTE: Input conditions at A1, B1, A2, B2, and C0 are used to determine outputs Σ1 and Σ2 and the value of the internal carry C2. The values at C2, A3, B3, A4, and B4 are then used to determine outputs Σ3, Σ4, and C4.

logic diagram

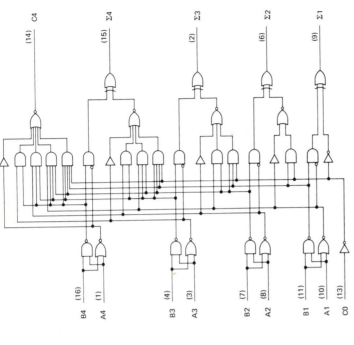

Pin numbers shown on logic notation are for D, J or N packages.

absolute maximum ratings over operating free-air temperature range (unless otherwise noted)

Supply voltage, VCC (see Note 1)	7 V
Input voltage: '83A	5.5 V
'LS83A	7 V
Interemitter voltage (see Note 2)	5.5 V
Operating free-air temperature range: SN5483A, SN54LS83A	−55°C to 125°C
SN7483A, SN74LS83A	0°C to 70°C
Storage temperature range	−65°C to 150°C

NOTES: 1. Voltage values, except interemitter voltage, are with respect to network ground terminal.
2. This is the voltage between two emitters of a multiple-emitter transistor. This rating applies for the '83A only between the following pairs: A1 and B1, A2 and B2, A3 and B3, A4 and B4.

TEXAS INSTRUMENTS
POST OFFICE BOX 225012 • DALLAS, TEXAS 75265

Recommended Operating Conditions

Sym	Parameter	DM5485 Min	DM5485 Nom	DM5485 Max	DM7485 Min	DM7485 Nom	DM7485 Max	Units
V_CC	Supply Voltage	4.5	5	5.5	4.75	5	5.25	V
V_IH	High Level Input Voltage	2			2			V
V_IL	Low Level Input Voltage			0.8			0.8	V
I_OH	High Level Output Current			−0.8			−0.8	mA
I_OL	Low Level Output Current			16			16	mA
T_A	Free Air Operating Temperature	−55		125	0		70	°C

Electrical Characteristics over recommended operating free air temperature (unless otherwise noted)

Sym	Parameter	Conditions		Min	Typ (Note 1)	Max	Units
V_I	Input Clamp Voltage	V_CC = Min, I_I = −12 mA				−1.5	V
V_OH	High Level Output Voltage	V_CC = Min, I_OH = Max, V_IL = Max, V_IH = Min		2.4			V
V_OL	Low Level Output Voltage	V_CC = Min, I_OL = Max, V_IH = Min, V_IL = Max				0.4	V
I_I	Input Current@Max Input Voltage	V_CC = Max, V_I = 5.5V				1	mA
I_IH	High Level Input Current	V_CC = Max, V_I = 2.4V	A < B			40	µA
			A > B			40	
			Others			120	
I_IL	Low Level Input Current	V_CC = Max, V_I = 0.4V	A < B			−1.6	mA
			A > B			−1.6	
			Others			−4.8	
I_OS	Short Circuit Output Current	V_CC = Max (Note 2)	DM54	−20		−55	mA
			DM74	−18		−55	
I_CC	Supply Current	V_CC = Max (Note 3)			55	88	mA

Note 1: All typicals are at V_CC = 5V, T_A = 25°C.
Note 2: Not more than one output should be shorted at a time.
Note 3: I_CC is measured with all outputs open, A = B input grounded and all other inputs at 4.5V.

National Semiconductor

DM5485/DM7485 4-Bit Magnitude Comparators

General Description

These 4-bit magnitude comparators perform comparison of straight binary or BCD codes. Three fully-decoded decisions about two 4-bit words (A, B) are made and are externally available at three outputs. These devices are fully expandable to any number of bits without external gates. Words of greater length may be compared by connecting comparators in cascade. The A > B, A < B, and A = B outputs of a stage handling less-significant bits are connected to the corresponding inputs of the next stage handling more-significant bits. The stage handling the least-significant bits must have a high-level voltage applied to the A = B input. The cascading paths are implemented with only a two-gate-level delay to reduce overall comparison times for long words.

Features

- Typical power dissipation 275 mW
- Typical delay (4-bit words) 23 ns

Absolute Maximum Ratings (Note 1)

Supply Voltage	7V
Input Voltage	5.5V
Storage Temperature Range	−65°C to 150°C

Note 1: The "Absolute Maximum Ratings" are those values beyond which the safety of the device can not be guaranteed. The device should not be operated at these limits. The parametric values defined in the "Electrical Characteristics" table are not guaranteed at the absolute maximum ratings. The "Recommended Operating Conditions" table will define the conditions for actual device operation.

Connection Diagram

Dual-In-Line Package

5485 (J)   7485 (N)

TL/F/6530-1

288

TYPES SN54ALS86, SN74ALS86
QUADRUPLE 2-INPUT EXCLUSIVE-OR GATES

D2661, APRIL 1982—REVISED MARCH 1984

- **Package Options Include Both Plastic and Ceramic Chip Carriers in Addition to Plastic and Ceramic DIPs**
- **Dependable Texas Instruments Quality and Reliability**

description

These devices contain four independent 2-input Exclusive-OR gates. They perform the Boolean functions $Y = A \oplus B = \overline{A}B + A\overline{B}$ in positive logic.

A common application is as a true/complement element. If one of the inputs is low, the other input will be reproduced in true form at the output. If one of the inputs is high, the signal on the other input will be reproduced inverted at the output.

The SN54ALS86 is characterized for operation over the full military temperature range of −55°C to 125°C. The SN74ALS86 is characterized for operation from 0°C to 70°C.

SN54ALS86 . . . J PACKAGE
SN74ALS86 . . . N PACKAGE
(TOP VIEW)

1A	1	14	VCC
1B	2	13	4B
1Y	3	12	4A
2A	4	11	4Y
2B	5	10	3B
2Y	6	9	3A
GND	7	8	3Y

SN54ALS86 . . . FH PACKAGE
SN74ALS86 . . . FN PACKAGE
(TOP VIEW)

NC—No internal connection

logic symbol

Pin numbers shown are for J and N packages

FUNCTION TABLE
(each gate)

INPUTS		OUTPUT
A	B	Y
L	L	L
L	H	H
H	L	H
H	H	L

exclusive-OR logic

An exclusive-OR gate has many applications, some of which can be represented better by alternative logic symbols.

These are five equivalent Exclusive-OR symbols valid for an 'ALS86 gate in positive logic; negation may be shown at any two ports.

EXCLUSIVE-OR

LOGIC IDENTITY ELEMENT

The output is active (low) if all inputs stand at the same logic level (i.e., A = B).

EVEN-PARITY

The output is active (low) if an even number of inputs (i.e., 0 or 2) are active.

ODD-PARITY ELEMENT

The output is active (high) if an odd number of inputs (i.e., only 1 of the 2) are active.

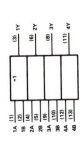

TEXAS INSTRUMENTS
POST OFFICE BOX 225012 • DALLAS, TEXAS 75265

---

absolute maximum ratings over operating free-air temperature range (unless otherwise noted)

Supply voltage, VCC		7 V
Input voltage		7 V
Operating free-air temperature range: SN54ALS86		−55°C to 125°C
SN74ALS86		0°C to 70°C
Storage temperature range		−65°C to 150°C

recommended operating conditions

		SN54ALS86			SN74ALS86			UNIT
		MIN	NOM	MAX	MIN	NOM	MAX	
VCC	Supply voltage	4.5	5	5.5	4.5	5	5.5	V
VIH	High-level input voltage	2			2			V
VIL	Low-level input voltage			0.8			0.8	V
IOH	High-level output current			−0.4			−0.4	mA
IOL	Low-level output current			4			8	mA
TA	Operating free-air temperature	−55		125	0		70	°C

electrical characteristics over recommended operating free-air temperature range (unless otherwise noted)

PARAMETER	TEST CONDITIONS	SN54ALS86			SN74ALS86			UNIT
		MIN	TYP†	MAX	MIN	TYP†	MAX	
VIK	VCC = 4.5 V, II = −18 mA			−1.5			−1.5	V
VOH	VCC = 4.5 V to 5.5 V, IOH = −0.4 mA	VCC − 2			VCC − 2			V
VOL	VCC = 4.5 V, IOL = 4 mA		0.25	0.4		0.25	0.4	V
	VCC = 4.5 V, IOL = 8 mA					0.35	0.5	
II	VCC = 5.5 V, VI = 7 V			0.1			0.1	mA
IIH	VCC = 5.5 V, VI = 2.7 V			20			20	µA
IIL	VCC = 5.5 V, VI = 0.4 V			−0.1			−0.1	mA
IO‡	VCC = 5.5 V, VO = 2.25 V	−30		−112	−30		−112	mA
ICC	VCC = 5.5 V, All inputs at 4.5 V		3.9	5.9		3.9	5.9	mA

†All typical values are at VCC = 5 V, TA = 25°C.
‡The output conditions have been chosen to produce a current that closely approximates one half of the true short-circuit output current, IOS.

switching characteristics (see Note 1)

PARAMETER	FROM (INPUT)	TO (OUTPUT)	VCC = 4.5 V to 5.5 V, CL = 50 pF, RL = 500 Ω, TA = MIN to MAX				UNIT
			SN54ALS86		SN74ALS86		
			MIN	MAX	MIN	MAX	
tPLH	A or B (other input low)	Y	3	22	3	17	ns
tPHL			2	14	2	12	
tPLH	A or B (other input high)	Y	3	22	3	17	ns
tPHL			2	12	2	10	

NOTE 1: For load circuit and voltage waveforms, see page 1-12 of the TTL Data Book, Volume 3.

TEXAS INSTRUMENTS
POST OFFICE BOX 225012 • DALLAS, TEXAS 75265

SN7489
64-BIT RANDOM-ACCESS READ/WRITE MEMORY

D1416, DECEMBER 1972 – REVISED FEBRUARY 1984

- For Application as a "Scratch Pad" Memory with Nondestructive Read-Out
- Fully Decoded Memory Organized as 16 Words of Four Bits Each
- Fast Access Time . . . 33 ns Typical
- Diode-Clamped, Buffered Inputs
- Open-Collector Outputs Provide Wire-AND Capability
- Typical Power Dissipation . . . 375 mW
- Compatible with Most TTL Circuits

description

This 64-bit active-element memory is a monolithic, high-speed, transistor-transistor logic (TTL) array of 64 flip-flop memory cells organized in a matrix to provide 16 words of four bits each. Each of the 16 words is addressed in straight binary with full on-chip decoding.

The buffered memory inputs consist of four address lines, four data inputs, a write enable, and a memory enable for controlling the entry and access of data. The memory has open-collector outputs which may be wired-AND connected to permit expansion up to 4704 words of N-bit length without additional output buffering. Access time is typically 33 nanoseconds; power dissipation is typically 375 milliwatts.

SN7489 . . . J OR N PACKAGE
(TOP VIEW)

A0	1	16	VCC
ME̅	2	15	A1
WE̅	3	14	A2
D1	4	13	A3
Q̅1	5	12	D4
D2	6	11	Q̅4
Q̅2	7	10	D3
GND	8	9	Q̅3

logic symbol

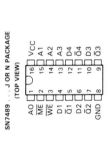

		RAM 16 × 4	
A0	(1)	0	
A1	(15)	A 0	
A2	(14)	15	
A3	(13)	3 1C2/G3	
ME̅	(2)	G1	
WE̅	(3)		
D1	(4)	1 A,2D A,1,3	Q̅1 (5)
D2	(6)		Q̅2 (7)
D3	(10)		Q̅3 (9)
D4	(12)		Q̅4 (11)

FUNCTION TABLE

ME	WE	OPERATION	CONDITION OF OUTPUTS
L	L	Write	Complement of Data Inputs
L	H	Read	Complement of Selected Word
H	L	Inhibit Storage	Complement of Data Inputs
H	H	Do Nothing	High

write operation

Information present at the data inputs is written into the memory by addressing the desired word and holding both the memory enable and write enable low. Since the internal output of the data input gate is common to the input of the sense amplifier, the sense output will assume the opposite state of the information at the data inputs when the write enable is low.

read operation

The complement of the information which has been written into the memory is nondestructively read out at the four sense outputs. This is accomplished by holding the memory enable low, the write enable high, and selecting the desired address.

SN7489
64-BIT RANDOM-ACCESS READ/WRITE MEMORY

logic diagram

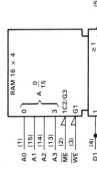

64-BIT RANDOM-ACCESS READ/WRITE MEMORY   SN7489

schematics of inputs and outputs

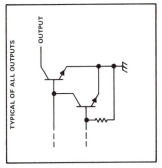

EQUIVALENT OF EACH INPUT

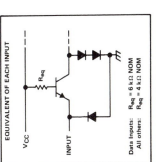

TYPICAL OF ALL OUTPUTS

Data Inputs: R_{eq} = 6 kΩ NOM
All others: R_{eq} = 4 kΩ NOM

absolute maximum ratings over operating free-air temperature range (unless otherwise noted)

Supply voltage, V_{CC} (see Note 1) . . . . 7 V
Input voltage (see Note 1) . . . . 5.5 V
High-level output voltage, V_{OH} (see Notes 1 and 2) . . . . 5.5 V
Operating free-air temperature range . . . . 0°C to 70°C
Storage temperature range . . . . −65°C to 150°C

NOTES: 1. Voltage values are with respect to network ground terminal.
2. This is the maximum voltage that should be applied to any output when it is in the off state.

recommended operating conditions

	MIN	NOM	MAX	UNIT
Supply voltage, V_{CC}	4.75	5	5.25	V
Width of write-enable pulse, t_w	40			ns
Setup time, data input with respect to write enable, t_{su} (see Figure 1)	40			ns
Hold time, data input with respect to write enable, t_h (see Figure 1)	5			ns
Select input setup time with respect to write enable, t_{su}	0			ns
Select input hold time after writing, t_h (see Figure 1)	5			ns
Operating free-air temperature, T_A	0		70	°C

electrical characteristics over recommended operating free-air temperature range (unless otherwise noted)

PARAMETER		TEST CONDITIONS[†]		MIN	TYP[‡]	MAX	UNIT
V_{IH}	High-level input voltage			2			V
V_{IL}	Low-level input voltage					0.8	V
V_{IK}	Input clamp voltage	V_{CC} = MIN,	I_I = −12 mA			−1.5	V
I_{OH}	High-level output current	V_{CC} = MIN, V_{IL} = 0.8 V,	V_{IH} = 2 V, V_{OH} = 5.5 V			20	µA
V_{OL}	Low-level output voltage	V_{CC} = MIN, V_{IL} = 0.8 V	V_{IH} = 2 V, I_{OL} = 12 mA			0.4	V
			I_{OL} = 16 mA			0.45	
I_I	Input current at maximum input voltage	V_{CC} = MAX,	V_I = 5.5 V			1	mA
I_{IH}	High-level input current	V_{CC} = MAX,	V_I = 2.4 V			40	µA
I_{IL}	Low-level input current	V_{CC} = MAX,	V_I = 0.4 V			−1.6	mA
I_{CC}	Supply current	See Note 3			75	105	mA
C_o	Off-state output capacitance	V_{CC} = 5 V, f = 1 MHz	V_O = 2.4 V,		6.5		pF

[†] For conditions shown as MIN or MAX, use the appropriate value specified under recommended operating conditions.
[‡] All typical values are at V_{CC} = 5 V, T_A = 25°C.
NOTE 3: I_{CC} is measured with the memory enable grounded, all other inputs at 4.5 V, and all outputs open.

switching characteristics, V_{CC} = 5 V, T_A = 25°C

PARAMETER		TEST CONDITIONS	MIN	TYP	MAX	UNIT
t_{PLH}	Propagation delay time, low-to-high-level output from memory enable			26	50	ns
t_{PHL}	Propagation delay time, high-to-low-level output from memory enable	C_L = 30 pF,		33	50	
t_{PLH}	Propagation delay time, low-to-high-level output from any address input	R_{L1} = 300 Ω, R_{L2} = 600 Ω,		30	60	ns
t_{PHL}	Propagation delay time, high-to-low-level output from any address input	See Figure 1		35	60	
t_{SR}	Sense recovery time	Output initially high		39	70	ns
	after writing	Output initially low		48	70	

TEXAS
INSTRUMENTS
POST OFFICE BOX 225012 ● DALLAS, TEXAS 75265

TEXAS
INSTRUMENTS
POST OFFICE BOX 225012 ● DALLAS, TEXAS 75265

TYPES SN5490A, SN5492A, SN5493A, SN54L90, SN54L93, SN54LS92, SN54LS93, SN7490A, SN7492A, SN7493A, SN74L90, SN74L93, SN74LS90, SN74LS92, SN74LS93
DECADE, DIVIDE-BY-TWELVE, AND BINARY COUNTERS

MARCH 1974 — REVISED DECEMBER 1983

'90A, 'L90, 'LS90 . . . DECADE COUNTERS
'92A, 'LS92 . . . DIVIDE-BY-TWELVE COUNTERS
'93A, 'LS93 . . . 4-BIT BINARY COUNTERS

TYPES	TYPICAL POWER DISSIPATION
'90A	145 mW
'L90	20 mW
'LS90	45 mW
'92A, '93A	130 mW
'LS92, 'LS93	45 mW
'L93	16 mW

description

Each of these monolithic counters contains four master-slave flip-flops and additional gating to provide a divide-by-two counter and a three-stage binary counter for which the count cycle length is divide-by-five for the '90A, 'L90, and 'LS90, divide-by-six for the '92A and 'LS92, and divide-by-eight for the '93A, 'L93, and 'LS93.

All of these counters have a gated zero reset and the '90A, 'L90, and 'LS90 also have gated set-to-nine inputs for use in BCD nine's complement applications.

To use their maximum count length (decade, divide-by-twelve, or four-bit binary) of these counters, the CKB input is connected to the QA output. The input count pulses are applied to CKA input and the outputs are as described in the appropriate function table. A symmetrical divide-by-ten count can be obtained from the '90A, 'L90, or 'LS90 counters by connecting the QD output to the CKA input and applying the input count to the CKB input which gives a divide-by-ten square wave at output QA.

SN5490A, SN54LS90 . . . J OR W PACKAGE
SN54L90 . . . J PACKAGE
SN7490A . . . J OR N PACKAGE
SN74LS90 . . . D, J OR N PACKAGE
(TOP VIEW)

```
CKB   1  U 14  CKA
R0(1) 2    13  NC
R0(2) 3    12  QA
NC    4    11  QD
VCC   5    10  GND
R9(1) 6     9  QB
R9(2) 7     8  QC
```

SN5492A, SN54LS92 . . . J OR W PACKAGE
SN7492A . . . J OR N PACKAGE
SN74LS92 . . . D, J OR N PACKAGE
(TOP VIEW)

```
CKB   1  U 14  CKA
NC    2    13  NC
NC    3    12  QA
NC    4    11  QB
VCC   5    10  QC
R0(1) 6     9  QD
R0(2) 7     8  QD
```

SN5493A, SN54L93, SN54LS93 . . . J OR W PACKAGE
SN7493A . . . J OR N PACKAGE
SN74LS93 . . . D, J OR N PACKAGE
(TOP VIEW)

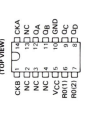

```
CKB   1  U 14  CKA
R0(1) 2    13  NC
R0(2) 3    12  QD
NC    4    11  GND
VCC   5    10  QB
NC    6     9  QC
NC    7     8  CKB
```

SN54L93 . . . J PACKAGE
(TOP VIEW)

```
R0(1) 1  U 14  CKA
R0(2) 2    13  NC
NC    3    12  QD
VCC   4    11  GND
NC    5    10  QB
NC    6     9  QC
NC    7     8  CKB
```

NC - No internal connection

For new chip carrier design, use 'LS290, 'LS292, and 'LS293.

'90A, 'L90, 'LS90
BCD COUNT SEQUENCE
(See Note A)

COUNT	QD	QC	QB	QA
0	L	L	L	L
1	L	L	L	H
2	L	L	H	L
3	L	L	H	H
4	L	H	L	L
5	L	H	L	H
6	L	H	H	L
7	L	H	H	H
8	H	L	L	L
9	H	L	L	H

'92A, 'LS92
COUNT SEQUENCE
(See Note C)

COUNT	QD	QC	QB	QA
0	L	L	L	L
1	L	L	L	H
2	L	L	H	L
3	L	L	H	H
4	L	H	L	L
5	L	H	L	H
6	H	L	L	L
7	H	L	L	H
8	H	L	H	L
9	H	L	H	H
10	H	H	L	L
11	H	H	L	H

'90A, 'L90, 'LS90
BI-QUINARY (5-2)
(See Note B)

COUNT	QA	QD	QC	QB
0	L	L	L	L
1	L	L	L	H
2	L	L	H	L
3	L	L	H	H
4	L	H	L	L
5	H	L	L	L
6	H	L	L	H
7	H	L	H	L
8	H	L	H	H
9	H	H	L	L

'90A, 'L90, 'LS90
RESET/COUNT FUNCTION TABLE

RESET INPUTS				OUTPUT			
R0(1)	R0(2)	R9(1)	R9(2)	QD	QC	QB	QA
H	H	L	X	L	L	L	L
H	H	X	L	L	L	L	L
X	X	H	H	H	L	L	H
X	L	X	L	COUNT			
L	X	L	X	COUNT			
L	X	X	L	COUNT			
X	L	L	X	COUNT			

'93A, 'L93, 'LS93
COUNT SEQUENCE
(See Note C)

COUNT	QD	QC	QB	QA
0	L	L	L	L
1	L	L	L	H
2	L	L	H	L
3	L	L	H	H
4	L	H	L	L
5	L	H	L	H
6	L	H	H	L
7	L	H	H	H
8	H	L	L	L
9	H	L	L	H
10	H	L	H	L
11	H	L	H	H
12	H	H	L	L
13	H	H	L	H
14	H	H	H	L
15	H	H	H	H

'92A, 'LS92, '93A, 'L93, 'LS93
RESET/COUNT FUNCTION TABLE

RESET INPUTS		OUTPUT			
R0(1)	R0(2)	QD	QC	QB	QA
H	H	L	L	L	L
L	X	COUNT			
X	L	COUNT			

NOTES: A. Output QA is connected to input CKB for BCD count.
B. Output QD is connected to input CKA for bi-quinary count.
C. Output QA is connected to input CKB.
D. H = high level, L = low level, X = irrelevant

TEXAS INSTRUMENTS
POST OFFICE BOX 225012 • DALLAS, TEXAS 75265

TEXAS INSTRUMENTS
POST OFFICE BOX 225012 • DALLAS, TEXAS 75265

TYPES SN5490A, SN5492A, SN5493A, SN7490A, SN7492A, SN7493A
DECADE, DIVIDE-BY-TWELVE, AND BINARY COUNTERS

absolute maximum ratings over operating free-air temperature range (unless otherwise noted)

Supply voltage, V_{CC} (see Note 1) . . . . 7 V
Input voltage . . . . 5.5 V
Interemitter voltage (see Note 2) . . . . 5.5 V
Operating free-air temperature range: SN5490A, SN5492A, SN5493A . . . . . −55°C to 125°C
  SN7490A, SN7492A, SN7493A . . . . . 0°C to 70°C
Storage temperature range . . . . −65°C to 150°C

NOTES: 1. Voltage values, except interemitter voltage, are with respect to network ground terminal.
2. This is the voltage between two emitters of a multiple emitter transistor. For these circuits, this rating applies between the two R_0 inputs, and for the '90A circuit, it also applies between the two R_9 inputs.

recommended operating conditions

		SN5490A, SN5492A SN5493A			SN7490A, SN7492A SN7493A			UNIT
		MIN	NOM	MAX	MIN	NOM	MAX	
Supply voltage, V_{CC}		4.5	5	5.5	4.75	5	5.25	V
High-level output current, I_{OH}				−800			−800	µA
Low-level output current, I_{OL}				16			16	mA
Count frequency, f_{count} (see Figure 1)	A input	0		32	0		32	MHz
	B input	0		16	0		16	
Pulse width, t_w	A input	15			15			ns
	B input	30			30			
Reset inactive-state setup time, t_{su}	Reset inputs	25			25			ns
Operating free-air temperature, T_A		−55		125	0		70	°C

electrical characteristics over recommended operating free-air temperature range (unless otherwise noted)

PARAMETER		TEST CONDITIONS†	'90A			'92A			'93A			UNIT
			MIN	TYP‡	MAX	MIN	TYP‡	MAX	MIN	TYP‡	MAX	
V_{IH} High-level input voltage			2			2			2			V
V_{IL} Low-level input voltage					0.8			0.8			0.8	V
V_{IK} Input clamp voltage		V_{CC} = MIN, I_I = −12 mA			−1.5			−1.5			−1.5	V
V_{OH} High-level output voltage		V_{CC} = MIN, V_{IH} = 2 V, V_{IL} = 0.8 V, I_{OH} = −800 µA	2.4	3.4		2.4	3.4		2.4	3.4		V
V_{OL} Low-level output voltage		V_{CC} = MIN, V_{IH} = 2 V, V_{IL} = 0.8 V, I_{OL} = 16 mA♦		0.2	0.4		0.2	0.4		0.2	0.4	V
I_I Input current at maximum input voltage		V_{CC} = MAX, V_I = 5.5 V			1			1			1	mA
I_{IH} High-level input current	Any reset	V_{CC} = MAX, V_I = 2.4 V			40			40			40	µA
	CKA				80			80			80	
	CKB				120			120			80	
I_{IL} Low-level input current	Any reset	V_{CC} = MAX, V_I = 0.4 V			−1.6			−1.6			−1.6	mA
	CKA				−3.2			−3.2			−3.2	
	CKB				−4.8			−4.8			−3.2	
I_{OS} Short-circuit output current§	SN54'	V_{CC} = MAX	−20		−57	−20		−57	−20		−57	mA
	SN74'		−18		−57	−18		−57	−18		−57	
I_{CC} Supply current		V_{CC} = MAX, See Note 3		29	42		26	39		26	39	mA

† For conditions shown as MIN or MAX, use the appropriate value specified under recommended operating conditions.
‡ All typical values are at V_{CC} = 5 V, T_A = 25°C.
§ Not more than one output should be shorted at a time.
♦ I_{OH} outputs are tested at I_{OL} = 16 mA plus the limit value for I_{IL} for the CKB input. This permits driving the CKB input while maintaining full fan-out capability.
NOTE 3: I_{CC} is measured with all outputs open, both R_0 inputs grounded following momentary connection to 4.5 V, and all other inputs grounded.

---

logic diagrams

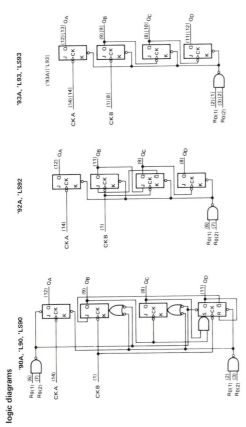

'90A, 'L90, 'LS90

'92A, 'LS92

'93A, 'L93, 'LS93

The J and K inputs shown without connection are for reference only and are functionally at a high level.
Pin numbers shown in ( ) are for the LS93 and '93A and pin numbers shown in [ ] are for the 54L93.

schematics of inputs and outputs

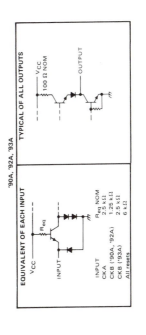

'90A, '92A, '93A

EQUIVALENT OF EACH INPUT	TYPICAL OF ALL OUTPUTS

INPUT	R_{eq} NOM
CKA	2.5 kΩ
CKB ('90A, '92A)	1.25 kΩ
CKB ('93A)	2.5 kΩ
All resets	6 kΩ

TEXAS INSTRUMENTS
POST OFFICE BOX 225012 • DALLAS, TEXAS 75265

TYPES SN54121, SN54L121, SN74121 MONOSTABLE MULTIVIBRATORS WITH SCHMITT-TRIGGER INPUTS

REVISED MAY 1983

- Programmable Output Pulse Width
  With R_{int} . . . 35 ns Typ
  With R_{ext}/C_{ext} . . . 40 ns to 28 Seconds
- Internal Compensation for Virtual Temperature Independence
- Jitter-Free Operation up to 90% Duty Cycle
- Inhibit Capability

SN54121 . . . J OR W PACKAGE
SN54L121 . . . J PACKAGE
SN74121 . . . J OR N PACKAGE

(TOP VIEW)

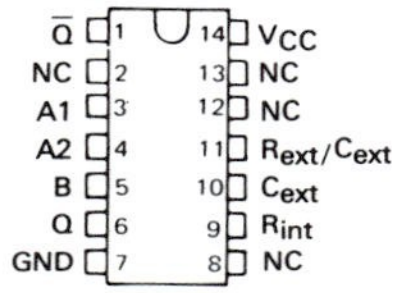

$\overline{Q}$ 1
NC 2
A1 3
A2 4
B 5
Q 6
GND 7
14 V_{CC}
13 NC
12 NC
11 R_{ext}/C_{ext}
10 C_{ext}
9 R_{int}
8 NC

NC - No internal connection.

FUNCTION TABLE

INPUTS			OUTPUTS	
A1	A2	B	Q	$\overline{Q}$
L	X	H	L	H
X	L	H	L†	H†
X	X	L	L†	H†
H	H	X	L†	H†
H	↓	H	⊓	⊔
↓	H	H	⊓	⊔
↓	↓	H	⊓	⊔
L	X	↑	⊓	⊔
X	L	↑	⊓	⊔

For explanation of function table symbols, see page
† These lines of the function table assume that the indicated steady-state conditions at the A and B inputs have been setup long enough to complete any pulse started before the setup.

description

These multivibrators feature dual negative-transition-triggered inputs and a single positive-transition-triggered input which can be used as an inhibit input. Complementary output pulses are provided.

Pulse triggering occurs at a particular voltage level and is not directly related to the transition time of the input pulse. Schmitt-trigger input circuitry (TTL hysteresis) for the B input allows jitter-free triggering from inputs with transition rates as slow as 1 volt/second, providing the circuit with an excellent noise immunity of typically 1.2 volts. A high immunity to V_{CC} noise of typically 1.5 volts is also provided by internal latching circuitry.

Once fired, the outputs are independent of further transitions of the inputs and are a function only of the timing components. Input pulses may be of any duration relative to the output pulse. Output pulse length may be varied from 40 nanoseconds to 28 seconds by choosing appropriate timing components. With no external timing components (i.e., R_{int} connected to V_{CC}, C_{ext} and R_{ext}/C_{ext} open), an output pulse of typically 30 or 35 nanoseconds is achieved which may be used as a d-c triggered reset signal. Output rise and fall times are TTL compatible and independent of pulse length.

Pulse width stability is achieved through internal compensation and is virtually independent of V_{CC} and temperature. In most applications, pulse stability will only be limited by the accuracy of external timing components.

Jitter-free operation is maintained over the full temperature and V_{CC} ranges for more than six decades of timing capacitance (10 pF to 10 μF) and more than one decade of timing resistance (2 kΩ to 30 kΩ for the SN54121/SN54L121 and 2 kΩ to 40 kΩ for the SN74121). Throughout these ranges, pulse width is defined by the relationship $t_{w(out)} = C_{ext}R_T \ln 2 \approx 0.7\, C_{ext}R_T$. In circuits where pulse cutoff is not critical, timing capacitance up to 1000 μF and timing resistance as low as 1.4 kΩ may be used. Also, the range of jitter-free output pulse widths is extended if V_{CC} is held to 5 volts and free-air temperature is 25°C. Duty cycles as high as 90% are achieved when using maximum recommended R_T. Higher duty cycles are available if a certain amount of pulse-width jitter is allowed.

PRODUCTION DATA
This document contains information current as of publication date. Products conform to specifications per the terms of Texas Instruments standard warranty. Production processing does not necessarily include testing of all parameters.

TYPES SN54121, SN54L121, SN74121 MONOSTABLE MULTIVIBRATORS WITH SCHMITT-TRIGGER INPUTS

logic diagram (positive logic)

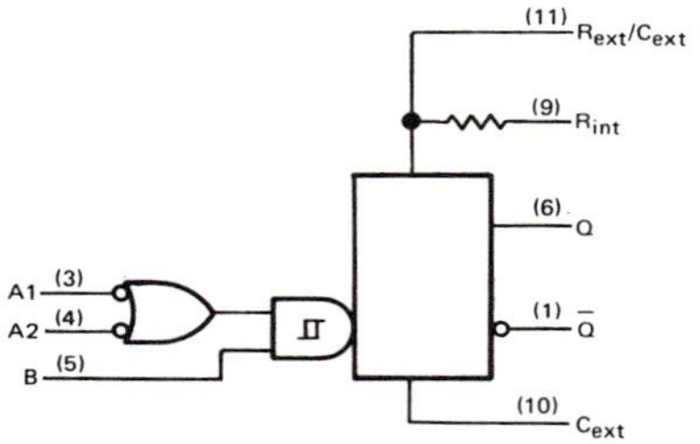

A1 (3)
A2 (4)
B (5)
(11) R_{ext}/C_{ext}
(9) R_{int}
(6) Q
(1) $\overline{Q}$
(10) C_{ext}

'121 . . . R_{int} = 2 kΩ NOM
'L121 . . . R_{int} = 4 kΩ NOM

Pin numbers shown on logic notation are for J or N packages.

NOTES: 1. An external capacitor may be connected between C_{ext} (positive) and R_{ext}/C_{ext}.
2. To use the internal timing resistor, connect R_{int} to V_{CC}. For improved pulse width accuracy and repeatability, connect an external resistor between R_{ext}/C_{ext} and V_{CC} with R_{int} open-circuited.

schematics of inputs and outputs

EQUIVALENT OF EACH INPUT

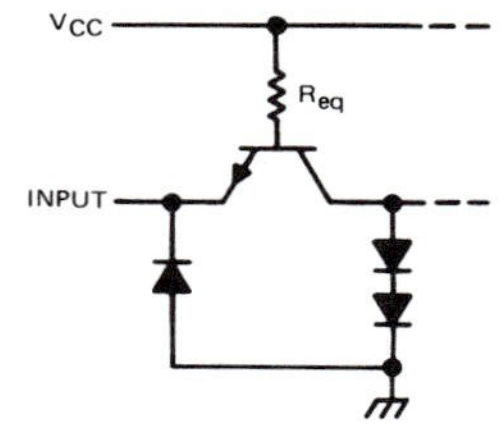

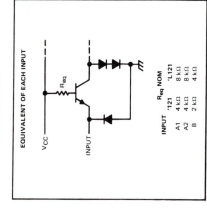

V_{CC}
R_{eq}
INPUT

INPUT	R_{eq} NOM '121	R_{eq} NOM 'L121
A1	4 kΩ	8 kΩ
A2	4 kΩ	8 kΩ
B	2 kΩ	4 kΩ

TYPICAL OF BOTH OUTPUTS

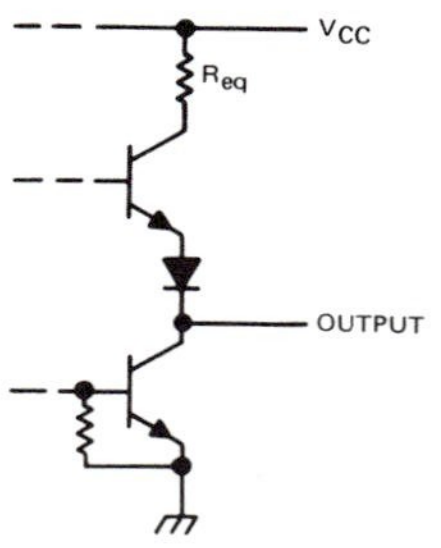

V_{CC}
R_{eq}
OUTPUT

'121: R_{eq} = 130 Ω NOM
'L121: R_{eq} = 260 Ω NOM

Courtesy of Texas Instruments Incorporated

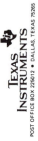

absolute maximum ratings over operating free-air temperature range (unless otherwise noted)

Supply voltage, V_{CC} (see Note 1) '121 .... 7 V
'L121 .... 8 V
Input voltage .... 5.5 V
Operating free-air temperature range: SN54121, SN54L121 .... -55°C to 125°C
SN74121 .... 0°C to 70°C
Storage temperature range .... -65°C to 150°C

NOTE 1: Voltage values are with respect to network ground terminal.

recommended operating conditions

			SN54121 SN74121			SN54L121			UNIT
			MIN	NOM	MAX	MIN	NOM	MAX	
V_{CC}	Supply voltage	54 Family	4.5	5	5.5	4.5	5	5.5	V
		74 Family	4.75	5	5.25				
I_{OH}	High-level output current				-0.4			-0.2	mA
I_{OL}	Low-level output current				16			8	mA
dv/dt	Rate of rise or fall of input pulse	Schmitt input,B			1			1	V/s
		Logic inputs, A1, A2			1			1	V/µs
$t_{w(in)}$	Input pulse width		50			100			ns
R_{ext}	External timing capacitance	54 Family	1.4		30	1.4		30	kΩ
		74 Family	1.4		40				
C_{ext}	External timing capacitance		0		1000	0		1000	µF
	Duty cycle	R_T = 2 kΩ			67			67	%
		R_T = MAX R_{ext}			90			90	
T_A	Operating free-air temperature	54 Family	-55		125	-55		125	°C
		74 Family	0		70				

electrical characteristics over recommended operating free-air temperature range (unless otherwise noted)

	PARAMETER	TEST CONDITIONS†		SN54121 SN74121			SN54L121			UNIT
				MIN	TYP‡	MAX	MIN	TYP‡	MAX	
V_{T+}	Positive-going threshold voltage at A input	V_{CC} = MIN			1.4	2		1.4	2	V
V_{T-}	Negative-going threshold voltage at A input	V_{CC} = MIN		0.8	1.4		0.8	1.4		V
V_{T+}	Positive-going threshold voltage at B input	V_{CC} = MIN			1.55	2		1.55	2	V
V_{T-}	Negative-going threshold voltage at B input	V_{CC} = MIN		0.8	1.35		0.8	1.35		V
V_{IK}	Input clamp voltage	V_{CC} = MIN, I_I = -12 mA				-1.5			-1.5	V
V_{OH}	High-level output voltage	V_{CC} = MIN, I_{OH} = MAX		2.4	3.4		2.4	3.4		V
V_{OL}	Low-level output voltage	V_{CC} = MIN, I_{OL} = MAX			0.2	0.4		0.2	0.4	V
I_I	Input current at maximum input voltage	V_{CC} = MAX, V_I = 5.5 V				1			1	mA
I_{IH}	High-level input current	V_{CC} = MAX, V_I = 2.4 V	A1 or A2			20			20	µA
			B			40			40	
I_{IL}	Low-level input current	V_{CC} = MAX, V_I = 0.4 V	A1 or A2			-0.8			-0.8	mA
			B			-1.6			-1.6	
I_{OS}	Short-circuit output current♦	V_{CC} = MAX	54 Family	-20		-55	-10		-27	mA
			74 Family	-18		-55				
I_{CC}	Supply current	V_{CC} = MAX	Quiescent		13	25		7	12	mA
			Triggered		23	40		9	20	

†For conditions shown as MIN or MAX, use the appropriate value specified under recommended operating conditions.
‡All typical values are at V_{CC} = 5 V, T_A = 25°C.
♦Not more than one output should be shorted at a time.

switching characteristics, V_{CC} = 5 V, T_A = 25°C

	PARAMETER	TEST CONDITIONS	'121			'L121			UNIT
			MIN	TYP	MAX	MIN	TYP	MAX	
t_{PLH}	Propagation delay time, low-to-high-level Q output from either A input		45	70				140	ns
t_{PLH}	Propagation delay time, low-to-high-level Q output from B input	C_L = 15 pF, R_L = 400 Ω for '121,	35	55				110	ns
t_{PHL}	Propagation delay time, high-to-low-level $\overline{Q}$ output from either A input	R_L = 800 Ω for 'L121, See Note 2	50	80				160	ns
t_{PHL}	Propagation delay time, high-to-low-level $\overline{Q}$ output from B input		40	65				130	ns
$t_{w(out)}$	Pulse width obtained using internal timing resistor	C_{ext} = 80 pF, R_{int} to V_{CC}	70	110	150	70	225	260	ns
$t_{w(out)}$	Pulse width obtained with zero timing capacitance	C_{ext} = 0, R_{int} to V_{CC}		30	50		35	70	ns
$t_{w(out)}$	Pulse width obtained using external timing resistor	C_{ext} = 100 pF, R_T = 10 kΩ	600	700	800	600	700	850	ns
		C_{ext} = 1 µF, R_T = 10 kΩ	6	7	8	6	7	8	ms

NOTE 2: See General Information Section for load circuits and voltage waveforms.

TEXAS INSTRUMENTS
POST OFFICE BOX 225012 • DALLAS, TEXAS 75265

TEXAS INSTRUMENTS
POST OFFICE BOX 225012 • DALLAS, TEXAS 75265

National Semiconductor

DM54125/DM74125 Quad TRI-STATE® Buffers

General Description

This device contains four independent gates each of which performs a non-inverting buffer function. The outputs have the TRI-STATE feature. When enabled, the outputs exhibit the low impedance characteristics of a standard TTL output with additional drive capability at the high Logic level to permit the driving of bus lines without external pull-up resistors. When disabled, both the output transistors are turned off presenting a high-impedance state to the bus line. Thus the output will act neither as a significant load nor as a driver. To minimize the possibility that two outputs will attempt to take a common bus to opposite logic levels, the disable time is shorter than the enable time of the outputs.

Absolute Maximum Ratings (Note 1)

Supply Voltage	7V
Input Voltage	5.5V
Storage Temperature Range	−65°C to 150°C

Note 1: The "Absolute Maximum Ratings" are those values beyond which the safety of the device can not be guaranteed. The device should not be operated at these limits. The parametric values defined in the "Electrical Characteristics" table are not guaranteed at the absolute maximum ratings. The "Recommended Operating Conditions" table will define the conditions for actual device operation.

Connection Diagram

Dual-In-Line Package

DM54125 (J)   DM74125 (N)

TL/F/6540-1

Function Table

Y = A

Input		Output
A	C	Y
L	L	L
H	L	H
X	H	Hi-Z

H = High Logic Level
L = Low Logic Level
X = Either Low or High Logic Level
Hi-Z = TRI-STATE (Outputs are disabled)

Recommended Operating Conditions

Sym	Parameter	DM54125 Min	DM54125 Nom	DM54125 Max	DM74125 Min	DM74125 Nom	DM74125 Max	Units
V_{CC}	Supply Voltage	4.5	5	5.5	4.75	5	5.25	V
V_{IH}	High Level Input Voltage	2			2			V
V_{IL}	Low Level Input Voltage			0.8			0.8	V
I_{OH}	High Level Output Current			−2			−5.2	mA
I_{OL}	Low Level Output Current			16			16	mA
T_A	Free Air Operating Temperature	−55		125	0		70	°C

Electrical Characteristics over recommended operating free air temperature (unless otherwise noted)

Sym	Parameter	Conditions	Min	Typ (Note 1)	Max	Units
V_I	Input Clamp Voltage	$V_{CC} = Min$, $I_I = -12$ mA			−1.5	V
V_{OH}	High Level Output Voltage	$V_{CC} = Min$, $I_{OH} = Max$ $V_{IL} = Max$, $V_{IH} = Min$	2.4	3.3		V
V_{OL}	Low Level Output Voltage	$V_{CC} = Min$, $I_{OL} = Max$ $V_{IH} = Min$, $V_{IL} = Max$		0.2	0.4	V
I_I	Input Current @ Max Input Voltage	$V_{CC} = Max$, $V_I = 5.5V$			1	mA
I_{IH}	High Level Input Current	$V_{CC} = Max$, $V_I = 2.4V$			40	μA
I_{IL}	Low Level Input Current	$V_{CC} = Max$, $V_I = 0.4V$			−1.6	mA
I_{IZL}	Off-State Input Current with Low Level Input Voltage Applied	$V_{CC} = Max$ $V_I = 0.4V$			−40	μA
I_{OZH}	Off-State Output Current with High Level Output Voltage Applied	$V_{CC} = Max$, $V_O = 2.4V$ $V_{IH} = Min$, $V_{IL} = Max$			40	μA
I_{OZL}	Off-State Output Current with Low Level Output Voltage Applied	$V_{CC} = Max$, $V_O = 0.4V$ $V_{IH} = Min$, $V_{IL} = Max$			−40	μA
I_{OS}	Short Circuit Output Current	$V_{CC} = Max$ (Note 2) DM54	−30		−70	mA
		DM74	−28		−70	mA
I_{CC}	Supply Current	$V_{CC} = Max$ (Note 3)		36	54	mA

Note 1: All typicals are at $V_{CC} = 5V$, $T_A = 25°C$.
Note 2: Not more than one output should be shorted at a time.
Note 3: I_{CC} is measured with the output control (C) inputs at 4.5V, the data inputs grounded, and the outputs open.

TYPES SN54LS139A, SN54S139, SN74LS139A, SN74S139
DUAL 2-LINE TO 4-LINE DECODERS/DEMULTIPLEXERS

REVISED APRIL 1985

- **Designed Specifically for High-Speed:**
  Memory Decoders
  Data Transmission Systems

- **Two Fully Independent 2-to-4-Line Decoders/Demultiplexers**

- **Schottky Clamped for High Performance**

description

These Schottky-clamped TTL MSI circuits are designed to be used in high-performance memory decoding or data-routing applications requiring very short propagation delay times. In high-performance memory systems these decoders can be used to minimize the effects of system decoding. When employed with high-speed memories utilizing a fast enable circuit the delay times of these decoders and the enable time of the memory are usually less than the typical access time of the memory. This means that the effective system delay introduced by the Schottky-clamped system decoder is negligible.

The circuit comprises two individual two-line to four-line decoders in a single package. The active-low enable input can be used as a data line in demultiplexing applications.

All of these decoders/demultiplexers feature fully buffered inputs, each of which represents only one normalized load to its driving circuit. All inputs are clamped with high-performance Schottky diodes to suppress line-ringing and to simplify system design. The SN54LS139A and SN54S139 are characterized for operation range of −55°C to 125°C. The SN74LS139A and SN74S139 are characterized for operation from 0°C to 70°C.

SN54LS139A, SN54S139 . . . J OR W PACKAGE
SN74LS139A, SN74S139 . . . D, J OR N PACKAGE
(TOP VIEW)

1G̅	1	16	V_CC
1A	2	15	2G̅
1B	3	14	2A
1Y0	4	13	2B
1Y1	5	12	2Y0
1Y2	6	11	2Y1
1Y3	7	10	2Y2
GND	8	9	2Y3

SN54LS139A, SN54S139 . . . FK PACKAGE
SN74LS139A, SN74S139 . . . FN PACKAGE
(TOP VIEW)

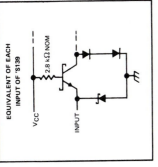

NC — No internal connection

FUNCTION TABLE

INPUTS			OUTPUTS			
ENABLE G̅	SELECT B	SELECT A	Y0	Y1	Y2	Y3
H	X	X	H	H	H	H
L	L	L	L	H	H	H
L	L	H	H	L	H	H
L	H	L	H	H	L	H
L	H	H	H	H	H	L

H = high level, L = low level, X = irrelevant

logic diagram

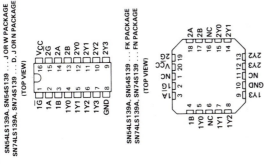

ENABLE 1G̅ (1)

SELECT INPUTS 1A (2), 1B (3)

ENABLE 2G̅ (15)

SELECT INPUTS 2A (14), 2B (13)

DATA OUTPUTS 1Y0 (4), 1Y1 (5), 1Y2 (6), 1Y3 (7), 2Y0 (12), 2Y1 (11), 2Y2 (10), 2Y3 (9)

Pin numbers shown on logic notation are for D, J or N packages.

TEXAS
INSTRUMENTS
POST OFFICE BOX 225012 ● DALLAS, TEXAS 75265

schematics of inputs and outputs

EQUIVALENT OF EACH INPUT OF 'LS139A
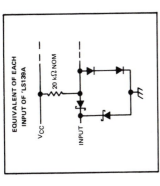
20 kΩ NOM
V_CC
INPUT

EQUIVALENT OF EACH INPUT OF 'S139
2.8 kΩ NOM
V_CC
INPUT

TYPICAL OF OUTPUTS OF 'LS139A
120 Ω NOM
V_CC
OUTPUT

TYPICAL OF OUTPUTS OF 'S139
50 Ω NOM
V_CC
OUTPUT

absolute maximum ratings over operating free-air temperature range (unless otherwise noted)

Supply voltage, V_CC (see Note 1) . . . . 7 V
Input voltage: 'LS139A, 'LS139 . . . . 7 V
       'S139 . . . . 5.5 V
Operating free-air temperature range: SN54LS139A, SN54S139 . . . . . . −55°C to 125°C
      SN74LS139A, SN74S139 . . . . . . 0°C to 70°C
Storage temperature range . . . . −65°C to 150°C

NOTE 1: Voltage values are with respect to network ground terminal.

TEXAS
INSTRUMENTS
POST OFFICE BOX 225012 ● DALLAS, TEXAS 75265

SN54S139, SN74S139

recommended operating conditions

		SN54S139			SN74S139			UNIT
		MIN	NOM	MAX	MIN	NOM	MAX	
V_{CC}	Supply voltage	4.5	5	5.5	4.75	5	5.25	V
V_{IH}	High-level input voltage	2			2			V
V_{IL}	Low-level input voltage			0.8			0.8	V
I_{OH}	High-level output current			−1			−1	mA
I_{OL}	Low-level output current			20			20	mA
T_A	Operating free-air temperature	−55		125	0		70	°C

electrical characteristics over recommended operating free-air temperature range (unless otherwise noted)

PARAMETER	TEST CONDITIONS†		SN54S139 SN74S138 MIN	TYP‡	MAX	UNIT
V_{IK}	V_{CC} = MIN,	I_I = 18 mA			−1.2	V
V_{OH}	V_{CC} = MIN, V_{IH} = 2 V, V_{IL} = 0.8 V, I_{OH} = −1 mA	SN54S'	2.5	3.4		V
		SN74S'	2.7	3.4		
V_{OL}	V_{CC} = MIN, V_{IH} = 2 V, V_{IL} = 0.8 V, I_{OL} = 20 mA				0.5	V
I_I	V_{CC} = MAX, V_I = 5.5 V				1	mA
I_{IH}	V_{CC} = MAX, V_I = 2.7 V				50	µA
I_{IL}	V_{CC} = MAX, V_I = 0.5 V				−2	mA
I_{OS}§	V_{CC} = MAX		−40		−100	mA
I_{CC}	V_{CC} = MAX, Outputs enabled and open	SN54S'		60	74	mA
		SN74S'		75	90	

†For conditions shown as MIN or MAX, use the appropriate value specified under recommended operating conditions.
‡All typical values are at V_{CC} = 5 V, T_A = 25°C.
§Not more than one output should be shorted at a time, and duration of the short circuit test should not exceed one second.

switching characteristics, V_{CC} = 5 V, T_A = 25°C (see note 2)

PARAMETER¶	FROM (INPUT)	TO (OUTPUT)	LEVELS OF DELAY	TEST CONDITIONS	SN54S139 SN74S139 MIN	TYP	MAX	UNIT
t_{PLH}	Binary Select	Any	2			5	7.5	ns
t_{PHL}						6.5	10	ns
t_{PLH}			3	R_L = 280 Ω, C_L = 15 pF		7	12	ns
t_{PHL}						8	12	ns
t_{PLH}	Enable	Any	2			5	8	ns
t_{PHL}						6.5	10	ns

¶t_{PLH} = propagation delay time, low to high-level output
t_{PHL} = propagation delay time, high to low-level output
NOTE 2: See General Information Section for load circuits and voltage waveforms.

TEXAS INSTRUMENTS
POST OFFICE BOX 225012 • DALLAS, TEXAS 75265

SN54LS139A, SN74LS139A

recommended operating conditions

		SN54LS139A			SN74LS139A			UNIT
		MIN	NOM	MAX	MIN	NOM	MAX	
V_{CC}	Supply voltage	4.5	5	5.5	4.75	5	5.25	V
V_{IH}	High-level input voltage	2			2			V
V_{IL}	Low-level input voltage			0.7			0.8	V
I_{OH}	High-level output current			−0.4			−0.4	mA
I_{OL}	Low-level output current			4			8	mA
T_A	Operating free-air temperature	−55		125	0		70	°C

electrical characteristics over recommended operating free-air temperature range (unless otherwise noted)

PARAMETER	TEST CONDITIONS†		SN54LS139A SN74LS139A MIN	TYP‡	MAX	UNIT
V_{IK}	V_{CC} = MIN,	I_I = −18 mA			−1.5	V
V_{OH}	V_{CC} = MIN, V_{IH} = 2 V, V_{IL} = MAX, I_{OH} = −0.4 mA		2.5	3.4		V
			2.7	3.4		
V_{OL}	V_{CC} = MIN, V_{IH} = 2 V, V_{IL} = MAX, I_{OL} = 4 mA			0.25	0.4	V
	I_{OL} = 8 mA			0.35	0.5	
I_I	V_{CC} = MAX, V_I = 7 V				0.1	mA
I_{IH}	V_{CC} = MAX, V_I = 2.7 V				20	µA
I_{IL}	V_{CC} = MAX, V_I = 0.4 V				−0.4	mA
I_{OS}§	V_{CC} = MAX		−20		−100	mA
I_{CC}	V_{CC} = MAX, Outputs enabled and open			6.8	11	mA

switching characteristics, V_{CC} = 5 V, T_A = 25°C (see note 2)

PARAMETER¶	FROM (INPUT)	TO (OUTPUT)	LEVELS OF DELAY	TEST CONDITIONS	SN54LS139A SN74LS139A MIN	TYP	MAX	UNIT
t_{PLH}	Binary Select	Any	2			13	20	ns
t_{PHL}						22	33	ns
t_{PLH}			3	R_L = 2 kΩ, C_L = 15 pF		18	29	ns
t_{PHL}						25	38	ns
t_{PLH}	Enable	Any	2			16	24	ns
t_{PHL}						21	32	ns

¶t_{PLH} = propagation delay time, low to high level output; t_{PHL} = propagation delay time, high-to-low-level output.
NOTE 2: See General Information Section for load circuits and voltage waveforms.

TEXAS INSTRUMENTS
POST OFFICE BOX 225012 • DALLAS, TEXAS 75265

logic diagram

'148, 'LS148

'147, 'LS147

Pin numbers shown on logic notation are for D, J or N packages.

'147, 'LS147

- Encodes 10-Line Decimal to 4-Line BCD

- Applications Include:

  Keyboard Encoding
  Range Selection: '148, 'LS148

- Encodes 8 Data Lines to 3-Line Binary (Octal)

- Applications Include:

  N-Bit Encoding
  Code Converters and Generators

TYPE	TYPICAL DATA DELAY	TYPICAL POWER DISSIPATION
'147	10 ns	225 mW
'148	10 ns	190 mW
'LS147	15 ns	60 mW
'LS148	15 ns	60 mW

description

These TTL encoders feature priority decoding of the inputs to ensure that only the highest-order data line is encoded. The '147 and 'LS147 encode nine data lines to four-line (8-4-2-1) BCD. The implied decimal zero condition requires no input condition as zero is encoded when all nine data lines are at a high logic level. The '148 and 'LS148 encode eight data lines to three-line (4-2-1) binary (octal). Cascading circuitry (enable input EI and enable output EO) has been provided to allow octal expansion without the need for external circuitry. For all types, data inputs and outputs are active at the low logic level. All inputs are buffered to represent one normalized Series 54/74 or 54LS/74LS load, respectively.

SN54147, SN54LS147,
SN54148, SN54LS148, SN74148 . . . J OR W PACKAGE
SN74147, SN74148 . . . J OR N PACKAGE
SN74LS147, SN74LS148 . . . D, J OR N PACKAGE
(TOP VIEW)

'147, 'LS147

4	1	16 VCC
5	2	15 D
6	3	14 C
7	4	13 B
8	5	12 1
C	6	11 9
B	7	10 9
GND	8	9 A

'148, 'LS148

4	1	16 VCC
5	2	15 EO
6	3	14 GS
7	4	13 3
EI	5	12 2
A2	6	11 1
A1	7	10 0
GND	8	9 A0

SN54LS147, SN54LS148 . . . FK PACKAGE
SN74LS147, SN74LS148 . . . FN PACKAGE
(TOP VIEW)

'147, 'LS147

'LS148

NC - No internal connection

'147, 'LS147
FUNCTION TABLE

INPUTS										OUTPUTS			
1	2	3	4	5	6	7	8	9	D	C	B	A
H	H	H	H	H	H	H	H	H	H	H	H	H
X	X	X	X	X	X	X	X	L	L	H	H	L
X	X	X	X	X	X	X	L	H	L	H	H	H
X	X	X	X	X	X	L	H	H	H	L	L	L
X	X	X	X	X	L	H	H	H	H	L	L	H
X	X	X	X	L	H	H	H	H	H	L	H	L
X	X	X	L	H	H	H	H	H	H	L	H	H
X	X	L	H	H	H	H	H	H	H	H	L	L
X	L	H	H	H	H	H	H	H	H	H	L	H
L	H	H	H	H	H	H	H	H	H	H	H	L

'148, 'LS148
FUNCTION TABLE

INPUTS									OUTPUTS				
EI	0	1	2	3	4	5	6	7	A2	A1	A0	GS	EO
H	X	X	X	X	X	X	X	X	H	H	H	H	H
L	H	H	H	H	H	H	H	H	H	H	H	H	L
L	X	X	X	X	X	X	X	L	L	L	L	L	H
L	X	X	X	X	X	X	L	H	L	L	H	L	H
L	X	X	X	X	X	L	H	H	L	H	L	L	H
L	X	X	X	X	L	H	H	H	L	H	H	L	H
L	X	X	X	L	H	H	H	H	H	L	L	L	H
L	X	X	L	H	H	H	H	H	H	L	H	L	H
L	X	L	H	H	H	H	H	H	H	H	L	L	H
L	L	H	H	H	H	H	H	H	H	H	H	L	H

H = high logic level, L = low logic level, X = irrelevant

TYPICAL APPLICATION DATA

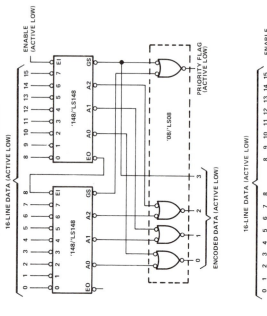

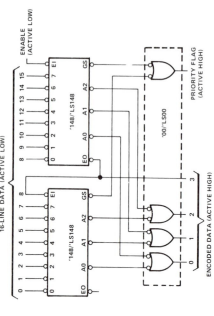

Since the '147/'LS147 and '148/'LS148 are combinational logic circuits, wrong addresses can appear during input transients. Moreover, for the '148/'LS148 a change from high to low at input EI can cause a transient low on the GS output when all inputs are high. This must be considered when strobing the outputs.

---

schematics of inputs and outputs

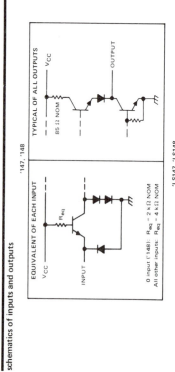

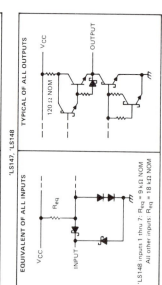

absolute maximum ratings over operating free-air temperature range (unless otherwise noted)

Supply voltage, V_{CC} (see Note 1) . . . . 7 V
Input voltage: '147, '148 . . . . 5.5 V
         'LS147, 'LS148 . . . . 7 V
Interemitter voltage: '148 only (see Note 2) . . . . 5.5 V
Operating free-air temperature range: SN54', SN54LS Circuits . . . . −55°C to 125°C
                        SN74', SN74LS Circuits . . . . 0°C to 70°C
Storage temperature range . . . . −65°C to 150°C

NOTES: 1. Voltage values, except interemitter voltage, are with respect to network ground terminal.
2. This is the voltage between two emitters of a multiple-emitter transistor. For '148 circuits, this rating applies between any two of the eight data lines, 0 through 7.

recommended operating conditions

	SN54'			SN74'			SN54LS'			SN74LS'			UNIT
	MIN	NOM	MAX	MIN	NOM	MAX	MIN	NOM	MAX	MIN	NOM	MAX	
Supply voltage, V_{CC}	4.5	5	5.5	4.75	5	5.25	4.5	5	5.5	4.75	5	5.25	V
High-level output current, I_{OH}			−800			−800			−400			−400	μA
Low-level output current, I_{OL}			16			16			4			8	mA
Operating free-air temperature, T_A	−55		125	0		70	−55		125	0		70	°C

TYPES SN54150, SN54151A, SN54152A, SN54LS151, SN54LS152, SN54S151, SN74151A, SN74LS151, SN74LS152, SN74S151 DATA SELECTORS/MULTIPLEXERS

DECEMBER 1972–REVISED DECEMBER 1983

SN54150 .... J OR W PACKAGE
SN74150 .... J OR N PACKAGE
(TOP VIEW)

- '150 Selects One-of-Sixteen Data Sources
- Others Select One-of-Eight Data Sources
- Performs Parallel-to-Serial Conversion
- Permits Multiplexing from N Lines to One Line
- Also For Use as Boolean Function Generator
- Input-Clamping Diodes Simplify System Design
- Fully Compatible with Most TTL Circuits

TYPE	TYPICAL AVERAGE PROPAGATION DELAY TIME DATA INPUT TO W OUTPUT	TYPICAL POWER DISSIPATION
'150	13 ns	200 mW
'151A	8 ns	145 mW
'152A	8 ns	130 mW
'LS151	13 ns	30 mW
'LS152	13 ns	28 mW
'S151	4.5 ns	225 mW

SN54151A, SN54152A, SN54S151 .... J OR W PACKAGE
SN74151A .... J OR W PACKAGE
SN74151A, SN74S151 .... D, J OR N PACKAGE
(TOP VIEW)

SN54LS151, SN54S151 .... FK PACKAGE
SN74LS151, SN74S151 .... FN PACKAGE
(TOP VIEW)

NC – No internal connection

SN54152A, SN54LS152 .... W PACKAGE
(TOP VIEW)

description

These monolithic data selectors/multiplexers contain full on-chip binary decoding to select the desired data source. The '150 selects one-of-sixteen data sources; the '151A, '152A, 'LS151, 'LS152, and 'S151 select one-of-eight data sources. The '150, '151A, 'LS151, and 'S151 have a strobe input which must be at a low logic level to enable these devices. A high level at the strobe forces the W output high, and the Y output (as applicable) low.

The '151A, 'LS151, and 'S151 feature complementary W and Y outputs whereas the '150, '152A, and 'LS152 have an inverted (W) output only.

The '151A and '152A incorporate address buffers which have symmetrical propagation delay times through the complementary paths. This reduces the possibility of transients occurring at the output(s) due to changes made at the select inputs, even when the '151A outputs are enabled (i.e., strobe low).

schematics of inputs and outputs

TYPICAL OF ALL OUTPUTS OF '150, '151A, '152A

TYPICAL OF ALL OUTPUTS OF 'LS151, 'LS152

TYPICAL OF ALL OUTPUTS OF 'S151

logic

'150 FUNCTION TABLE

INPUTS					OUTPUT
SELECT				STROBE	W
D	C	B	A	$\overline{G}$	W
X	X	X	X	H	H
L	L	L	L	L	$\overline{E0}$
L	L	L	H	L	$\overline{E1}$
L	L	H	L	L	$\overline{E2}$
L	L	H	H	L	$\overline{E3}$
L	H	L	L	L	$\overline{E4}$
L	H	L	H	L	$\overline{E5}$
L	H	H	L	L	$\overline{E6}$
L	H	H	H	L	$\overline{E7}$
H	L	L	L	L	$\overline{E8}$
H	L	L	H	L	$\overline{E9}$
H	L	H	L	L	$\overline{E10}$
H	L	H	H	L	$\overline{E11}$
H	H	L	L	L	$\overline{E12}$
H	H	L	H	L	$\overline{E13}$
H	H	H	L	L	$\overline{E14}$
H	H	H	H	L	$\overline{E15}$

'151A, 'LS151, 'S151 FUNCTION TABLE

INPUTS				OUTPUTS	
SELECT			STROBE		
C	B	A	$\overline{G}$	Y	W
X	X	X	H	L	H
L	L	L	L	D0	$\overline{D0}$
L	L	H	L	D1	$\overline{D1}$
L	H	L	L	D2	$\overline{D2}$
L	H	H	L	D3	$\overline{D3}$
H	L	L	L	D4	$\overline{D4}$
H	L	H	L	D5	$\overline{D5}$
H	H	L	L	D6	$\overline{D6}$
H	H	H	L	D7	$\overline{D7}$

'152A, 'LS152 FUNCTION TABLE

SELECT INPUTS			OUTPUT
C	B	A	W
L	L	L	$\overline{D0}$
L	L	H	$\overline{D1}$
L	H	L	$\overline{D2}$
L	H	H	$\overline{D3}$
H	L	L	$\overline{D4}$
H	L	H	$\overline{D5}$
H	H	L	$\overline{D6}$
H	H	H	$\overline{D7}$

H = high level, L = low level, X = irrelevant
E0, E1 ... E15 = the complement of the level of the respective E input
D0, D1 ... D7 = the level of the D respective input

PRODUCTION DATA
This document contains information current as of publication date. Products conform to specifications per the terms of Texas Instruments standard warranty. Production processing does not necessarily include testing of all parameters.

For SN54LS152 Chip Carrier Information, Contact The Factory.

TEXAS INSTRUMENTS
POST OFFICE BOX 225012 • DALLAS, TEXAS 75265

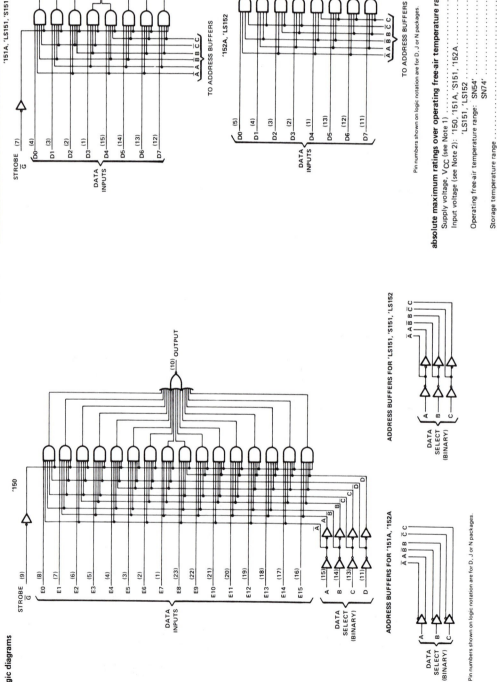

'151A, 'LS151, 'S151

'152A, 'LS152

TO ADDRESS BUFFERS

absolute maximum ratings over operating free-air temperature range (unless otherwise noted)

Supply voltage, V_{CC} (see Note 1) .... 7 V
Input voltage (see Note 2): '150, '151A, 'S151, '152A .... 5.5 V
              'LS151, 'LS152 .... 7 V
Operating free-air temperature range: SN54' .... −55°C to 125°C
              SN74' .... 0°C to 70°C
Storage temperature range .... −65°C to 150°C

NOTES: 1. Voltage values are with respect to network ground terminal.
        2. For the '150, input voltages must be zero or positive with respect to network ground terminal.

Pin numbers shown on logic notation are for D, J or N packages.

TEXAS INSTRUMENTS
POST OFFICE BOX 225012 • DALLAS, TEXAS 75265

---

logic diagrams

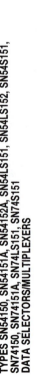

'150

ADDRESS BUFFERS FOR '151A, '152A

ADDRESS BUFFERS FOR 'LS151, 'S151, 'LS152

Pin numbers shown on logic notation are for D, J or N packages.

TEXAS INSTRUMENTS
POST OFFICE BOX 225012 • DALLAS, TEXAS 75265

TYPES SN54LS151, SN54LS152, SN74LS151 DATA SELECTORS/MULTIPLEXERS

recommended operating conditions

	SN54LS' MIN	NOM	MAX	SN74LS' MIN	NOM	MAX	UNIT
Supply voltage, V_{CC}	4.5	5	5.5	4.75	5	5.25	V
High-level output current, I_{OH}			-400			-400	µA
Low-level output current, I_{OL}			4			8	mA
Operating free-air temperature, T_A	-55		125	0		70	°C

electrical characteristics over recommended operating free-air temperature range (unless otherwise noted)

PARAMETER	TEST CONDITIONS†	SN54LS' MIN	TYP‡	MAX	SN74LS' MIN	TYP‡	MAX	UNIT
V_{IH} High-level input voltage		2			2			V
V_{IL} Low-level input voltage				0.7			0.8	V
V_{IK} Input clamp voltage	V_{CC} = MIN, I_I = -18 mA			-1.5			-1.5	V
V_{OH} High-level output voltage	V_{CC} = MIN, V_{IH} = 2 V, V_{IL} = V_{IL} max, I_{OH} = -400 µA	2.5	3.4		2.7	3.4		V
V_{OL} Low-level output voltage	V_{CC} = MIN, V_{IH} = 2 V, V_{IL} = V_{IL} max, I_{OL} = 4 mA	0.25	0.4		0.25		0.4	V
	I_{OL} = 8 mA		0.35	0.5				V
I_I Input current at maximum input voltage	V_{CC} = MAX, V_I = 7 V			0.1			0.1	mA
I_{IH} High-level input current	V_{CC} = MAX, V_I = 2.7 V			20			20	µA
I_{IL} Low-level input current	V_{CC} = MAX, V_I = 0.4 V			-0.4			-0.4	mA
I_{OS} Short-circuit output current§	V_{CC} = MAX	-20		-100	-20		-100	mA
I_{CC} Supply current	V_{CC} = MAX, Outputs open, All inputs at 4.5 V — 'LS151		6.0	10		6.0	10	mA
	'LS152		5.6	9				

† For conditions shown as MIN or MAX, use the appropriate value specified under recommended operating conditions for the applicable device type.
‡ All typical values are at V_{CC} = 5 V, T_A = 25°C.
§ Not more than one output should be shorted at a time and duration of short-circuit should not exceed one second.

switching characteristics, V_{CC} = 5 V, T_A = 25°C

PARAMETER¶	FROM (INPUT)	TO (OUTPUT)	TEST CONDITIONS	SN54LS', SN74LS' MIN	TYP	MAX	UNIT
t_{PLH}	A, B, or C (4 levels)	Y			27	43	ns
t_{PHL}					18	30	ns
t_{PLH}	A, B, or C (3 levels)	W			14	23	ns
t_{PHL}					20	32	ns
t_{PLH}	Strobe $\overline{G}$	Y	C_L = 15 pF,		26	42	ns
t_{PHL}			R_L = 2 kΩ,		20	32	ns
t_{PLH}	Strobe $\overline{G}$	W	See Note 4		15	24	ns
t_{PHL}					18	30	ns
t_{PLH}	Any D	Y			20	32	ns
t_{PHL}					16	26	ns
t_{PLH}	Any D	W			13	21	ns
t_{PHL}					12	20	ns

¶ t_{PLH} ≡ propagation delay time, low-to-high-level output
t_{PHL} ≡ propagation delay time, high-to-low-level output
NOTE 4: See General Information Section for load circuits and voltage waveforms.

TYPES SN54150, SN54151A, SN54152A, SN74150, SN74151A DATA SELECTORS/MULTIPLEXERS

recommended operating conditions

	SN54' MIN	NOM	MAX	SN74' MIN	NOM	MAX	UNIT
Supply voltage, V_{CC}	4.5	5	5.5	4.75	5	5.25	V
High-level output current, I_{OH}			-800			-800	µA
Low-level output current, I_{OL}			16			16	mA
Operating free-air temperature, T_A	-55		125	0		70	°C

electrical characteristics over recommended operating free-air temperature range (unless otherwise noted)

PARAMETER	TEST CONDITIONS†	'150 MIN	TYP‡	MAX	'151A, '152A MIN	TYP‡	MAX	UNIT
V_{IH} High-level input voltage		2			2			V
V_{IL} Low-level input voltage				0.8			0.8	V
V_{IK} Input clamp voltage	V_{CC} = MIN, I_I = -8 mA			-1.5			-1.5	V
V_{OH} High-level output voltage	V_{CC} = MIN, V_{IH} = 2 V, I_{OH} = -800 µA	2.4	3.4		2.4	3.4		V
V_{OL} Low-level output voltage	V_{CC} = MIN, V_{IL} = 0.8 V, I_{OL} = 16 mA		0.2	0.4		0.2	0.4	V
I_I Input current at maximum input voltage	V_{CC} = MAX, V_I = 5.5 V			1			1	mA
I_{IH} High-level input current	V_{CC} = MAX, V_I = 2.4 V			40			40	µA
I_{IL} Low-level input current	V_{CC} = MAX, V_I = 0.4 V			-1.6			-1.6	mA
I_{OS} Short-circuit output current§	V_{CC} = MAX — SN54'	-20		-55				mA
	SN74'	-18		-55				
I_{CC} Supply current	V_{CC} = MAX, See Note 3 — '150		40	68				mA
	'151A					29	48	
	'152A					26	43	

† For conditions shown as MIN or MAX, use the appropriate value specified under recommended operating conditions for the applicable device type.
‡ All typical values at V_{CC} = 5 V, T_A = 25°C.
§ Not more than one output of the '151A should be shorted at a time.
NOTE 3: I_{CC} is measured with the strobe and data select inputs at 4.5 V, all other inputs and outputs open.

switching characteristics, V_{CC} = 5 V, T_A = 25°C

PARAMETER¶	FROM (INPUT)	TO (OUTPUT)	TEST CONDITIONS	'150 MIN	TYP	MAX	'151A, '152A MIN	TYP	MAX	UNIT
t_{PLH}	A, B, or C (4 levels)	Y						25	38	ns
t_{PHL}								25	38	ns
t_{PLH}	A, B, C, or D (3 levels)	W			23	35		17	26	ns
t_{PHL}					22	33		19	30	ns
t_{PLH}	Strobe $\overline{G}$	Y	C_L = 15 pF,					21	33	ns
t_{PHL}			R_L = 400 Ω,					22	33	ns
t_{PLH}	Strobe $\overline{G}$	W	See Note 4		15.5	24		14	21	ns
t_{PHL}					21	30		15	23	ns
t_{PLH}	D0 thru D7	Y						13	20	ns
t_{PHL}								18	27	ns
t_{PLH}	E0 thru E15, or D0 thru D7	W			8.5	14		8	14	ns
t_{PHL}					13	20		8	14	ns

¶ t_{PLH} ≡ propagation delay time, low-to-high-level output
t_{PHL} ≡ propagation delay time, high-to-low-level output
NOTE 4: See General Information Section for load circuits and voltage waveforms.

TEXAS INSTRUMENTS
POST OFFICE BOX 225012 • DALLAS, TEXAS 75265

TEXAS INSTRUMENTS
POST OFFICE BOX 225012 • DALLAS, TEXAS 75265

TYPES SN54165, SN54LS165A, SN74165, SN74LS165A
PARALLEL-LOAD 8-BIT SHIFT REGISTERS

OCTOBER 1976—REVISED APRIL 1985

- **Complementary Outputs**
- **Direct Overriding Load (Data) Inputs**
- **Gated Clock Inputs**
- **Parallel-to-Serial Data Conversion**

TYPE	TYPICAL MAXIMUM CLOCK FREQUENCY	TYPICAL POWER DISSIPATION
'165	26 MHz	210 mW
'LS165A	35 MHz	90 mW

description

The '165 and 'LS165A are 8-bit serial shift registers that shift the data in the direction of Q_A toward Q_H when clocked. Parallel-in access to each stage is made available by eight individual direct data inputs that are enabled by a low level at the shift/load input. These registers also feature gated clock inputs and complementary outputs from the eighth bit. All inputs are diode-clamped to minimize transmission-line effects, thereby simplifying system design.

Clocking is accomplished through a 2-input positive-NOR gate, permitting one input to be used as a clock-inhibit function. Holding either of the clock inputs high inhibits clocking and holding either clock input low with the shift/load input high enables the other clock input. The clock-inhibit input should be changed to the high level only while the clock input is high. Parallel loading is inhibited as long as the shift/load input is high. Data at the parallel inputs are loaded directly into the register while the shift/load input is low independently of the levels of the clock, clock inhibit, or serial inputs.

SN54165, SN54LS165A . . . J OR W PACKAGE
SN74165 . . . J OR N PACKAGE
SN74LS165A . . . D, J OR N PACKAGE
(TOP VIEW)

SH/LD	1	16 VCC
CLK	2	15 CLK INH
E	3	14 D
F	4	13 C
G	5	12 B
H	6	11 A
$\overline{Q_H}$	7	10 SER
GND	8	9 Q_H

SN54LS165A . . . FK PACKAGE
SN74LS165A . . . FN PACKAGE
(TOP VIEW)

FUNCTION TABLE

INPUTS				INTERNAL OUTPUTS		OUTPUT
SHIFT/ LOAD	CLOCK INHIBIT	CLOCK	SERIAL	PARALLEL A . . . H	Q_A Q_B	Q_H
				a . . . h	a b	
L	X	X	X	a . . . h	a b	h
H	L	↑	H	X	H Q_{A0}	Q_{G0}
H	L	↑	L	X	L Q_{An}	Q_{Gn}
H	L	L	X	X	Q_{A0} Q_{B0}	Q_{H0}
H	H	X	X	X	Q_{A0} Q_{B0}	Q_{H0}

logic diagram (positive logic)

Pin numbers shown on logic notation are for D, J or N packages.

TEXAS INSTRUMENTS
POST OFFICE BOX 225012 • DALLAS, TEXAS 75265

This document contains information current as of publication date. Products conform to specifications per the terms of Texas Instruments standard warranty. Production processing does not necessarily include testing of all parameters.

304

Courtesy of Texas Instruments Incorporated

typical shift, load, and inhibit sequences

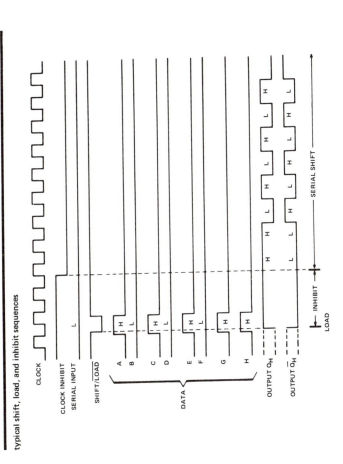

absolute maximum ratings over operating free-air temperature range (unless otherwise noted)

Supply voltage, V_{CC} (see Note 1) .... 7 V
Input voltage: SN54165, SN74165 .... 5.5 V
    SN54LS165A, SN74LS165A .... 7 V
Interemitter voltage (see Note 2) .... 5.5 V
Operating free-air temperature range: SN54165, SN54LS165A .... −55°C to 125°C
    SN74165, SN74LS165A .... 0°C to 70°C
Storage temperature range .... −65°C to 150°C

NOTES: 1. Voltage values, except interemitter voltage, are with respect to network ground terminal.
    2. This is the voltage between two emitters of a multiple-emitter transistor. This rating applies for the '165 to the shift/load input in conjunction with the clock-inhibit inputs.

---

recommended operating conditions

	SN54165			SN74165			UNIT
	MIN	NOM	MAX	MIN	NOM	MAX	
Supply voltage, V_{CC}	4.5	5	5.5	4.75	5	5.25	V
High-level output current, I_{OH}			−800			−800	μA
Low-level output current, I_{OL}			16			16	mA
Clock frequency, f_{clock}	0		20	0		20	MHz
Width of clock input pulse, $t_{w(clock)}$	25			25			ns
Width of load input pulse, $t_{w(load)}$	15			15			ns
Clock-enable setup time, t_{su} (see Figure 1)	30			30			ns
Parallel input setup time, t_{su} (see Figure 1)	10			10			ns
Serial input setup time, t_{su} (see Figure 2)	20			20			ns
Shift setup time, t_{su} (see Figure 2)	45			45			ns
Hold time at any input, t_h	0			0			ns
Operating free-air temperature, T_A	−55		125	0		70	°C

electrical characteristics over recommended operating free-air temperature range (unless otherwise noted)

PARAMETER		TEST CONDITIONS	SN54165			SN74165			UNIT
			MIN	TYP‡	MAX	MIN	TYP‡	MAX	
V_{IH}	High-level input voltage		2			2			V
V_{IL}	Low-level input voltage				0.8			0.8	V
V_{IK}	Input clamp voltage	V_{CC} = MIN, I_I = −12 mA			−1.5			−1.5	V
V_{OH}	High-level output voltage	V_{CC} = MIN, V_{IH} = 2 V, V_{IL} = 0.8 V, I_{OH} = −800 μA	2.4	3.4		2.4	3.4		V
V_{OL}	Low-level output voltage	V_{CC} = MIN, V_{IH} = 2 V, V_{IL} = 0.8 V, I_{OL} = 16 mA		0.2	0.4		0.2	0.4	V
I_I	Input current at maximum input voltage	V_{CC} = MAX, V_I = 5.5 V			1			1	mA
I_{IH}	High-level input current	V_{CC} = MAX, V_I = 2.4 V			80			80	μA
I_{IL}	Low-level input current	Shift/load	V_{CC} = MAX, V_I = 0.4 V			−3.2			−3.2	mA
		Other inputs				−1.6			−1.6	mA
I_{OS}	Short-circuit output current§	V_{CC} = MAX	−20		−55	−18		−55	mA
I_{CC}	Supply current	V_{CC} = MAX, See Note 3		42	63		42	63	mA

NOTE 3: With the outputs open, clock inhibit and clock at 4.5 V, and a clock pulse applied to the shift/load input, I_{CC} is measured first with the parallel inputs at 4.5 V, then with the parallel inputs grounded.
†For conditions shown as MIN or MAX, use the appropriate value specified under recommended operating conditions.
‡All typical values are at V_{CC} = 5 V, T_A = 25°C.
§Not more than one output should be shorted at a time.

switching characteristics, V_{CC} = 5 V, T_A = 25°C

PARAMETER¶	FROM (INPUT)	TO (OUTPUT)	TEST CONDITIONS	MIN	TYP	MAX	UNIT
f_{max}				20	26		MHz
t_{PLH}	Load	Any	C_L = 15 pF, R_L = 400 Ω, See figures 1 thru 3		21	31	ns
t_{PHL}					27	40	ns
t_{PLH}	Clock	Any			16	24	ns
t_{PHL}					21	31	ns
t_{PLH}	H	Q_H			11	17	ns
t_{PHL}					24	36	ns
t_{PLH}	H	$\overline{Q}_H$			18	27	ns
t_{PHL}					18	27	ns

¶f_{max} ≡ maximum clock frequency
t_{PLH} ≡ propagation delay time, low-to-high-level output
t_{PHL} ≡ propagation delay time, high-to-low-level output

TYPES SN54174, SN54175, SN54LS174, SN54LS175, SN54S175, SN74174, SN74175, SN74LS174, SN74LS175, SN74S174, SN74S175
HEX/QUADRUPLE D-TYPE FLIP-FLOPS WITH CLEAR

DECEMBER 1972—REVISED DECEMBER 1983

- '174, 'LS174, 'S174 . . . HEX D-TYPE FLIP-FLOPS
- '175, 'LS175, 'S175 . . . QUADRUPLE D-TYPE FLIP-FLOPS

- **'174, 'LS174, 'S174 Contain Six Flip-Flops with Single-Rail Outputs**
- **'175, 'LS175, 'S175 Contain Four Flip-Flops with Double-Rail Outputs**
- **Three Performance Ranges Offered: See Table Lower Right**
- **Buffered Clock and Direct Clear Inputs**
- **Individual Data Input to Each Flip-Flop**
- **Applications include:**
  Buffer/Storage Registers
  Shift Registers
  Pattern Generators

description

These monolithic, positive-edge-triggered flip-flops utilize TTL circuitry to implement D-type flip-flop logic. All have a direct clear input, and the '175, 'LS175, and 'S175 feature complementary outputs from each flip-flop.

Information at the D inputs meeting the setup time requirements is transferred to the Q outputs on the positive-going edge of the clock pulse. Clock triggering occurs at a particular voltage level and is not directly related to the transition time of the positive-going pulse. When the clock input is at either the high or low level, the D input signal has no effect at the output.

These circuits are fully compatible for use with most TTL circuits.

SN54174, SN54LS174, SN54S174 . . . J OR W PACKAGE
SN74174, SN74LS174, SN74S174 . . . J OR N PACKAGE
(TOP VIEW)

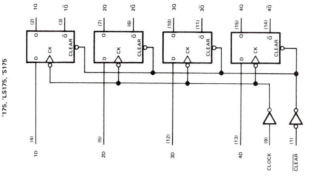

'174, 'LS174, 'S174

SN54175, SN54LS175, SN54S175 . . . J OR W PACKAGE
SN74175, SN74LS175, SN74S175 . . . J OR N PACKAGE
(TOP VIEW)

SN54LS174, SN54S174 . . . FK PACKAGE
SN74LS174, SN74S174 . . . FN PACKAGE
(TOP VIEW)

SN54LS175, SN54S175 . . . FK PACKAGE
SN74LS175, SN74S175 . . . FN PACKAGE
(TOP VIEW)

NC – No internal connection

FUNCTION TABLE
(EACH FLIP-FLOP)

INPUTS		OUTPUTS	
CLEAR	CLOCK	D	Q	Q̄
L	X	X	L	H
H	↑	H	H	L
H	↑	L	L	H
H	L	X	Q₀	Q̄₀

H = high level (steady state)
L = low level (steady state)
X = irrelevant
↑ = transition from low to high level
Q₀ = the level of Q before the indicated steady-state input conditions were established.
† = '175, 'LS175, and 'S175 only.

TYPES	TYPICAL MAXIMUM CLOCK FREQUENCY	TYPICAL POWER DISSIPATION PER FLIP-FLOP
'174, '175	35 MHz	38 mW
'LS174, 'LS175	40 MHz	14 mW
'S174, 'S175	110 MHz	75 mW

logic diagrams

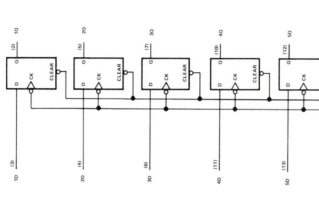

'174, 'LS174, 'S174

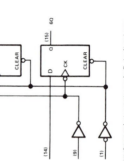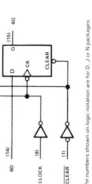

'175, 'LS175, 'S175

Pin numbers shown on logic notation are for D, J or N packages.

TEXAS INSTRUMENTS
POST OFFICE BOX 225012 • DALLAS, TEXAS 75265

TYPES SN54181, SN54LS181, SN54S181, SN74181, SN74LS181, SN74S181
ARITHMETIC LOGIC UNITS/FUNCTION GENERATORS
DECEMBER 1972 – REVISED DECEMBER 1983

- **Full Look-Ahead for High-Speed Operations on Long Words**
- **Input Clamping Diodes Minimize Transmission-Line Effects**
- **Darlington Outputs Reduce Turn-Off Time**
- **Arithmetic Operating Modes:**
  Addition
  Subtraction
  Shift Operand A One Position
  Magnitude Comparison
  Plus Twelve Other Arithmetic Operations
- **Logic Function Modes:**
  Exclusive-OR
  Comparator
  AND, NAND, OR, NOR
  Plus Ten Other Logic Operations

description

The '181, 'LS181, and 'S181 are arithmetic logic units (ALU)/function generators that have a complexity of 75 equivalent gates on a monolithic chip. These circuits perform 16 binary arithmetic operations on two 4-bit words as shown in Tables 1 and 2. These operations are selected by the four function-select lines (S0, S1, S2, S3) and include addition, subtraction, decrement, and straight transfer. When performing arithmetic manipulations, the internal carries must be enabled by applying a low-level voltage to the mode control input (M). A full carry look-ahead scheme is made available in these devices for fast, simultaneous carry generation by means of two cascade-outputs (pins 15 and 17) for the four bits in the package. When used in conjunction with the SN54182, SN54S182, SN74182, or SN74S182, full carry look-ahead circuits, high-speed arithmetic operations can be performed. The typical addition times shown above illustrate the little additional time required for addition of longer words when full carry look ahead is employed. The method of cascading '182 or 'S182 circuits with these ALU's to provide multi-level full carry look-ahead is illustrated under typical applications data for the '182 and 'S182.

If high speed is not of importance, a ripple-carry input (C_n) and a ripple-carry output (C_{n+4}) are available. However, the ripple-carry delay has also been minimized so that arithmetic manipulations for small word lengths can be performed without external circuitry.

SN54181, SN54LS181, SN54S181 . . . J OR W PACKAGE
SN74181 . . . J OR N PACKAGE
SN74LS181, SN74S181 . . . DW, J OR N PACKAGE
(TOP VIEW)

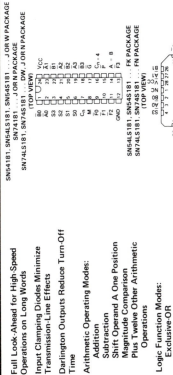

SN54LS181, SN54S181 . . . FK PACKAGE
SN74LS181, SN74S181 . . . FN PACKAGE
(TOP VIEW)

NC – No internal connection

TYPICAL ADDITION TIMES

NUMBER OF BITS	ADDITION TIMES				PACKAGE COUNT			CARRY METHOD BETWEEN ALU's
	USING '181	USING 'LS181	USING 'S181		ARITHMETIC/LOGIC UNITS	LOOK-AHEAD CARRY GENERATORS		
	AND '182	AND '182	AND 'S182					
1 to 4	24 ns	24 ns	11 ns		1			NONE
5 to 8	36 ns	40 ns	18 ns		2			RIPPLE
9 to 16	36 ns	44 ns	19 ns		3 or 4	1		FULL LOOK-AHEAD
17 to 64	60 ns	68 ns	28 ns		5 to 16	2 to 5		FULL LOOK-AHEAD

description (continued)

The '181, 'LS181, and 'S181 will accommodate active-high or active-low data if the pin designations are interpreted as follows:

PIN NUMBER	2	1	23	22	21	20	19	18	9	10	11	13	7	16	15	17
Active-low data (Table 1)	$\overline{A_0}$	$\overline{B_0}$	$\overline{A_1}$	$\overline{B_1}$	$\overline{A_2}$	$\overline{B_2}$	$\overline{A_3}$	$\overline{B_3}$	$\overline{F_0}$	$\overline{F_1}$	$\overline{F_2}$	$\overline{F_3}$	C_n	C_{n+4}	P	$\overline{G}$
Active-high data (Table 2)	A_0	B_0	A_1	B_1	A_2	B_2	A_3	B_3	F_0	F_1	F_2	F_3	$\overline{C_n}$	$\overline{C_{n+4}}$	X	Y

Subtraction is accomplished by 1's complement addition where the 1's complement of the subtrahend is generated internally. The resultant output is A–B–1, which requires an end-around or forced carry to provide A–B.

The '181, 'LS181, or 'S181 can also be utilized as a comparator. The A = B output is internally decoded from the function outputs (F0, F1, F2, F3) so that when two words of equal magnitude are applied at the A and B inputs, it will assume a high level to indicate equality (A = B). The ALU must be in the subtract mode with C_n = H when performing this comparison. The A = B output is open-collector so that it can be wire-AND connected to give a comparison for more than four bits. The carry output (C_{n+4}) can also be used to supply relative magnitude information. Again, the ALU must be placed in the subtract mode by placing the function select inputs S3, S2, S1, S0 at L, H, H, L, respectively.

INPUT C_n	OUTPUT C_{n+4}	ACTIVE-LOW DATA (FIGURE 1)	ACTIVE-HIGH DATA (FIGURE 2)
H	H	A > B	A < B
H	L	A < B	A > B
L	H	A ≥ B	A ≤ B
L	L	A ≤ B	A ≥ B

These circuits have been designed to not only incorporate all of the designer's requirements for arithmetic operations, but also to provide 16 possible functions of two Boolean variables without the use of external circuitry. These logic functions are selected by use of the four function-select inputs (S0, S1, S2, S3) with the mode-control input (M) at a high level to disable the internal carry. The 16 logic functions are detailed in Tables 1 and 2 and include exclusive-OR, NAND, AND, NOR, and OR functions.

Series 54, 54LS, and 54S devices are characterized for operation over the full military temperature range of –55°C to 125°C; Series 74, 74LS, and 74S devices are characterized for operation from 0°C to 70°C.

signal designations

The '181, 'LS181, and 'S181 together with the '182 and 'S182 can be used with the signal designations of either Figure 1 or Figure 2. The inversion indicators (○) and the bars over the terminal letter symbols (e.g., $\overline{C}$) each indicate that the associated input or output is active with respect to the selected function of the device when that input or output is low. That is, a low at $\overline{C}$ means "do carry" while a high means "do not carry".

The logic functions and arithmetic operations obtained with signal designations of Figure 1 are given in Table 1; those obtained with signal designations of Figure 2 are given in Table 2.

TEXAS INSTRUMENTS
POST OFFICE BOX 225012 • DALLAS, TEXAS 75265

TEXAS INSTRUMENTS
POST OFFICE BOX 225012 • DALLAS, TEXAS 75265

TYPES SN54181, SN54LS181, SN54S181, SN74181, SN74LS181, SN74S181
ARITHMETIC LOGIC UNITS/FUNCTION GENERATORS

signal designations (continued)

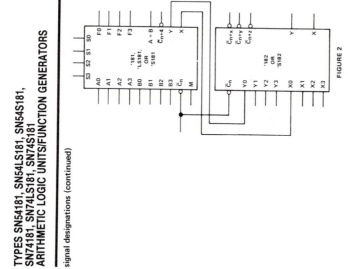

FIGURE 1

signal designations (continued)

FIGURE 2

TABLE 1

SELECTION				M = H	M = L; ARITHMETIC OPERATIONS	
				ACTIVE-LOW DATA		
				LOGIC FUNCTIONS	C_n = L (no carry)	C_n = H (with carry)
S3	S2	S1	S0			
L	L	L	L	F = Ā	F = A MINUS 1	F = A
L	L	L	H	F = $\overline{AB}$	F = AB MINUS 1	F = AB
L	L	H	L	F = $\overline{A}$ + B	F = $A\overline{B}$ MINUS 1	F = $A\overline{B}$
L	L	H	H	F = 1	F = MINUS 1 (2's COMP)	F = ZERO
L	H	L	L	F = $\overline{A + B}$	F = A PLUS (A + $\overline{B}$)	F = A PLUS (A + $\overline{B}$) PLUS 1
L	H	L	H	F = $\overline{B}$	F = AB PLUS (A + $\overline{B}$)	F = AB PLUS (A + $\overline{B}$) PLUS 1
L	H	H	L	F = $\overline{A \oplus B}$	F = A MINUS B MINUS 1	F = A MINUS B
L	H	H	H	F = A + $\overline{B}$	F = A + $\overline{B}$	F = (A + $\overline{B}$) PLUS 1
H	L	L	L	F = $\overline{A}B$	F = A PLUS (A + B)	F = A PLUS (A + B) PLUS 1
H	L	L	H	F = A $\oplus$ B	F = A PLUS B	F = A PLUS B PLUS 1
H	L	H	L	F = B	F = $A\overline{B}$ PLUS (A + B)	F = $A\overline{B}$ PLUS (A + B) PLUS 1
H	L	H	H	F = A + B	F = (A + B)	F = (A + B) PLUS 1
H	H	L	L	F = 0	F = A	F = A PLUS A PLUS 1
H	H	L	H	F = $A\overline{B}$	F = AB PLUS A	F = AB PLUS A PLUS 1
H	H	H	L	F = AB	F = $A\overline{B}$ PLUS A	F = $A\overline{B}$ PLUS A PLUS 1
H	H	H	H	F = A	F = A	F = A PLUS 1

TABLE 2

SELECTION				M = H	M = L; ARITHMETIC OPERATIONS	
				ACTIVE-HIGH DATA		
				LOGIC FUNCTIONS	$\overline{C}_n$ = H (no carry)	$\overline{C}_n$ = L (with carry)
S3	S2	S1	S0			
L	L	L	L	F = $\overline{A}$	F = A	F = A PLUS 1
L	L	L	H	F = $\overline{A + B}$	F = A + B	F = (A + B) PLUS 1
L	L	H	L	F = $\overline{A}B$	F = A + $\overline{B}$	F = (A + $\overline{B}$) PLUS 1
L	L	H	H	F = 0	F = MINUS 1 (2's COMPL)	F = ZERO
L	H	L	L	F = $\overline{AB}$	F = A PLUS $A\overline{B}$	F = A PLUS $A\overline{B}$ PLUS 1
L	H	L	H	F = $\overline{B}$	F = (A + B) PLUS $A\overline{B}$	F = (A + B) PLUS $A\overline{B}$ PLUS 1
L	H	H	L	F = A $\oplus$ B	F = A MINUS B MINUS 1	F = A MINUS B
L	H	H	H	F = $A\overline{B}$	F = $A\overline{B}$ MINUS 1	F = $A\overline{B}$
H	L	L	L	F = $\overline{A} + B$	F = A PLUS AB	F = A PLUS AB PLUS 1
H	L	L	H	F = $\overline{A \oplus B}$	F = A PLUS B	F = A PLUS B PLUS 1
H	L	H	L	F = B	F = (A + $\overline{B}$) PLUS AB	F = (A + $\overline{B}$) PLUS AB PLUS 1
H	L	H	H	F = AB	F = AB MINUS 1	F = AB
H	H	L	L	F = 1	F = A PLUS A	F = A PLUS A PLUS 1
H	H	L	H	F = A + $\overline{B}$	F = (A + B) PLUS A	F = (A + B) PLUS A PLUS 1
H	H	H	L	F = A + B	F = (A + $\overline{B}$) PLUS A	F = (A + $\overline{B}$) PLUS A PLUS 1
H	H	H	H	F = A	F = A MINUS 1	F = A

TEXAS INSTRUMENTS
POST OFFICE BOX 225012 • DALLAS, TEXAS 75265

TEXAS INSTRUMENTS
POST OFFICE BOX 225012 • DALLAS, TEXAS 75265

TYPES SN54181, SN74181
ARITHMETIC LOGIC UNITS/FUNCTION GENERATORS

absolute maximum ratings over operating free-air temperature range (unless otherwise noted)

Supply voltage, V_{CC} (see Note 1) . . . . 7 V
Input voltage . . . . 5.5 V
Interemitter voltage (see Note 2) . . . . 5.5 V
Operating free-air temperature range: SN54181 . . . . −55°C to 125°C
    SN74181 . . . . 0°C to 70°C
Storage temperature range . . . . −65°C to 150°C

NOTES: 1. Voltage values, except interemitter voltage, are with respect to network ground terminal.
    2. This is the voltage between two emitters of a multiple-emitter transistor. For this circuit, this rating applies to each Ā input in conjunction with inputs S2 or S3, and to each B input in conjunction with inputs S0 or S3.

recommended operating conditions

	SN54181			SN74181			UNIT
	MIN	NOM	MAX	MIN	NOM	MAX	
Supply voltage, V_{CC}	4.5	5	5.5	4.75	5	5.25	V
High-level output current, I_{OH} (All outputs except A = B)			−800			−800	µA
Low-level output current, I_{OL}			16			16	mA
Operating free-air temperature, T_A	−55		125	0		70	°C

electrical characteristics over recommended operating free-air temperature range (unless otherwise noted)

PARAMETER		TEST CONDITIONS†	SN54181			SN74181			UNIT
			MIN	TYP‡	MAX	MIN	TYP‡	MAX	
V_{IH}	High-level input voltage		2			2			V
V_{IL}	Low-level input voltage				0.8			0.8	V
V_{IK}	Input clamp voltage	V_{CC} = MIN, I_I = −12 mA			−1.5			−1.5	V
V_{OH}	High-level output voltage, any output except A = B	V_{CC} = MIN, V_{IH} = 2 V, V_{IL} = 0.8 V, I_{OH} = −800 µA	2.4	3.4		2.4	3.4		V
I_{OH}	High-level output current, A = B output only	V_{CC} = MIN, V_{IH} = 2 V, V_{IL} = 0.8 V, V_{OH} = 5.5 V			250			250	µA
V_{OL}	Low-level output voltage	V_{CC} = MIN, V_{IH} = 2 V, V_{IL} = 0.8 V, I_{OL} = 16 mA		0.2	0.4		0.2	0.4	V
I_I	Input current at maximum input voltage	V_{CC} = MAX, V_I = 5.5 V			1			1	mA
I_{IH}	High-level input current	Mode input	V_{CC} = MAX, V_I = 2.4 V			40			40	µA
		Any Ā or B̄ input				120			120	
		Any S input				160			160	
		Carry input				200			200	
I_{IL}	Low-level input current	Mode input	V_{CC} = MAX, V_I = 0.4 V			−1.6			−1.6	mA
		Any Ā or B̄ input				−4.8			−4.8	
		Any S input				−6.4			−6.4	
		Carry input				−8			−8	
I_{OS}	Short-circuit output current, any output except A = B§	V_{CC} = MAX	−20		−55	−18		−57	mA
I_{CC}	Supply current	V_{CC} = MAX, Condition A		88	127		88	140	mA
		See Note 3, Condition B		94	135		94	150	mA

† For conditions shown as MIN or MAX, use the appropriate value specified under recommended operating conditions.
‡ All typical values are at V_{CC} = 5 V, T_A = 25°C.
§ Not more than one output should be shorted at a time.
NOTE 3: With outputs open, I_{CC} is measured for the following conditions:
    A. S0 through S3, M, and Ā inputs are at 4.5 V, all other inputs are grounded.
    B. S0 through S3 and M are at 4.5 V, all other inputs are grounded.

TEXAS INSTRUMENTS
POST OFFICE BOX 225012 • DALLAS, TEXAS 75265

TYPES SN54181, SN54LS181, SN54S181, SN74181, SN74LS181, SN74S181
ARITHMETIC LOGIC UNITS/FUNCTION GENERATORS

logic diagram

Pin numbers shown on logic notation are for DW, J or N packages.

TEXAS INSTRUMENTS
POST OFFICE BOX 225012 • DALLAS, TEXAS 75265

TYPES SN54190, SN54191, SN54LS190, SN54LS191, SN74190, SN74191, SN74LS190, SN74LS191 SYNCHRONOUS UP/DOWN COUNTERS WITH DOWN/UP MODE CONTROL

DECEMBER 1972–REVISED DECEMBER 1983

- Counts 8-4-2-1 BCD or Binary
- Single Down/Up Count Control Line
- Count Enable Control Input
- Ripple Clock Output for Cascading
- Asynchronously Presettable with Load Control
- Parallel Outputs
- Cascadable for n-Bit Applications

TYPE	AVERAGE PROPAGATION DELAY	TYPICAL MAXIMUM CLOCK FREQUENCY	TYPICAL POWER DISSIPATION
'190, '191	20ns	25MHz	325mW
'LS190, 'LS191	20ns	25MHz	100mW

description

The '190, 'LS190, '191, and 'LS191 are synchronous, reversible up/down counters having a complexity of 58 equivalent gates. The '191 and 'LS191 are 4-bit binary counters and the '190 and 'LS190 are BCD counters. Synchronous operation is provided by having all flip-flops clocked simultaneously so that the outputs change coincident with each other when so instructed by the steering logic. This mode of operation eliminates the output counting spikes normally associated with asynchronous (ripple clock) counters.

The outputs of the four master-slave flip-flops are triggered on a low-to-high transition of the clock input if the enable input is low. A high at the enable input inhibits counting. Level changes at the enable input should be made only when the clock input is high. The direction of the count is determined by the level of the down/up input. When low, the counter count up and when high, it counts down. A false clock may occur if the down/up input changes while the clock is low. A false ripple carry may occur if both the clock and enable are low and the down/up input is high during a load pulse.

These counters are fully programmable; that is, the outputs may be preset to either level by placing a low on the load input and entering the desired data at the data inputs. The output will change to agree with the data inputs independently of the level of the clock input. This feature allows the counters to be used as modulo-N dividers by simply modifying the count length with the preset inputs.

The clock, down/up, and load inputs are buffered to lower the drive requirement which significantly reduces the number of clock drivers, etc., required for long parallel words.

Two outputs have been made available to perform the cascading function: ripple clock and maximum/minimum count. The latter output produces a high-level output pulse with a duration approximately equal to one complete cycle of the clock when the counter overflows or underflows. The ripple clock output produces a low-level output pulse equal in width to the low-level portion of the clock input when an overflow or underflow condition exists. The counters can be easily cascaded by feeding the ripple clock output to the enable input of the succeeding counter if parallel clocking is used, or to the clock input if parallel enabling is used. The maximum/minimum count output can be used to accomplish look-ahead for high-speed operation.

Series 54' and 54LS' are characterized for operation over the full military temperature range of −55°C to 125°C; Series 74' and 74LS' are characterized for operation from 0°C to 70°C.

SN54190, SN54191, SN54LS190,
SN54LS191 . . . J OR W PACKAGE
SN74190, SN74191 . . . J OR N PACKAGE
SN74LS190, SN74LS191 . . . D, J OR N PACKAGE
(TOP VIEW)

B	1 U 16	V_CC
Q_B	2 15	A
Q_A	3 14	CLK
CTEN	4 13	RCO
D/Ū	5 12	MAX/MIN
Q_C	6 11	LOAD
Q_D	7 10	C
GND	8 9	D

SN54LS190, SN54LS191 . . . FK PACKAGE
SN74LS190, SN74LS191 . . . FN PACKAGE
(TOP VIEW)

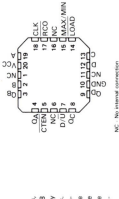

NC - No internal connection

TEXAS INSTRUMENTS
POST OFFICE BOX 225012 • DALLAS, TEXAS 75265

TYPES SN54191, SN54LS191, SN74191, SN74LS191 SYNCHRONOUS UP/DOWN COUNTERS WITH DOWN/UP MODE CONTROL

logic diagram

'191, 'LS191 BINARY COUNTERS

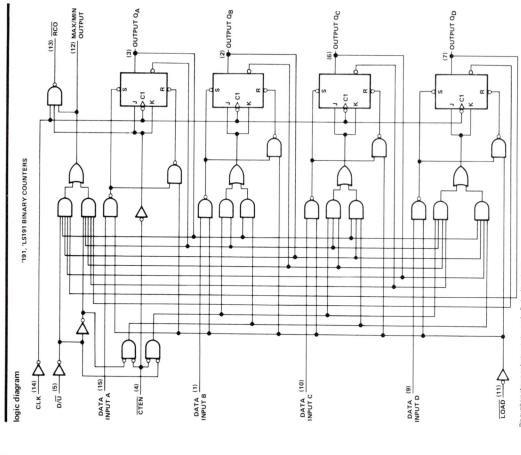

Pin numbers shown on logic notation are for D, J or N packages.

TEXAS INSTRUMENTS
POST OFFICE BOX 225012 • DALLAS, TEXAS 75265

TYPES SN54190, SN54191, SN54LS190, SN54LS191, SN74190, SN74191, SN74LS190, SN74LS191
SYNCHRONOUS UP/DOWN COUNTERS WITH DOWN/UP MODE CONTROL

absolute maximum ratings over operating free-air temperature range (unless otherwise noted)

Supply voltage, V_{CC} (see Note 1)		7 V
Input voltage: SN54', SN74' Circuits		5.5 V
SN54LS', SN74LS' Circuits		7 V
Operating free-air temperature range: SN54', SN54LS' Circuits		−55°C to 125°C
SN74', SN74LS' Circuits		0°C to 70°C
Storage temperature range		−65°C to 150°C

NOTE 1: Voltage values are with respect to network ground terminal.

recommended operating conditions

			SN54190, SN54191			SN74190, SN74191			UNIT
			MIN	NOM	MAX	MIN	NOM	MAX	
V_{CC}	Supply voltage		4.5	5	5.5	4.75	5	5.25	V
I_{OH}	High-level output current				−0.8			−0.8	mA
I_{OL}	Low-level output current				16			16	mA
f_{clock}	Input clock frequency		0		20	0		20	MHz
$t_{w(clock)}$	Width of clock input pulse		25			25			ns
$t_{w(load)}$	Width of load input pulse		35			35			ns
t_{su}	Setup time	Data, high or low (See Figure 1 and 2)	20			20			ns
		Load inactive state	20			20			
t_{hold}	Data hold time		0			0			ns
T_A	Operating free-air temperature		−55		125	0		70	°C

electrical characteristics over recommended operating free-air temperature range (unless otherwise noted)

PARAMETER		TEST CONDITIONS†	SN54190, SN54191			SN74190, SN74191			UNIT
			MIN	TYP‡	MAX	MIN	TYP‡	MAX	
V_{IH}	High-level input voltage	V_{CC} = MIN	2			2			V
V_{IL}	Low-level input voltage	V_{CC} = MIN			0.8			0.8	V
V_{IK}	Input clamp voltage	V_{CC} = MIN, I_I = −12 mA			−1.5			−1.5	V
V_{OH}	High-level output voltage	V_{CC} = MIN, V_{IH} = 2 V, V_{IL} = 0.8 V, I_{OH} = −0.8 mA	2.4	3.4		2.4	3.4		V
V_{OL}	Low-level output voltage	V_{CC} = MIN, V_{IH} = 2 V, V_{IL} = 0.8 V, I_{OL} = 16 mA		0.2	0.4		0.2	0.4	V
I_I	High-level input current at maximum input voltage	V_{CC} = MAX, V_I = 5.5 V			1			1	mA
I_{IH}	High-level input current at any input except enable	V_{CC} = MAX, V_I = 2.4 V			40			40	µA
I_{IH}	High-level input current at enable input				120			120	µA
I_{IL}	Low-level input current at any input except enable	V_{CC} = MAX, V_I = 0.4 V			−1.6			−1.6	mA
I_{IL}	Low-level input current at enable input				−4.8			−4.8	mA
I_{OS}	Short-circuit output current§	V_{CC} = MAX	−20		−65	−18		−65	mA
I_{CC}	Supply current	V_{CC} = MAX, See Note 2		65	99		65	105	mA

†For conditions shown as MAX or MIN, use appropriate value specified under recommended operating conditions.
‡All typical values are at V_{CC} = 5 V, T_A = 25°C.
§Not more than one output should be shorted at a time.
NOTE 2: I_{CC} is measured with all inputs grounded and all outputs open.

TYPES SN54191, SN54LS191, SN74191, SN74LS191
SYNCHRONOUS UP/DOWN COUNTERS WITH DOWN/UP MODE CONTROL

'191, 'LS191 BINARY COUNTERS

typical load, count, and inhibit sequences

Illustrated below is the following sequence:

1. Load (preset) to binary thirteen.
2. Count up to fourteen, fifteen (maximum), zero, one, and two.
3. Inhibit.
4. Count down to one, zero (minimum), fifteen, fourteen, and thirteen.

TEXAS INSTRUMENTS
POST OFFICE BOX 225012 • DALLAS, TEXAS 75265

Courtesy of Texas Instruments Incorporated

311

TYPES SN54195, SN54LS195A, SN54S195, SN74195, SN74LS195A, SN74S195
4-BIT PARALLEL-ACCESS SHIFT REGISTERS

MARCH 1974 – REVISED APRIL 1985

- Synchronous Parallel Load
- Positive-Edge-Triggered Clocking
- Parallel Inputs and Outputs from Each Flip-Flop
- Direct Overriding Clear
- J and $\overline{K}$ Inputs to First Stage
- Complementary Outputs from Last Stage
- For Use in High Performance:
  Accumulators/Processors
  Serial-to-Parallel, Parallel-to-Serial
  Converters

description

These 4-bit registers feature parallel inputs, parallel outputs, J-$\overline{K}$ serial inputs, shift/load control input, and a direct overriding clear. All inputs are buffered to lower the input drive requirements. The registers have two modes of operation:

Parallel (broadside) load
Shift (in the direction Q_A toward Q_D)

Parallel loading is accomplished by applying the four bits of data and taking the shift/load control input low. The data is loaded into the associated flip-flop and appears at the outputs after the positive transition of the clock input. During loading, serial data flow is inhibited.

Shifting is accomplished synchronously when the shift/load control input is high. Serial data for this mode is entered at the J-$\overline{K}$ inputs. These inputs permit the first stage to perform as a J-K, D, or T-type flip-flop as shown in the function table.

The high-performance 'S195, with a 105-megahertz typical maximum shift-frequency, is particularly attractive for very-high-speed data processing systems. In most cases existing systems can be upgraded merely by using this Schottky-clamped shift register.

SN54195, SN54LS195A, SN54S195 . . . J OR W PACKAGE
SN74195 . . . J OR N PACKAGE
SN74LS195A, SN74S195 . . . D, J OR N PACKAGE
(TOP VIEW)

$\overline{CLR}$	1	16 V_{CC}
J	2	15 Q_A
$\overline{K}$	3	14 Q_B
A	4	13 Q_C
B	5	12 Q_D
C	6	11 $\overline{Q_D}$
D	7	10 CLK
GND	8	9 SH/$\overline{LD}$

SN54LS195, SN54S195 . . . FK PACKAGE
SN74LS195, SN74S195 . . . FN PACKAGE
(TOP VIEW)

NC – No internal connection

TYPE	TYPICAL MAXIMUM CLOCK FREQUENCY	TYPICAL POWER DISSIPATION
'195	39 MHz	195 mW
'LS195A	39 MHz	70 mW
'S195	105 MHz	350 mW

logic diagram

†This connection is made on '195 only.
Pin numbers shown on logic notation are for J, J or N packages.

FUNCTION TABLE

INPUTS									OUTPUTS				
CLEAR	SHIFT/LOAD	CLOCK	SERIAL		PARALLEL				Q_A	Q_B	Q_C	Q_D	$\overline{Q_D}$
			J	$\overline{K}$	A	B	C	D					
L	X	X	X	X	X	X	X	X	L	L	L	L	H
H	L	↑	X	X	a	b	c	d	a	b	c	d	$\overline{d}$
H	H	L	X	X	X	X	X	X	Q_{A0}	Q_{B0}	Q_{C0}	Q_{D0}	$\overline{Q_{D0}}$
H	H	↑	L	H	X	X	X	X	Q_{A0}	Q_{An}	Q_{Bn}	Q_{Cn}	$\overline{Q_{Cn}}$
H	H	↑	L	L	X	X	X	X	L	Q_{An}	Q_{Bn}	Q_{Cn}	$\overline{Q_{Cn}}$
H	H	↑	H	H	X	X	X	X	H	Q_{An}	Q_{Bn}	Q_{Cn}	$\overline{Q_{Cn}}$
H	H	↑	H	L	X	X	X	X	$\overline{Q_{An}}$	Q_{An}	Q_{Bn}	Q_{Cn}	$\overline{Q_{Cn}}$

H = high level (steady state)
L = low level (steady state)
X = irrelevant (any input, including transitions)
↑ = transition from low to high level
a, b, c, d = the level of steady state input at A, B, C, or D respectively
Q_{A0}, Q_{B0}, Q_{C0}, Q_{D0} = the level of Q_A, Q_B, Q_C, or Q_D, respectively, before the indicated steady state input conditions were established
Q_{An}, Q_{Bn}, Q_{Cn} = the level of Q_A, Q_B, or Q_C, respectively, before the most-recent transition of the clock

TEXAS INSTRUMENTS
POST OFFICE BOX 225012 • DALLAS, TEXAS 75265

absolute maximum ratings over operating free-air temperature range (unless otherwise noted)

Supply voltage, V_{CC} (see Note 1) . . . . 7 V
Input voltage . . . . 5.5 V
Operating free-air temperature range: SN54195 . . . . −55°C to 125°C
                                         SN74195 . . . . 0°C to 70°C
Storage temperature range . . . . −65°C to 150°C

NOTE 1: Voltage values are with respect to network ground terminal.

recommended operating conditions

	SN54195 MIN	NOM	MAX	SN74195 MIN	NOM	MAX	UNIT
Supply voltage, V_{CC}	4.5	5	5.5	4.75	5	5.25	V
High-level output current, I_{OH}			−800			−800	µA
Low-level output current, I_{OL}			16			16	mA
Clock frequency, f_{clock}	0		30	0		30	MHz
Width of clock input pulse, $t_{w(clock)}$	16			16			ns
Width of clear input pulse, $t_{w(clear)}$	12			12			ns
Setup time, t_{su} (see Figure 1) Shift/load	25			25			ns
Serial and parallel data	20			20			
Clear inactive-state	25			25			
Shift/load release time, $t_{release}$ (see Figure 1)			20			10	ns
Serial and parallel data hold time, t_h (see Figure 1)	0			0			ns
Operating free-air temperature, T_A	−55		125	0		70	°C

electrical characteristics over recommended operating free-air temperature range (unless otherwise noted)

PARAMETER		TEST CONDITIONS†	MIN	TYP‡	MAX	UNIT
V_{IH}	High-level input voltage		2			V
V_{IL}	Low-level input voltage				0.8	V
V_{IK}	Input clamp voltage	V_{CC} = MIN, I_I = −12 mA			−1.5	V
V_{OH}	High-level output voltage	V_{CC} = MIN, V_{IH} = 2 V, V_{IL} = 0.8 V, I_{OH} = −800 µA	2.4	3.4		V
V_{OL}	Low-level output voltage	V_{CC} = MIN, V_{IH} = 2 V, V_{IL} = 0.8 V, I_{OL} = 16 mA		0.2	0.4	V
I_I	Input current at maximum input voltage	V_{CC} = MAX, V_I = 5.5 V			1	mA
I_{IH}	High-level input current	V_{CC} = MAX, V_I = 2.4 V			40	µA
I_{IL}	Low-level input current	V_{CC} = MAX, V_I = 0.4 V			−1.6	mA
I_{OS}	Short-circuit output current§	V_{CC} = MAX SN54195	−20		−57	mA
		SN74195	−18		−57	
I_{CC}	Supply current	V_{CC} = MAX, See Note 2		39	63	mA

†For conditions shown as MIN or MAX, use the appropriate value specified under recommended operating conditions.
‡All typical values are at V_{CC} = 5 V, T_A = 25°C.
§Not more than one output should be shorted at a time.
NOTE 2: With all outputs open, shift/load grounded, and 4.5 V applied to the J, $\overline{K}$, and data inputs, I_{CC} is measured by applying a momentary ground, followed by 4.5 V, to clear and then applying a momentary ground, followed by 4.5 V, to clock.

switching characteristics, V_{CC} = 5 V, T_A = 25°C

PARAMETER	TEST CONDITIONS	MIN	TYP	MAX	UNIT
f_{max} Maximum clock frequency	C_L = 15 pF,	30	39		MHz
t_{PHL} Propagation delay time, high-to-low-level output from clear	R_L = 400 Ω,		19	30	ns
t_{PLH} Propagation delay time, low-to-high-level output from clock	See Figure 1		14	22	ns
t_{PHL} Propagation delay time, high-to-low-level output from clock			17	26	ns

TEXAS
INSTRUMENTS
POST OFFICE BOX 225012 • DALLAS, TEXAS 75265

typical clear, shift, and load sequences

CLK
$\overline{CLR}$
SERIAL INPUTS   J, $\overline{K}$
SH/$\overline{LD}$
PARALLEL DATA INPUTS   A, B, C, D
OUTPUTS Q_A, Q_B, Q_C, Q_D

CLEAR   SERIAL SHIFT   LOAD   SERIAL SHIFT

TEXAS
INSTRUMENTS
POST OFFICE BOX 225012 • DALLAS, TEXAS 75265

National Semiconductor

CD4069M/CD4069C Inverter Circuits

General Description

The CD4069B consists of six inverter circuits and is manufactured using complementary MOS (CMOS) to achieve wide power supply operating range, low power consumption, high noise immunity, and symmetric controlled rise and fall times.

This device is intended for all general purpose inverter applications where the special characteristics of the MM74C901, MM74C903, MM74C907, and CD4049A Hex Inverter/Buffers are not required. In those applications requiring larger noise immunity the MM74C14 or MM74C914 Hex Schmitt Trigger is suggested.

All inputs are protected from damage due to static discharge by diode clamps to V_{DD} and V_{SS}.

Features

- Wide supply voltage range — 3.0 V to 15 V
- High noise immunity — 0.45 V_{DD} typ.
- Low power TTL compatibility — fan out of 2 driving 74L or 1 driving 74LS
- Equivalent to MM54C04/MM74C04

Absolute Maximum Ratings

(Notes 1 and 2)

V_{DD} dc Supply Voltage	−0.5 to +18 V_{DC}
V_{IN} Input Voltage	−0.5 to V_{DD} +0.5 V_{DC}
T_S Storage Temperature Range	−65°C to +150°C
P_D Package Dissipation	500 mW
T_L Lead Temperature (Soldering, 10 seconds)	300°C

Recommended Operating Conditions

(Note 2)

V_{DD} dc Supply Voltage	3 to 15 V_{DC}
V_{IN} Input Voltage	0 to V_{DD} V_{DC}
T_A Operating Temperature Range	
CD4069M	−55°C to +125°C
CD4069C	−40°C to +85°C

DC Electrical Characteristics

CD4069M (Note 2)

PARAMETER		CONDITIONS	−55°C		25°C			125°C		UNITS
			MIN	MAX	MIN	TYP	MAX	MIN	MAX	
I_{DD}	Quiescent Device Current	V_{DD} = 5V		0.25			0.25		7.5	μA
		V_{DD} = 10V		0.5			0.5		15	μA
		V_{DD} = 15V		1.0			1.0		30	μA
V_{OL}	Low Level Output Voltage	$|I_O| < 1μA$								
		V_{DD} = 5V		0.05		0	0.05		0.05	V
		V_{DD} = 10V		0.05		0	0.05		0.05	V
		V_{DD} = 15V		0.05		0	0.05		0.05	V
V_{OH}	High Level Output Voltage	$|I_O| < 1μA$								
		V_{DD} = 5V	4.95		4.95	5		4.95		V
		V_{DD} = 10V	9.95		9.95	10		9.95		V
		V_{DD} = 15V	14.95		14.95	15		14.95		V
V_{IL}	Low Level Input Voltage	$|I_O| < 1μA$								
		V_{DD} = 5V, V_O = 4.5V		1.5			1.5		1.5	V
		V_{DD} = 10V, V_O = 9V		3.0			3.0		3.0	V
		V_{DD} = 15V, V_O = 13.5V		4.0			4.0		4.0	V
V_{IH}	High Level Input Voltage	$|I_O| < 1μA$								
		V_{DD} = 5V, V_O = 0.5V	3.5		3.5			3.5		V
		V_{DD} = 10V, V_O = 1V	7.0		7.0			7.0		V
		V_{DD} = 15V, V_O = 1.5V	11.0		11.0			11.0		V
I_{OL}	Low Level Output Current	V_{DD} = 5V, V_O = 0.4V	0.64		0.51	0.88		0.36		mA
		V_{DD} = 10V, V_O = 0.5V	1.6		1.3	2.25		0.9		mA
		V_{DD} = 15V, V_O = 1.5V	4.2		3.4	8.8		2.4		mA
I_{OH}	High Level Output Current	V_{DD} = 5V, V_O = 4.6V	−0.64		−0.51	−0.88		−0.36		mA
		V_{DD} = 10V, V_O = 9.5V	−1.6		−1.3	−2.25		−0.9		mA
		V_{DD} = 15V, V_O = 13.5V	−4.2		−3.4	−8.8		−2.4		mA
I_{IN}	Input Current	V_{DD} = 15V, V_{IN} = 0V		−0.10		-10^{-5}	−0.10		−1.0	μA
		V_{DD} = 15V, V_{IN} = 15V		0.10		10^{-5}	0.10		1.0	μA

Schematic and Connection Diagrams

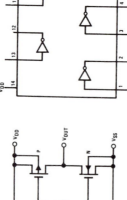

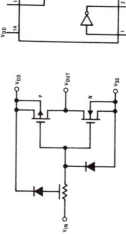

Dual-In-Line Package

TOP VIEW

AC Test Circuits and Switching Time Waveforms

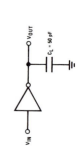

$t_r = t_f = 20$ ns

Absolute Maximum Ratings

(Notes 1 and 2)

Voltage at Any Pin	-0.5V to V_DD + 0.5V
Package Dissipation	500 mW
V_DD Range	-0.5 V_DC to +18 V_DC
Storage Temperature	-65°C to +150°C
Lead Temperature (Soldering, 10 seconds)	260°C

Operating Conditions

Operating V_DD Range	3 V_DC to 15 V_DC
Operating Temperature Range	
CD4071BM, CD4081BM	-55°C to +125°C
CD4071BC, CD4081BC	-40°C to +85°C

DC Electrical Characteristics — CD4071BM/CD4081BM (Note 2)

SYM	PARAMETER	CONDITIONS	-55°C MIN	-55°C MAX	+25°C MIN	+25°C TYP	+25°C MAX	+125°C MIN	+125°C MAX	UNITS
I_{DD}	Quiescent Device Current	$V_{DD}=5V$		0.25		0.004	0.25		7.5	µA
		$V_{DD}=10V$		0.50		0.005	0.50		15	µA
		$V_{DD}=15V$		1.0		0.006	1.0		30	µA
V_{OL}	Low Level Output Voltage	$V_{DD}=5V$ $\|I_O\|<1µA$		0.05		0	0.05		0.05	V
		$V_{DD}=10V$ $\|I_O\|<1µA$		0.05		0	0.05		0.05	V
		$V_{DD}=15V$ $\|I_O\|<1µA$		0.05		0	0.05		0.05	V
V_{OH}	High Level Output Voltage	$V_{DD}=5V$ $\|I_O\|<1µA$	4.95		4.95	5		4.95		V
		$V_{DD}=10V$ $\|I_O\|<1µA$	9.95		9.95	10		9.95		V
		$V_{DD}=15V$ $\|I_O\|<1µA$	14.95		14.95	15		14.95		V
V_{IL}	Low Level Input Voltage	$V_{DD}=5V$, $V_O=0.5V$		1.5		2	1.5		1.5	V
		$V_{DD}=10V$, $V_O=1.0V$		3.0		4	3.0		3.0	V
		$V_{DD}=15V$, $V_O=1.5V$		4.0		6	4.0		4.0	V
V_{IH}	High Level Input Voltage	$V_{DD}=5V$, $V_O=4.5V$	3.5		3.5	3		3.5		V
		$V_{DD}=10V$, $V_O=9.0V$	7.0		7.0	6		7.0		V
		$V_{DD}=15V$, $V_O=13.5V$	11.0		11.0	9		11.0		V
I_{OL}	Low Level Output Current (Note 3)	$V_{DD}=5V$, $V_O=0.4V$	0.64		0.51	0.88		0.36		mA
		$V_{DD}=10V$, $V_O=0.5V$	1.6		1.3	2.25		0.9		mA
		$V_{DD}=15V$, $V_O=1.5V$	4.2		3.4	8.8		2.4		mA
I_{OH}	High Level Output Current (Note 3)	$V_{DD}=5V$, $V_O=4.6V$	-0.64		-0.51	-0.88		-0.36		mA
		$V_{DD}=10V$, $V_O=9.5V$	-1.6		-1.3	-2.25		-0.9		mA
		$V_{DD}=15V$, $V_O=13.5V$	-4.2		-3.4	-8.8		-2.4		mA
I_{IN}	Input Current	$V_{DD}=15V$, $V_{IN}=0V$		-0.10		-10^{-5}	-0.10		-1.0	µA
		$V_{DD}=15V$, $V_{IN}=15V$		0.10		10^{-5}	0.10		1.0	µA

Note 1: "Absolute Maximum Ratings" are those values beyond which the safety of the device cannot be guaranteed. Except for "Operating Temperature Range" they are not meant to imply that the devices should be operated at these limits. The table of "Electrical Characteristics" provides conditions for actual device operation.

Note 2: All voltages measured with respect to V_SS unless otherwise specified.

Note 3: I_OH and I_OL are tested one output at a time.

National Semiconductor

CD4071BM/CD4071BC Quad 2-Input OR Buffered B Series Gate
CD4081BM/CD4081BC Quad 2-Input AND Buffered B Series Gate

General Description

These quad gates are monolithic complementary MOS (CMOS) integrated circuits constructed with N- and P-channel enhancement mode transistors. They have equal source and sink current capabilities and conform to standard B series output drive. The devices also have buffered outputs which improve transfer characteristics by providing very high gain.

All inputs protected against static discharge with diodes to V_DD and V_SS.

Features

- Low power TTL compatibility
- 5V-10V-15V parametric ratings
- Symmetrical output characteristics
- Maximum input leakage 1µA at 15V over full temperature range
- fan out of 2 driving 74L or 1 driving 74LS

Schematic and Connection Diagrams

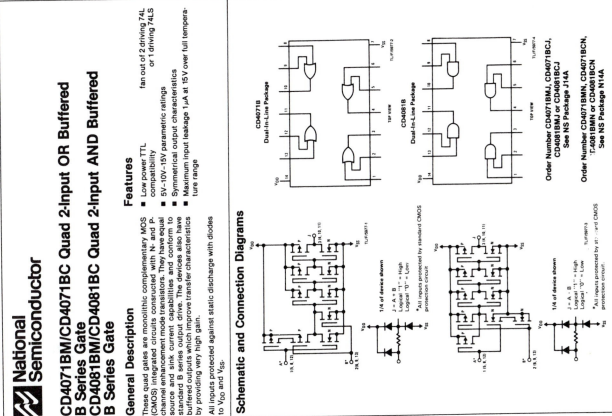

CD4071B Dual-In-Line Package
TOP VIEW

CD4081B Dual-In-Line Package
TOP VIEW

1/4 of device shown

J = A + B
Logical "1" = High
Logical "0" = Low
*All inputs protected by standard CMOS protection circuit

J = A · B
Logical "1" = High
Logical "0" = Low
*All inputs protected by standard CMOS protection circuit

Order Number CD4071BMJ, CD4071BCJ, CD4081BMJ or CD4081BCJ
See NS Package J14A

Order Number CD4071BMN, CD4071BCN, CD4081BMN or CD4081BCN
See NS Package N14A

AC Electrical Characteristics CD4081BC/CD4081BM

$T_A = 25°C$, Input t_r; $t_f = 20$ ns, $C_L = 50$ pF, $R_L = 200K$ Typical temperature coefficient is 0.3%/°C

SYMBOL	PARAMETER	CONDITIONS	TYP	MAX	UNITS
tPHL	Propagation Delay Time, High-to-Low Level	V_{DD} = 5V	100	250	ns
		V_{DD} = 10V	40	100	ns
		V_{DD} = 15V	30	70	ns
tPLH	Propagation Delay Time, Low-to-High Level	V_{DD} = 5V	120	250	ns
		V_{DD} = 10V	50	100	ns
		V_{DD} = 15V	35	70	ns
tTHL, tTLH	Transition Time	V_{DD} = 5V	90	200	ns
		V_{DD} = 10V	50	100	ns
		V_{DD} = 15V	40	80	ns
CIN	Average Input Capacitance	Any Input	5	7.5	pF
CPD	Power Dissipation Capacity	Any Gate	18		pF

Typical Performance Characteristics

FIGURE 1. Typical Transfer Characteristics
FIGURE 2. Typical Transfer Characteristics
FIGURE 3. Typical Transfer Characteristics
FIGURE 4. Typical Transfer Characteristics
FIGURE 5
FIGURE 6

DC Electrical Characteristics   CD4071BC/CD4081BC (Note 2)

SYM	PARAMETER	CONDITIONS	-40°C MIN	-40°C MAX	+25°C MIN	+25°C TYP	+25°C MAX	+85°C MIN	+85°C MAX	UNITS
IDD	Quiescent Device Current	V_{DD} = 5V		1		0.004	1		7.5	μA
		V_{DD} = 10V		2		0.005	2		15	μA
		V_{DD} = 15V		4		0.006	4		30	μA
VOL	Low Level Output Voltage	V_{DD} = 5V		0.05		0	0.05		0.05	V
		V_{DD} = 10V $|I_{OL}| < 1μA$		0.05		0	0.05		0.05	V
		V_{DD} = 15V		0.05		0	0.05		0.05	V
VOH	High Level Output Voltage	V_{DD} = 5V	4.95		4.95	5		4.95		V
		V_{DD} = 10V $|I_{OL}| < 1μA$	9.95		9.95	10		9.95		V
		V_{DD} = 15V	14.95		14.95	15		14.95		V
VIL	Low Level Input Voltage	V_{DD} = 5V, V_O = 0.5V		1.5		2	1.5		1.5	V
		V_{DD} = 10V, V_O = 1.0V		3.0		4	3.0		3.0	V
		V_{DD} = 15V, V_O = 1.5V		4.0		6	4.0		4.0	V
VIH	High Level Input Voltage	V_{DD} = 5V, V_O = 4.5V	3.5		3.5	3		3.5		V
		V_{DD} = 10V, V_O = 9.0V	7.0		7.0	6		7.0		V
		V_{DD} = 15V, V_O = 13.5V	11.0		11.0	9		11.0		V
IOL	Low Level Output Current (Note 3)	V_{DD} = 5V, V_O = 0.4V	0.52		0.44	0.88		0.36		mA
		V_{DD} = 10V, V_O = 0.5V	1.3		1.1	2.25		0.9		mA
		V_{DD} = 15V, V_O = 1.5V	3.6		3.0	8.8		2.4		mA
IOH	High Level Output Current (Note 3)	V_{DD} = 5V, V_O = 4.6V	-0.52		-0.44	-0.88		-0.36		mA
		V_{DD} = 10V, V_O = 9.5V	-1.3		-1.1	-2.25		-0.9		mA
		V_{DD} = 15V, V_O = 13.5V	-3.6		-3.0	-8.8		-2.4		mA
IIN	Input Current	V_{DD} = 15V, V_{IN} = 0V		-0.30		-10^{-5}	-0.30		-1.0	μA
		V_{DD} = 15V, V_{IN} = 15V		0.30		10^{-5}	0.30		1.0	μA

AC Electrical Characteristics   CD4071BC/CD4071BM

$T_A = 25°C$, Input t_r; $t_f = 20$ ns, $C_L = 50$ pF, $R_L = 200KΩ$ Typical temperature coefficient is 0.3%/°C

SYMBOL	PARAMETER	CONDITIONS	TYP	MAX	UNITS
tPHL	Propagation Delay Time, High-to-Low Level	V_{DD} = 5V	100	250	ns
		V_{DD} = 10V	40	100	ns
		V_{DD} = 15V	30	70	ns
tPLH	Propagation Delay Time, Low-to-High Level	V_{DD} = 5V	90	250	ns
		V_{DD} = 10V	40	100	ns
		V_{DD} = 15V	30	70	ns
tTHL, tTLH	Transition Time	V_{DD} = 5V	90	200	ns
		V_{DD} = 10V	50	100	ns
		V_{DD} = 15V	40	80	ns
CIN	Average Input Capacitance	Any Input	5	7.5	pF
CPD	Power Dissipation Capacity	Any Gate	18		pF

Note 1: "Absolute Maximum Ratings" are those values beyond which the safety of the device cannot be guaranteed. Except for "Operating Temperature Range" they are not meant to imply that the devices should be operated at these limits. The table of "Electrical Characteristics" provides conditions for actual device operation.

Note 2: All voltages measured with respect to V_{SS} unless otherwise specified.

Note 3: I_{OH} and I_{OL} are tested one output at a time.

316

MOTOROLA

MC14051B
MC14052B
MC14053B

CMOS MSI
(LOW-POWER COMPLEMENTARY MOS)

ANALOG MULTIPLEXERS/ DEMULTIPLEXERS

ANALOG MULTIPLEXERS/DEMULTIPLEXERS

The MC14051B, MC14052B, and MC14053B analog multiplexers are digitally-controlled analog switches. The MC14051B effectively implements an SP8T solid state switch, the MC14052B a DP4T, and the MC14053B a Triple SPDT. All three devices feature low ON impedance and very low OFF leakage current. Control of analog signals up to the complete supply voltage range can be achieved.

- Diode Protection on All Inputs
- Supply Voltage Range = 3.0 Vdc to 18 Vdc
- Analog Voltage Range ($V_{DD} - V_{EE}$) = 3 to 18 V
  Note: V_{EE} must be ≤ V_{SS}
- Linearized Transfer Characteristics
- Low-Noise – 12 nV/$\sqrt{Cycle}$, f ≥ 1 kHz typical
- Pin-for-Pin Replacement for CD4051, CD4052, and CD4053
- For 4PDT Switch, See MC14551B
- For Lower R_{ON}, Use the HC4051, HC4052, or HC4053 High-Speed CMOS Devices

MAXIMUM RATINGS*

Symbol	Parameter	Value	Unit
V_{DD}	DC Supply Voltage (Referenced to V_{EE}; $V_{SS} \geq V_{EE}$)	–0.5 to +18.0	V
V_{in}, V_{out}	Input or Output Voltage (DC or Transient) (Referenced to V_{SS} for Control Inputs and V_{EE} for Switch I/O)	–0.5 to V_{DD} +0.5	V
I_{in}	Input Current (DC or Transient), per Control Pin	±10	mA
I_{sw}	Switch Through Current	±25	mA
P_D	Power Dissipation, per Package†	500	mW
T_{stg}	Storage Temperature	–65 to +150	°C
T_L	Lead Temperature (8-Second Soldering)	260	°C

*Maximum Ratings are those values beyond which damage to the device may occur.
†Temperature Derating: Plastic "P" Package: –12mW/°C from 65°C to 85°C
Ceramic "L" Package: –12mW/°C from 100°C to 125°C

MC14051B
8-Channel Analog Multiplexer/Demultiplexer
Controls: 6 Inhibit, 11 A, 10 B, 9 C
13 X0, 14 X1, 15 X2, 12 X3, 1 X4, 5 X5, 2 X6, 4 X7
X 3 Common Out/In
V_{DD} = Pin 16, V_{SS} = Pin 8, V_{EE} = Pin 7

MC14052B
Dual 4-Channel Analog Multiplexer/Demultiplexer
Controls: 6 Inhibit, 10 A, 9 B
12 X0, 14 X1, 15 X2, 11 X3, 1 Y0, 5 Y1, 2 Y2, 4 Y3
X 13, Y 3 Commons Out/In
V_{DD} = Pin 16, V_{SS} = Pin 8, V_{EE} = Pin 7

MC14053B
Triple 2-Channel Analog Multiplexer/Demultiplexer
Controls: 6 Inhibit, 11 A, 10 B, 9 C
12 X0, 13 X1, 2 Y0, 1 Y1, 5 Z0, 3 Z1
X 14, Y 15, Z 4 Commons Out/In
V_{DD} = Pin 16, V_{SS} = Pin 8, V_{EE} = Pin 7

Note: Control inputs referenced to V_{SS}. Analog Inputs and Outputs reference to V_{EE}. V_{EE} must be <V_{SS}.

ELECTRICAL CHARACTERISTICS

Characteristic	Symbol	V_{DD}	Test Conditions	T_{low}* Min	T_{low}* Max	25°C Min	25°C Typ#	25°C Max	T_{high}* Min	T_{high}* Max	Unit
SUPPLY REQUIREMENTS (Voltages Referenced to V_{EE})											
Power Supply Voltage Range	V_{DD}		$V_{DD} - 3 \geq V_{SS} \geq V_{EE}$	3	18	3	—	18	3	18	V
Quiescent Current Per Package (AL Device)	I_{DD}	5 / 10 / 15	Control Inputs $V_{in} = V_{SS}$ or V_{DD}, Switch I/O: $V_{EE} \leq V_{I/O} \leq V_{DD}$ and $\Delta V_{switch} \leq 500$ mV***	— / — / —	5 / 10 / 20	— / — / —	0.005 / 0.010 / 0.015	5 / 10 / 20	— / — / —	150 / 300 / 600	μA
Quiescent Current Per Package (CL/CP Device)	I_{DD}	5 / 10 / 15	Control Inputs $V_{in} = V_{SS}$ or V_{DD}, Switch I/O: $V_{EE} \leq V_{I/O} \leq V_{DD}$ and $\Delta V_{switch} \leq 500$ mV***	— / — / —	20 / 40 / 80	— / — / —	0.005 / 0.010 / 0.015	20 / 40 / 80	— / — / —	150 / 300 / 600	μA
Total Supply Current (Dynamic Plus Quiescent, Per Package)	$I_{D(AV)}$		T_A = 25°C only (The channel component, $(V_{in} - V_{out})/R_{ON}$, is not included)			Typical $\begin{cases}(0.07\ \mu A/kHz)f + I_{DD}\\(0.20\ \mu A/kHz)f + I_{DD}\\(0.36\ \mu A/kHz)f + I_{DD}\end{cases}$					μA
CONTROL INPUTS — INHIBIT, A, B, C (Voltages Referenced to V_{SS})											
Low-Level Input Voltage	V_{IL}	5 / 10 / 15	R_{ON} = per spec, I_{off} = per spec	— / — / —	1.5 / 3.0 / 4.0	— / — / —	2.25 / 4.50 / 6.75	1.5 / 3.0 / 4.0	— / — / —	1.5 / 3.0 / 4.0	V
High-Level Input Voltage	V_{IH}	5 / 10 / 15	R_{ON} = per spec, I_{off} = per spec	3.5 / 7.0 / 11.0	— / — / —	3.5 / 7.0 / 11.0	2.75 / 5.50 / 8.25	— / — / —	3.5 / 7.0 / 11.0	— / — / —	V
Input Leakage Current (AL Device)	I_{in}	15	V_{in} = 0 or V_{DD}	—	±0.1	—	±0.00001	±0.1	—	±1.0	μA
Input Leakage Current (CL/CP Device)	I_{in}	15	V_{in} = 0 or V_{DD}	—	±0.3	—	±0.00001	±0.3	—	±1.0	μA
Input Capacitance	C_{in}			—	—	—	5.0	7.5	—	—	pF
SWITCHES IN/OUT AND COMMONS OUT/IN – X, Y, Z (Voltages Referenced to V_{EE})											
Recommended Peak-to-Peak Voltage Into or Out of the Switch	$V_{I/O}$		Channel On or Off	0	V_{DD}	0	—	V_{DD}	0	V_{DD}	V_{PP}
Recommended Static or Dynamic Voltage Across the Switch** (Figure 5)	ΔV_{switch}		Channel On	—	600	—	—	600	—	300	mV
Output Offset Voltage	V_{OO}		V_{in} = 0 V, No load	—	—	—	10	—	—	—	μV
ON Resistance (AL Device)	R_{ON}	5 / 10 / 15	$\Delta V_{switch} \leq 500$ mV**, $V_{in} = V_{IL}$ or V_{IH} (Control), and V_{in} = 0 to V_{DD} (Switch)	— / — / —	800 / 400 / 220	— / — / —	250 / 120 / 80	1050 / 500 / 280	— / — / —	1300 / 550 / 320	Ω
ON Resistance (CL/CP Device)	R_{ON}	5 / 10 / 15	$\Delta V_{switch} \leq 500$ mV**, $V_{in} = V_{IL}$ or V_{IH} (Control), and V_{in} = 0 to V_{DD} (Switch)	— / — / —	880 / 450 / 250	— / — / —	250 / 120 / 80	1050 / 500 / 280	— / — / —	1200 / 520 / 300	Ω
Δ ON Resistance Between Any Two Channels in the Same Package	ΔR_{ON}	5 / 10 / 15	$V_{in} = V_{IL}$ or V_{IH} (Control) Channel to Channel or Any One Channel	— / — / —	70 / 50 / 45	— / — / —	25 / 10 / 10	70 / 50 / 45	— / — / —	135 / 95 / 65	Ω
Off-Channel Leakage Current (AL Device) (Figure 10)	I_{off}	15	$V_{in} = V_{IL}$ or V_{IH} (Control) Channel to Channel or Any One Channel	—	±100	—	±0.05	±100	—	±1000	nA
Off-Channel Leakage Current (CL/CP Device) (Figure 10)	I_{off}	15	$V_{in} = V_{IL}$ or V_{IH} (Control) Channel to Channel or Any One Channel	—	±300	—	±0.05	±300	—	±1000	nA
Capacitance, Switch I/O	$C_{I/O}$	15	Inhibit = V_{DD}	—	—	—	10	—	—	—	pF
Capacitance, Common O/I	C_{Out}		Inhibit = V_{DD} (MC14051B) (MC14052B) (MC14053B)	—	—	—	60 / 32 / 17	—	—	—	pF
Capacitance, Feedthrough (Channel Off)	$C_{I/O}$		Pins Not Adjacent / Pins Adjacent	—	—	—	0.15 / 0.47	—	—	—	pF

* T_{low} = –55°C for AL Device, –40° for CL/CP Device.
  T_{high} = +125°C for AL Device, +85°C for CL/CP Device.
Data labeled "Typ" is not to be used for design purposes, but is intended as an indication of the IC's potential performance.
**For voltage drops across the switch (ΔV_{switch}) >600 mV (>300 mV at high temperature), excessive V_{DD} current may be drawn; i.e. the current out of the switch may contain both V_{DD} and switch input components. The reliability of the device will be unaffected unless the Maximum Ratings are exceeded. (See first page of this data sheet.)

MOTOROLA

MC14532B

8-BIT PRIORITY ENCODER

The MC14532B is constructed with complementary MOS (CMOS) enhancement mode devices. The primary function of a priority encoder is to provide a binary address for the active input with the highest priority. Eight data inputs (D0 thru D7) and an enable input (E$_{in}$) are provided. Five outputs are available, three are address outputs (Q0 thru Q2), one group select (GS) and one enable output (E$_{out}$).

- Diode Protection on All Inputs
- Supply Voltage Range = 3.0 Vdc to 18 Vdc
- Capable of Driving Two Low-power TTL Loads or One Low-Power Schottky TTL Load over the Rated Temperature Range

CMOS MSI
(LOW-POWER COMPLEMENTARY MOS)

8-BIT PRIORITY ENCODER

L SUFFIX
CERAMIC PACKAGE
CASE 620

P SUFFIX
PLASTIC PACKAGE
CASE 648

ORDERING INFORMATION

A Series: −55°C to +125°C
MC14XXXBAL (Ceramic Package Only)

C Series: −40°C to +85°C
MC14XXXBCP (Plastic Package)
MC14XXXBCL (Ceramic Package)

PIN ASSIGNMENT

D4	1		16	VDD
D5	2		15	Eout
D6	3		14	GS
D7	4		13	D3
Ein	5		12	D2
Q2	6		11	D1
Q1	7		10	D0
VSS	8		9	Q0

MAXIMUM RATINGS* (Voltages Referenced to V$_{SS}$)

Symbol	Parameter	Value	Unit
V$_{DD}$	DC Supply Voltage	−0.5 to +18.0	V
V$_{in}$, V$_{out}$	Input or Output Voltage (DC or Transient)	−0.5 to V$_{DD}$ +0.5	V
I$_{in}$, I$_{out}$	Input or Output Current (DC or Transient), per Pin	±10	mA
P$_D$	Power Dissipation, per Package†	500	mW
T$_{stg}$	Storage Temperature	−65 to +150	°C
T$_L$	Lead Temperature (8-Second Soldering)	260	°C

*Maximum Ratings are those values beyond which damage to the device may occur.
†Temperature Derating: Plastic "P" Package: −12mW/°C from 65°C to 85°C
Ceramic "L" Package: −12mW/°C from 100°C to 125°C

TRUTH TABLE

INPUT										OUTPUT				
Ein	D7	D6	D5	D4	D3	D2	D1	D0	GS	Q2	Q1	Q0	Eout
0	X	X	X	X	X	X	X	X	0	0	0	0	0
1	0	0	0	0	0	0	0	0	0	0	0	0	1
1	1	X	X	X	X	X	X	X	1	1	1	1	0
1	0	1	X	X	X	X	X	X	1	1	1	0	0
1	0	0	1	X	X	X	X	X	1	1	0	1	0
1	0	0	0	1	X	X	X	X	1	1	0	0	0
1	0	0	0	0	1	X	X	X	1	0	1	1	0
1	0	0	0	0	0	1	X	X	1	0	1	0	0
1	0	0	0	0	0	0	1	X	1	0	0	1	0
1	0	0	0	0	0	0	0	1	1	0	0	0	0

X = Don't Care

This device contains protection circuitry to guard against damage due to high static voltages or electric fields. However, precautions must be taken to avoid applications of any voltage higher than maximum rated voltages to this high-impedance circuit. For proper operation, V$_{in}$ and V$_{out}$ should be constrained to the range V$_{SS}$ ≤ (V$_{in}$ or V$_{out}$) ≤ V$_{DD}$.
Unused inputs must always be tied to an appropriate logic voltage level (e.g., either V$_{SS}$ or V$_{DD}$). Unused outputs must be left open.

MC14532B

ELECTRICAL CHARACTERISTICS (Voltages Referenced to V$_{SS}$)

Characteristic	Symbol	V$_{DD}$ Vdc	T$_{low}$* Min	T$_{low}$* Max	25°C Min	25°C Typ #	25°C Max	T$_{high}$* Min	T$_{high}$* Max	Unit
Output Voltage "0" Level	V$_{OL}$	5.0	—	0.05	0	0	0.05	—	0.05	Vdc
V$_{in}$ = V$_{DD}$ or 0		10	—	0.05	0	0	0.05	—	0.05	
		15	—	0.05	0	0	0.05	—	0.05	
"1" Level	V$_{OH}$	5.0	4.95	—	4.95	5.0	—	4.95	—	Vdc
V$_{in}$ = 0 or V$_{DD}$		10	9.95	—	9.95	10	—	9.95	—	
		15	14.95	—	14.95	15	—	14.95	—	
Input Voltage "0" Level	V$_{IL}$	5.0	—	1.5	—	2.25	1.5	—	1.5	Vdc
(V$_O$ = 4.5 or 0.5 Vdc)		10	—	3.0	—	4.50	3.0	—	3.0	
(V$_O$ = 9.0 or 1.0 Vdc)										
(V$_O$ = 13.5 or 1.5 Vdc)		15	—	4.0	—	6.75	4.0	—	4.0	
"1" Level	V$_{IH}$	5.0	3.5	—	3.5	2.75	—	3.5	—	Vdc
(V$_O$ = 0.5 or 4.5 Vdc)		10	7.0	—	7.0	5.50	—	7.0	—	
(V$_O$ = 1.0 or 9.0 Vdc)										
(V$_O$ = 1.5 or 13.5 Vdc)		15	11.0	—	11.0	8.25	—	11.0	—	
Output Drive Current (AL Device) Source	I$_{OH}$	5.0	−3.0	—	−2.4	−4.2	—	−1.7	—	mAdc
(V$_{OH}$ = 2.5 Vdc)		5.0	−0.64	—	−0.51	−0.88	—	−0.36	—	
(V$_{OH}$ = 4.6 Vdc)		10	−1.6	—	−1.3	−2.25	—	−0.9	—	
(V$_{OH}$ = 9.5 Vdc)		15	−4.2	—	−3.4	−8.8	—	−2.4	—	
(V$_{OH}$ = 13.5 Vdc)										
Sink	I$_{OL}$	5.0	0.64	—	0.51	0.88	—	0.36	—	mAdc
(V$_{OL}$ = 0.4 Vdc)		10	1.6	—	1.3	2.25	—	0.9	—	
(V$_{OL}$ = 0.5 Vdc)		15	4.2	—	3.4	8.8	—	2.4	—	
(V$_{OL}$ = 1.5 Vdc)										
Output Drive Current (CL/CP Device) Source	I$_{OH}$	5.0	−2.5	—	−2.1	−2.4	—	−1.7	—	mAdc
(V$_{OH}$ = 2.5 Vdc)		5.0	−0.52	—	−0.44	−0.88	—	−0.36	—	
(V$_{OH}$ = 4.6 Vdc)		10	−1.3	—	−1.1	−2.25	—	−0.9	—	
(V$_{OH}$ = 9.5 Vdc)		15	−3.6	—	−3.0	−8.8	—	−2.4	—	
(V$_{OH}$ = 13.5 Vdc)										
Sink	I$_{OL}$	5.0	0.52	—	0.44	0.88	—	0.36	—	mAdc
(V$_{OL}$ = 0.4 Vdc)		10	1.3	—	1.1	2.25	—	0.9	—	
(V$_{OL}$ = 0.5 Vdc)		15	3.6	—	3.0	8.8	—	2.4	—	
(V$_{OL}$ = 1.5 Vdc)										
Input Current (AL Device)	I$_{in}$	15	—	±0.1	—	±0.00001	±0.1	—	±1.0	µAdc
Input Current (CL/CP Device)	I$_{in}$	15	—	±0.3	—	±0.00001	±0.3	—	±1.0	µAdc
Input Capacitance (V$_{in}$ = 0)	C$_{in}$	—	—	—	—	5.0	7.5	—	—	pF
Quiescent Current (AL Device) (Per Package)	I$_{DD}$	5.0	—	5.0	—	0.005	5.0	—	150	µAdc
		10	—	10	—	0.010	10	—	300	
		15	—	20	—	0.015	20	—	600	
Quiescent Current (CL/CP Device) (Per Package)	I$_{DD}$	5.0	—	20	—	0.005	20	—	150	µAdc
		10	—	40	—	0.010	40	—	300	
		15	—	80	—	0.015	80	—	600	
Total Supply Current**† (Dynamic plus Quiescent, Per Package) (C$_L$ = 50 pF on all outputs, all buffers switching)	I$_T$	5.0			I$_T$ = (1.74 µA/kHz) f + I$_{DD}$					µAdc
		10			I$_T$ = (3.65 µA/kHz) f + I$_{DD}$					
		15			I$_T$ = (5.73 µA/kHz) f + I$_{DD}$					

*T$_{low}$ = −55°C for AL Device, −40°C for CL/CP Device.
T$_{high}$ = +125°C for AL Device, +85°C for CL/CP Device.
#Data labelled "Typ" is not to be used for design purposes but is intended as an indication of the IC's potential performance.

**The formulas given are for the typical characteristics only at 25°C.
†To calculate total supply current at loads other than 50 pF:
I$_T$(C$_L$) = I$_T$(50 pF) + (C$_L$ − 50) Vfk

where: I$_T$ is in µA (per package), C$_L$ in pF, V = (V$_{DD}$ −V$_{SS}$) in volts, f in kHz is input frequency, and k = 0.005.

National Semiconductor

Industrial Blocks

LM555/LM555C Timer

General Description

The LM555 is a highly stable device for generating accurate time delays or oscillation. Additional terminals are provided for triggering or resetting if desired. In the time delay mode of operation, the time is precisely controlled by one external resistor and capacitor. For astable operation as an oscillator, the free running frequency and duty cycle are accurately controlled with two external resistors and one capacitor. The circuit may be triggered and reset on falling waveforms, and the output circuit can source or sink up to 200 mA or drive TTL circuits.

Features

- Direct replacement for SE555/NE55b
- Timing from microseconds through hours
- Operates in both astable and monostable modes
- Adjustable duty cycle
- Output can source or sink 200 mA
- Output and supply TTL compatible
- Temperature stability better than 0.005% per °C
- Normally on and normally off output

Applications

- Precision timing
- Pulse generation
- Sequential timing
- Time delay generation
- Pulse width modulation
- Pulse position modulation
- Linear ramp generator

Absolute Maximum Ratings

Supply Voltage	+18V
Power Dissipation (Note 1)	600 mW
Operating Temperature Ranges	
LM555C	0°C to +70°C
LM555	−55°C to +125°C
Storage Temperature Range	−65°C to +150°C
Lead Temperature (Soldering, 10 seconds)	300°C

Electrical Characteristics ($T_A = 25°C$, $V_{CC} = +5V$ to $+15V$, unless otherwise specified)

PARAMETER	CONDITIONS	LM555 MIN	LM555 TYP	LM555 MAX	LM555C MIN	LM555C TYP	LM555C MAX	UNITS
Supply Voltage		4.5		18	4.5		16	V
Supply Current	$V_{CC} = 5V$, $R_L = \infty$		3	5		3	6	mA
	$V_{CC} = 15V$, $R_L = \infty$ (Low State) (Note 2)		10	12		10	15	mA
Timing Error, Monostable								
Initial Accuracy	R_A, $R_B = 1k$ to 100 k, $C = 0.1\mu F$. (Note 3)		0.5			1		%
Drift with Temperature			30			50		ppm/°C
Accuracy over Temperature			1.5			1.5		%
Drift with Supply			0.05			0.1		%/V
Timing Error, Astable								
Initial Accuracy			1.5			2.25		%
Drift with Temperature			90			150		ppm/°C
Accuracy over Temperature			2.5			3.0		%
Drift with Supply			0.15			0.30		%/V
Threshold Voltage			0.667			0.667		x V_{CC}
Trigger Voltage	$V_{CC} = 15V$	4.8	5	5.2		5		V
	$V_{CC} = 5V$	1.45	1.67	1.9		1.67		V
Trigger Current			0.01	0.5		0.5	0.9	µA
Reset Voltage		0.4	0.5	1	0.4	0.5	1	V
Reset Current			0.1	0.4		0.1	0.4	mA
Threshold Current	(Note 4)		0.1	0.25		0.1	0.25	µA
Control Voltage Level	$V_{CC} = 15V$	9.6	10	10.4	9	10	11	V
	$V_{CC} = 5V$	2.9	3.33	3.8	2.6	3.33	4	V
Pin 7 Leakage Output High			1	100		1	100	nA
Pin 7 Sat (Note 5)								
Output Low	$V_{CC} = 15V$, $I_7 = 15$ mA		150			180	200	mV
Output Low	$V_{CC} = 4.5V$, $I_7 = 4.5$ mA		70	100		80		mV
Output Voltage Drop (Low)	$V_{CC} = 15V$							
	$I_{SINK} = 10$ mA		0.1	0.15		0.1	0.25	V
	$I_{SINK} = 50$ mA		0.4	0.5		0.4	0.75	V
	$I_{SINK} = 100$ mA		2	2.2		2	2.5	V
	$I_{SINK} = 200$ mA		2.5			2.5		V
	$V_{CC} = 5V$							
	$I_{SINK} = 8$ mA		0.1	0.25				V
	$I_{SINK} = 5$ mA					0.25	0.35	V
Output Voltage Drop (High)	$I_{SOURCE} = 200$ mA, $V_{CC} = 15V$		12.5			12.5		V
	$I_{SOURCE} = 100$ mA, $V_{CC} = 15V$	13	13.3		12.75	13.3		V
	$V_{CC} = 5V$	3	3.3		2.75	3.3		V
Rise Time of Output			100			100		ns
Fall Time of Output			100			100		ns

Note 1: For operating at elevated temperatures the device must be derated based on a +150°C maximum junction temperature and a thermal resistance of +45°C/W junction to case for TO-5 and +150°C/W junction to ambient for both packages.

Note 2: Supply current when output high typically 1 mA less at $V_{CC} = 5V$.

Note 3: Tested at $V_{CC} = 5V$ and $V_{CC} = 15V$.

Note 4: This will determine the maximum value of $R_A + R_B$ for 15V operation. The maximum total $(R_A + R_B)$ is 20 MΩ.

Note 5: No protection against excessive pin 7 current is necessary providing the package dissipation rating will not be exceeded.

Schematic Diagram

Connection Diagrams

Metal Can Package

Pins: GND, TRIGGER, OUTPUT, RESET, V_{CC}, DISCHARGE, THRESHOLD, CONTROL VOLTAGE

TOP VIEW

Order Number LM555H, LM555CH
See NS Package H08C

Dual-In-Line Package

Pins: GND 1, TRIGGER 2, OUTPUT 3, RESET 4, CONTROL VOLTAGE 5, THRESHOLD 6, DISCHARGE 7, $+V_{CC}$ 8

TOP VIEW

Order Number LM555CN
See NS Package N08B

Order Number LM555CJ or LM555CJ
See NS Package J08A

LM741/LM741A/LM741C/LM741E Operational Amplifier

General Description

The LM741 series are general purpose operational amplifiers which feature improved performance over industry standards like the LM709. They are direct, plug-in replacements for the 709C, LM201, MC1439 and 748 in most applications.

The amplifiers offer many features which make their application nearly foolproof: overload pro-tection on the input and output, no latch-up when the common mode range is exceeded, as well as freedom from oscillations.

The LM741C/LM741E are identical to the LM741/LM741A except that the LM741C/LM741E have their performance guaranteed over a 0°C to +70°C temperature range, instead of −55°C to +125°C.

Absolute Maximum Ratings

	LM741A	LM741	LM741E	LM741C
Supply Voltage	±22V	±22V	±22V	±18V
Power Dissipation (Note 1)	500 mW	500 mW	500 mW	500 mW
Differential Input Voltage	±30V	±30V	±30V	±30V
Input Voltage (Note 2)	±15V	±15V	±15V	±15V
Output Short Circuit Duration	Indefinite	Indefinite	Indefinite	Indefinite
Operating Temperature Range	−55°C to +125°C	−55°C to +125°C	0°C to +70°C	0°C to +70°C
Storage Temperature Range	−65°C to +150°C	−65°C to +150°C	−65°C to +150°C	−65°C to +150°C
Lead Temperature (Soldering, 10 seconds)	300°C	300°C	300°C	300°C

Electrical Characteristics (Note 3)

PARAMETER	CONDITIONS	LM741A/LM741E MIN	TYP	MAX	LM741 MIN	TYP	MAX	LM741C MIN	TYP	MAX	UNITS
Input Offset Voltage	$T_A = 25°C$										
	$R_S \leq 10\ k\Omega$					1.0	5.0		2.0	6.0	mV
	$R_S \leq 50\Omega$		0.8	3.0							mV
	$T_{AMIN} \leq T_A \leq T_{AMAX}$										
	$R_S \leq 50\Omega$			4.0							mV
	$R_S \leq 10\ k\Omega$						6.0			7.5	mV
Average Input Offset Voltage Drift				15							µV/°C
Input Offset Voltage Adjustment Range	$T_A = 25°C$, $V_S = ±20V$	±10				±15			±15		mV
Input Offset Current	$T_A = 25°C$		3.0	30		20	200		20	200	nA
	$T_{AMIN} \leq T_A \leq T_{AMAX}$			70		85	500			300	nA
Average Input Offset Current Drift				0.5							nA/°C
Input Bias Current	$T_A = 25°C$		30	80		80	500		80	500	nA
	$T_{AMIN} \leq T_A \leq T_{AMAX}$			0.210			1.5			0.8	µA
Input Resistance	$T_A = 25°C$, $V_S = ±20V$	1.0	6.0		0.3	2.0		0.3	2.0		MΩ
	$T_{AMIN} \leq T_A \leq T_{AMAX}$, $V_S = ±20V$	0.5									MΩ
Input Voltage Range	$T_A = 25°C$							±12	±13		V
	$T_{AMIN} \leq T_A \leq T_{AMAX}$				±12	±13					V
Large Signal Voltage Gain	$T_A = 25°C$, $R_L \geq 2\ k\Omega$										
	$V_S = ±20V$, $V_O = ±15V$	50									V/mV
	$V_S = ±15V$, $V_O = ±10V$				50	200		20	200		V/mV
	$T_{AMIN} \leq T_A \leq T_{AMAX}$, $R_L \geq 2\ k\Omega$										
	$V_S = ±20V$, $V_O = ±15V$	32									V/mV
	$V_S = ±15V$, $V_O = ±10V$				25			15			V/mV
	$V_S = ±5V$, $V_O = ±2V$	10									V/mV
Output Voltage Swing	$V_S = ±20V$										
	$R_L \geq 10\ k\Omega$	±16									V
	$R_L \geq 2\ k\Omega$	±15									V
	$V_S = ±15V$										
	$R_L \geq 10\ k\Omega$				±12	±14		±12	±14		V
	$R_L \geq 2\ k\Omega$				±10	±13		±10	±13		V
Output Short Circuit Current	$T_A = 25°C$	10	25	35		25			25		mA
	$T_{AMIN} \leq T_A \leq T_{AMAX}$	10		40							mA
Common-Mode Rejection Ratio	$T_{AMIN} \leq T_A \leq T_{AMAX}$										
	$R_S \leq 10\ k\Omega$, $V_{CM} = ±12V$				70	90		70	90		dB
	$R_S \leq 50\ k\Omega$, $V_{CM} = ±12V$	80	95								dB

Schematic and Connection Diagrams (Top Views)

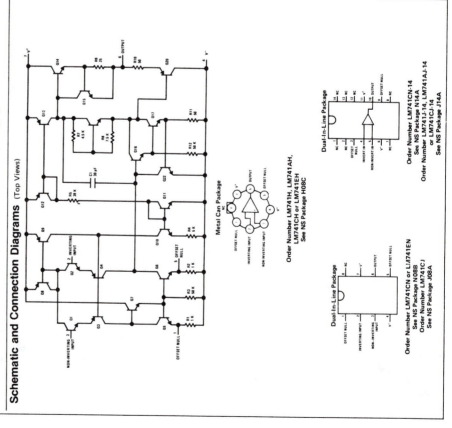

Metal Can Package

Order Number LM741H, LM741AH, LM741CH or LM741EH
See NS Package H08C

Dual-In-Line Package

Order Number LM741CN or LM741EN
See NS Package N08B
Order Number LM741CJ
See NS Package J08A

Dual-In-Line Package

Order Number LM741CN-14
See NS Package N14A
Order Number LM741J-14, LM741AJ-14
or LM741CJ-14
See NS Package J14A

MAXIMUM RATINGS (TA = +25°C unless otherwise noted.)

Rating	Symbol	Value	Unit
Power Supply Voltage	VCC / VEE	+5.5 / -16.5	Vdc
Digital Input Voltage	V5 thru V12	0 to +5.5	Vdc
Applied Output Voltage	VO	+0.5, -5.2	Vdc
Reference Current	I14	5.0	mA
Reference Amplifier Inputs	V14, V15	VCC, VEE	Vdc
Operating Temperature Range MC1508 / MC1408 Series	TA	-55 to +125 / 0 to +75	°C
Storage Temperature Range	Tstg	-65 to +150	°C

ELECTRICAL CHARACTERISTICS (VCC = +5.0 Vdc, VEE = -15 Vdc, Vref/R14 = 2.0 mA, MC1508L8: TA = -55°C to +125°C. MC1408L Series: TA = 0 to +75°C unless otherwise noted. All digital inputs at high logic level.)

Characteristic	Figure	Symbol	Min	Typ	Max	Unit
Relative Accuracy (Error relative to full scale IO)	4	Er				%
MC1508L8, MC1408L8, MC1408P8			—	—	±0.19	
MC1408P7, MC1408L7, See Note 1			—	—	±0.39	
MC1408P6, MC1408L6, See Note 1			—	—	±0.78	
Settling Time to within ±1/2 LSB (includes tpLH)(TA = +25°C)See Note 2	5	ts	—	300	—	ns
Propagation Delay Time TA = +25°C	5	tpLH, tpHL	—	30	100	ns
Output Full Scale Current Drift	—	TCIO	—	-20	—	PPM/°C
Digital Input Logic Levels (MSB)	3					Vdc
High Level, Logic "1"		VIH	2.0	—	—	
Low Level, Logic "0"		VIL	—	—	0.8	
Digital Input Current (MSB)	3					mA
High Level, VIH = 5.0 V		IIH	—	0	0.04	
Low Level, VIL = 0.8 V		IIL	—	-0.4	-0.8	
Reference Input Bias Current (Pin 15)	3	I15	—	-1.0	-5.0	µA
Output Current Range	3	IOR				mA
VEE = -5.0 V			0	2.0	2.1	
VEE = -15 V, TA = 25°C			0	2.0	4.2	
Output Current Vref = 2.000 V, R14 = 1000 Ω	3	IO	1.9	1.99	2.1	mA
Output Current (All bits low)	3	IO(min)	—	0	4.0	µA
Output Voltage Compliance (Er ≤ 0.19% at TA = +25°C)	3	VO				Vdc
Pin 1 grounded			—	—	-0.55, +0.4	
Pin 1 open, VEE below -10 V			—	—	-5.0, +0.4	
Reference Current Slew Rate	6	SR Iref	—	4.0	—	mA/µs
Output Current Power Supply Sensitivity	—	PSRR(-)	—	0.5	2.7	µA/V
Power Supply Current (All bits low)	3	ICC / IEE	—	+13.5 / -7.5	+22 / -13	mA
Power Supply Voltage Range (TA = +25°C)	3	VCCR / VEER	+4.5 / -4.5	+5.0 / -15	+5.5 / -16.5	Vdc
Power Dissipation	3	PD				mW
All bits low VEE = -5.0 Vdc			—	105	170	
VEE = -15 Vdc			—	190	305	
All bits high VEE = -5.0 Vdc			—	90	—	
VEE = -15 Vdc			—	160	—	

Note 1. All current switches are tested to guarantee at least 50% of rated output current.
Note 2. All bits switched.

MC1408
MC1508

Specifications and Applications Information

EIGHT-BIT MULTIPLYING DIGITAL-TO-ANALOG CONVERTER

... designed for use where the output current is a linear product of an eight-bit digital word and an analog input voltage.

- Eight-Bit Accuracy Available in Both Temperature Ranges Relative Accuracy: ±0.19% Error maximum (MC1408L8, MC1408P8, MC1508L8)
- Seven and Six-Bit Accuracy Available with MC1408 Designated by 7 or 6 Suffix after Package Suffix
- Fast Settling Time – 300 ns typical
- Noninverting Digital Inputs are MTTL and CMOS Compatible
- Output Voltage Swing – +0.4 V to -5.0 V
- High-Speed Multiplying Input Slew Rate 4.0 mA/µs
- Standard Supply Voltages: +5.0 V and -5.0 V to -15 V

EIGHT-BIT MULTIPLYING DIGITAL-TO-ANALOG CONVERTER

SILICON MONOLITHIC INTEGRATED CIRCUIT

L SUFFIX CERAMIC PACKAGE CASE 620-02

P SUFFIX PLASTIC PACKAGE CASE 648-05

FIGURE 2 – BLOCK DIAGRAM

FIGURE 1 – D-to-A TRANSFER CHARACTERISTICS

IO, OUTPUT CURRENT (mA)

INPUT DIGITAL WORD

(00000000)   (11111111)

TYPICAL APPLICATIONS

- Tracking A-to-D Converters
- Successive Approximation A-to-D Converters
- 2 1/2 Digit Panel Meters and DVM's
- Waveform Synthesis
- Sample and Hold
- Peak Detector
- Programmable Gain and Attenuation
- CRT Character Generation
- Audio Digitizing and Decoding
- Programmable Power Supplies
- Analog-Digital Multiplication
- Digital-Digital Multiplication
- Analog-Digital Division
- Digital Addition and Subtraction
- Speech Compression and Expansion
- Stepping Motor Drive

MOTOROLA LINEAR/INTERFACE DEVICES

2N3905 / 2N3906

CASE 29-04, STYLE 1
TO-92 (TO-226AA)

GENERAL PURPOSE TRANSISTOR
PNP SILICON

MAXIMUM RATINGS

Rating	Symbol	Value	Unit
Collector-Emitter Voltage	VCEO	40	Vdc
Collector-Base Voltage	VCBO	40	Vdc
Emitter-Base Voltage	VEBO	5.0	Vdc
Collector Current — Continuous	IC	200	mAdc
Total Device Dissipation @ TA = 25°C Derate above 25°C	PD	625 5.0	mW mW/°C
Total Power Dissipation @ TA = 60°C	PD	250	mW
Total Device Dissipation @ TC = 25°C Derate above 25°C	PD	1.5 12	Watts mW/°C
Operating and Storage Junction Temperature Range	TJ, Tstg	-55 to +150	°C

*THERMAL CHARACTERISTICS

Characteristic	Symbol	Max	Unit
Thermal Resistance, Junction to Case	RθJC	83.3	°C/W
Thermal Resistance, Junction to Ambient	RθJA	200	°C/W

ELECTRICAL CHARACTERISTICS (TA = 25°C unless otherwise noted.)

Characteristic		Symbol	Min	Max	Unit
OFF CHARACTERISTICS					
Collector-Emitter Breakdown Voltage(1) (IC = 1.0 mAdc, IB = 0)		V(BR)CEO	40	—	Vdc
Collector-Base Breakdown Voltage (IC = 10 μAdc, IE = 0)		V(BR)CBO	40	—	Vdc
Emitter-Base Breakdown Voltage (IE = 10 μAdc, IC = 0)		V(BR)EBO	5.0	—	Vdc
Base Cutoff Current (VCE = 30 Vdc, VBE = 3.0 Vdc)		IBL	—	50	nAdc
Collector Cutoff Current (VCE = 30 Vdc, VBE = 3.0 Vdc)		ICEX	—	50	nAdc
ON CHARACTERISTICS(1)					
DC Current Gain (IC = 0.1 mAdc, VCE = 1.0 Vdc)	2N3905 2N3906	hFE	30 60	— —	
(IC = 1.0 mAdc, VCE = 1.0 Vdc)	2N3905 2N3906		40 80	— —	
(IC = 10 mAdc, VCE = 1.0 Vdc)	2N3905 2N3906		50 100	150 300	
(IC = 50 mAdc, VCE = 1.0 Vdc)	2N3905 2N3906		30 60	— —	
(IC = 100 mAdc, VCE = 1.0 Vdc)	2N3905 2N3906		15 30	— —	
Collector-Emitter Saturation Voltage (IC = 10 mAdc, IB = 1.0 mAdc) (IC = 50 mAdc, IB = 5.0 mAdc)		VCE(sat)	— —	0.25 0.4	Vdc
Base-Emitter Saturation Voltage (IC = 10 mAdc, IB = 1.0 mAdc) (IC = 50 mAdc, IB = 5.0 mAdc)		VBE(sat)	0.65 —	0.85 0.95	Vdc
SMALL-SIGNAL CHARACTERISTICS					
Current-Gain — Bandwidth Product (IC = 10 mAdc, VCE = 20 Vdc, f = 100 MHz)	2N3905 2N3906	fT	200 250	—	MHz
Output Capacitance (VCB = 5.0 Vdc, IE = 0, f = 100 kHz)		Cobo	—	4.5	pF

MOTOROLA SMALL-SIGNAL SEMICONDUCTORS

2N3903 / 2N3904

CASE 29-04, STYLE 1
TO-92 (TO-226AA)

GENERAL PURPOSE TRANSISTOR
NPN SILICON

MAXIMUM RATINGS

Rating	Symbol	Value	Unit
Collector-Emitter Voltage	VCEO	40	Vdc
Collector-Base Voltage	VCBO	60	Vdc
Emitter-Base Voltage	VEBO	6.0	Vdc
Collector Current — Continuous	IC	200	mAdc
Total Device Dissipation @ TA = 25°C Derate above 25°C	PD	625 5.0	mW mW/°C
*Total Device Dissipation @ TC = 25°C Derate above 25°C	PD	1.5 12	Watts mW/°C
Operating and Storage Junction Temperature Range	TJ, Tstg	-55 to +150	°C

*THERMAL CHARACTERISTICS

Characteristic	Symbol	Max	Unit
Thermal Resistance, Junction to Case	RθJC	83.3	°C/W
Thermal Resistance, Junction to Ambient	RθJA	200	°C/W

*Indicates Data in addition to JEDEC Requirements.

ELECTRICAL CHARACTERISTICS (TA = 25°C unless otherwise noted.)

Characteristic		Symbol	Min	Max	Unit
OFF CHARACTERISTICS					
Collector-Emitter Breakdown Voltage(1) (IC = 1.0 mAdc, IB = 0)		V(BR)CEO	40	—	Vdc
Collector-Base Breakdown Voltage (IC = 10 μAdc, IE = 0)		V(BR)CBO	60	—	Vdc
Emitter-Base Breakdown Voltage (IE = 10 μAdc, IC = 0)		V(BR)EBO	6.0	—	Vdc
Base Cutoff Current (VCE = 30 Vdc, VEB = 3.0 Vdc)		IBL	—	50	nAdc
Collector Cutoff Current (VCE = 30 Vdc, VEB = 3.0 Vdc)		ICEX	—	50	nAdc
ON CHARACTERISTICS					
DC Current Gain(1) (IC = 0.1 mAdc, VCE = 1.0 Vdc)	2N3903 2N3904	hFE	20 40	— —	
(IC = 1.0 mAdc, VCE = 1.0 Vdc)	2N3903 2N3904		35 70	— —	
(IC = 10 mAdc, VCE = 1.0 Vdc)	2N3903 2N3904		50 100	150 300	
(IC = 50 mAdc, VCE = 1.0 Vdc)	2N3903 2N3904		30 60	— —	
(IC = 100 mAdc, VCE = 1.0 Vdc)	2N3903 2N3904		15 30	— —	
Collector-Emitter Saturation Voltage(1) (IC = 10 mAdc, IB = 1.0 mAdc) (IC = 50 mAdc, IB = 5.0 mAdc)		VCE(sat)	— —	0.2 0.3	Vdc
Base-Emitter Saturation Voltage(1) (IC = 10 mAdc, IB = 1.0 mAdc) (IC = 50 mAdc, IB = 5.0 mAdc)		VBE(sat)	0.65 —	0.85 0.95	Vdc
SMALL-SIGNAL CHARACTERISTICS					
Current-Gain — Bandwidth Product (IC = 10 mAdc, VCE = 20 Vdc, f = 100 MHz)	2N3903 2N3904	fT	250 300	—	MHz

MOTOROLA SMALL-SIGNAL SEMICONDUCTORS